THE SUN

by the same author

PADRE ANGELO SECCHI (*Agnelli, Milan*)
SCIENZA D'OGGI (*Bompiani, Milan*)
ESPLORAZIONI CELESTI (*Hoepli, Milan*)
AMICI E NEMICI DI GALILEO (*Bompiani, Milan*)
LE STELLE E I PIANETI (*Einaudi, Turin*)
THE HISTORY OF ASTRONOMY (*Sidgwick & Jackson*)
IL SOLE, FONTE DI VITA (*La Scuola, Brescia*)

by J. B. Sidgwick

INTRODUCING ASTRONOMY (*Faber & Faber*)
AMATEUR ASTRONOMER'S HANDBOOK (*Faber & Faber*)
OBSERVATIONAL ASTRONOMY FOR AMATEURS (*Faber & Faber*)
THE HEAVENS ABOVE: A RATIONALE OF ASTRONOMY (*Oxford University Press*)

as editor

THE SHORTER POEMS OF WALTER SAVAGE LANDOR
(*Cambridge University Press*)

as translator

THE EXPANSION OF THE UNIVERSE, by PAUL COUDERC
(*Faber & Faber*)

THE SUN

by

GIORGIO ABETTI, *1882–*

translated by

J. B. SIDGWICK

FABER AND FABER

24 Russell Square

London

First published in mcmlvii
by Faber and Faber Limited
24 Russell Square, London, W.C.1
Second edition, revised, mcmlxiii
Made and printed in Great Britain
by William Clowes and Sons, Limited,
London and Beccles

TO
GEORGE ELLERY HALE

.... In them hath he set a tabernacle for the sun,
Which is as a bridegroom coming out of his
chamber, and rejoiceth as a strong man to run a
race.
His going forth is from the end of the heaven,
and his circuit unto the ends of it: and there is
nothing hid from the heat thereof.

PSALM XIX

CONTENTS

*see appendix for additional material

9

ILLUSTRATIONS

PLATES

13

ILLUSTRATIONS

ILLUSTRATIONS

Figures

ILLUSTRATIONS

PREFACE TO THE FIRST EDITION

SOME years ago I had occasion to write the chapter on solar physics for the *Handbuch der Astrophysik*, published in Berlin by Springer. Since then the continual and rapid advance of our knowledge of the Sun, as well as the requests that I have received for a similar monograph in Italian, have decided me to rewrite and extend this chapter, at the same time incorporating the results of other solar researches, such as those carried out during total eclipses and those relating to radiation and temperature. The present volume is the result. Whilst necessarily not being exhaustive, it may be considered to give a general picture of our present knowledge of the star to which life on Earth owes its existence.

The reader should be advised that the book is not narrowly technical: it has not been my intention, that is, to treat its various subjects in a manner suited solely to the specialist, but to display them in a manner which will render the methods employed in solar research, and the results so far obtained, intelligible to any student conversant with the rudiments of physics and mathematics.

In recent years the investigation of solar problems has, in fact, acquired an interest not only for astrophysicists but also for an ever-widening circle of students of other sciences: because the Sun, which so abundantly dispenses energy and life, has an undeniably immense and varied influence upon phenomena occurring on the Earth.

For these reasons I hope that my work may not have been in vain. Specialists will find here a *résumé* of much recent work, and will without difficulty be able to trace this to its original sources in the technical journals; at the same time I believe that the reader with no astronomical knowledge will be given a comprehensive bird's-eye view of our present knowledge of the Sun and of what may reasonably be hoped for from future work.

A list of the works consulted will be found at the end of the book; besides these, attention has of course also been given to most of the technical papers in such journals as the *Memorie degli Spettroscopisti italiani*, later continued in those of the *Società Astronomica Italiana*, the *Monthly Notices of the Royal Astronomical Society*, the *Astrophysical Journal*, the *Zeitschrift für Astrophysik* and the Memoirs and Annals of the various observatories.

I believe that today it is safe to predict for solar studies an ever-increasing importance, not only in the narrow field of astrophysics but also in such allied and applied sciences as geophysics, biology and agriculture, which every day demand a wide and thorough knowledge of solar phenomena and their explanations, as well as those terrestrial phenomena which are more or less directly attributable to the Sun's agency.

I am happy to extend my heartfelt thanks for their kind assistance to Signora Castelnuovo-Tedesco, Professor F. Zagar, L. Taffara and M. G. Fracastoro, as also to those colleagues who have so kindly provided me with some of the illustrations.

GIORGIO ABETTI

Arcetri Observatory, Florence
October 1934

PREFACE TO THE SECOND EDITION

GREAT progress has been made in astrophysics of recent years in the observational and experimental fields—through the continual development and improvement of the instruments employed—and also in the field of theoretical research.

In the more specialised branch of solar physics it can, I think, be maintained that even greater advances have been made, owing to the continually increasing interest shown in solar studies; for the Sun is the nearest of all the stars, and the Earth is dependent upon it not only gravitationally but also in respect of those numerous classes of terrestrial phenomena that are caused by solar events.

During the 15 years that have elapsed since the appearance of the first edition of this book the literature of solar physics has become so abundant as to comprise a considerable part of the whole body of astrophysical literature. The detailed study of the Sun's visible and invisible radiations, together with the parallel theoretical work, has greatly clarified our understanding of the physical conditions obtaining on the Sun, and has allowed important conclusions to be deduced concerning the great variety of stars both younger and older than the Sun.

In another direction, progress in geophysics has been so rapid that it has been possible to establish the origin on the Sun—the ultimate source of every form of terrestrial life—of a large class of hitherto more or less mysterious terrestrial phenomena. Further, the observation and study of these phenomena have already led to an improved understanding of the solar events to which they owe their origin, and it may reasonably be assumed that in the near future this advance will be continued.

Astrophysics, geophysics and radio technology all play their part in these investigations, and it has grown increasingly desirable that the more reliable and recently obtained results should be collected and discussed.

The layout and arrangement of the various sections of this book remain the same as in the first edition; also unchanged are those passages describing work which has now been superseded by more recent discoveries but which nevertheless has a lasting historical value and which, moreover, assists in an understanding of the unfolding story of solar physics. Naturally I have endeavoured to refer to all the work of recent years which seems to be important and necessary to the formation of an up-to-date picture. Omissions will no doubt be found, since one's acquaintance with the vast literature must necessarily be incomplete; also I have been anxious to maintain the descriptive character of the text, and there are certain researches (both experimental and theoretical) which do not lend themselves to a treatment of this sort.

Reference to recent work—see the Bibliography, and also the technical journals—will allow anyone wishing to go more deeply into the various topics to fill in the gaps for himself. It is hoped that these pages will be adequate for the student to gain a general picture of the present state of our knowledge of the Sun.

I am deeply indebted to my foreign colleagues, distinguished authorities in solar physics—Lucien d'Azambuja, Bernard Lyot, Seth B. Nicholson, Walter Orr Roberts and others—for their generosity in providing me with original and invaluable illustrations. These are better capable of revealing the processes occurring on our Sun than lengthy verbal descriptions.

GIORGIO ABETTI

Arcetri Observatory, Florence
July 1951

PREFACE TO THE SECOND ENGLISH EDITION

THE previous edition of this book was published in its excellent English translation by the late J. B. Sidgwick in 1957.

Since then the Sun has continued to be one of the main subjects, if not the main subject, studied by astrophysicists. Two very important facts have enabled them to increase their knowledge of our nearest star considerably.

One is the possibility of extending our sphere of observation and research into solar physics to the upper parts of our atmosphere and beyond by means of balloons, rockets and artificial satellites. The other is the possibility of receiving, by means of radio-telescopes, the radio-waves of various wavelengths emitted by the Sun.

Countless investigations have been carried out in recent years in both these fields as well as in the more traditional ones with equipment which is being constantly improved and becoming increasingly powerful. New theories and new hypotheses have been advanced to explain the mysterious phenomena which the Sun presents in such abundance.

The extremely successful International Geophysical Year (1957–58) coincided with the maximum of activity of the 19th eleven-year solar cycle, which happened to be higher than that of any previous cycle, and it contributed greatly to the progress of research in solar physics. The international collaboration proved to be so effective that it was possible to keep a twenty-four-hour watch on the Sun every day. A glance at the diagrams of the hours of observation of the Sun published in the *Quarterly Bulletin on Solar Activity* will show that there are hardly any gaps in the observations throughout the whole of the solar day.

The course of the many and various solar phenomena is followed the whole time, and we are now beginning to understand both the circumstances which produce them and their development better, as well as the influence that such phenomena have on terrestrial phenomena.

The observations obtained at the limits of, or outside, our own atmosphere have already led to some knowledge of the ultra-violet region of the solar spectrum down to a very short wavelength. And we can expect new knowledge from the study of this region. Observation of the radio-emission from the Sun has led to a knowledge of the radio Sun, very different from the Sun, which we may call the optical Sun, and to a knowledge of the progressive development of the phenomena of activity through the various layers of the solar atmosphere.

Finally, there have also been important developments in the utilisation of solar energy, and important applications are following rapidly.

It would not be possible to embody all the findings of the past few years within the limits of this book. We have attempted, however, to bring it up to date by adding information about the most outstanding and important developments to the various chapters and sections, so that our readers may gain an insight into, and obtain some guidance with regard to, the new developments in solar physics.†

GIORGIO ABETTI

Arcetri Observatory, Florence
April 1962

† The new information is contained in an appendix at the end of the book. The sections of the book for which there are additions in the appendix are marked with an asterisk (*).

TRANSLATOR'S NOTE

FOR over twenty years Professor Abetti's book, based on his *Handbuch der Astrophysik* monograph, has been the recognised text on the Sun. Five years ago a revised and enlarged edition was published in Italy, and it is this edition that is here translated. So rapid, however, is the progress of solar research, that a five-year-old work is already to some extent out of date, and Professor Abetti has therefore supplied a large number of revisions, additions and new illustrations for this English translation.

I should like to record here my indebtedness to Mr J. N. Swannell and Mr F. T. Prince for their assistance in elucidating mediaeval Italian, and to Dr P. A. Wayman who very kindly looked over the proofs and made a number of valuable suggestions.

J. B. SIDGWICK

Pretoria
August 1955

INTRODUCTION

From earliest times the Sun has been an object of veneration, revered by all the peoples of primitive civilisations. This veneration was not without some justification, for were the Sun to fail or were the radiation which it pours forth so profusely to undergo even a slight variation, life on this Earth would no longer be possible.

In ancient Egyptian temples we find the Sun worshipped under diverse guises: among the major divinities are to be found numerous representations of the powerful god Ra, the ruler of human destinies. In the Bible the firmament, together with the stars and the Sun, are the works of God's hand, and a witness to His glory and to the grandeur of Creation. Moreover the Bible contains many warnings against worshipping the stars and the Sun as gods. Fr Secchi wrote in the Preface to his famous work, *The Sun*, published in Paris in 1875: 'Several peoples of antiquity worshipped the Sun, an error perhaps less degrading than many another since this star is the most perfect image of the Divine, the instrument whereby the Creator communicates almost all his blessings in the physical sphere. Although to our eyes the Sun is simply a material body, its study is nevertheless one of the most exalted occupations to which the savant can apply himself, and the story of the conquests made in this inexhaustible field will always be one most deserving of our attention, and most capable of edifying us.' The Preface concludes with the verse from the psalm, *in sole posuit tabernaculum suum Altissimus*.

Whilst unsuccessful attempts were made in ancient times—particularly by the Greek astronomers—to determine the Sun's size and distance from the Earth, its effective physical study dates from the invention of the telescope. It is true to say that from that epoch up to the present time the Sun has been ever more diligently observed—first to provide a continuous record of the phenomena of its surface and their variations, later in an attempt to elucidate its composition and physical constitution. Of the latter we now have a fair degree of comprehension, not only qualitatively but also quantitatively. We are today able to form some idea of, and advance hypotheses concerning, the origin of the Sun and the production of the enormous quantity of energy that it has been radiating for

34

millions of years in the past and will continue to radiate in the future.

Another problem of great interest has in recent years engaged the attention of the astrophysicist, the geophysicist and the radio technician: that of the influence of solar upon terrestrial phenomena—a dependence not only upon the regular and almost constant radiant flux which we receive, but also upon its possible variations. Astrophysicists, geologists and radio technicians work together in isolating and defining the two classes of phenomena, and in establishing correlations between them. These investigations, conducted without interruption through international collaboration, have brought to light certain periodic phenomena which occur with greater or less violence on the Sun, and have elucidated the various ways in which these disturb the conditions of the terrestrial atmosphere and of the Earth itself. Because such solar events develop and change with remarkable rapidity (especially when the Sun is very active) they need to be kept under as nearly continuous observation as possible, and it is therefore important that the Sun be observed from many observatories, scattered over the whole world. This is nowadays possible by virtue of international collaboration, initiated some years ago and steadily growing under the auspices of the International Astronomical Union.

In this review of the main practical problems of solar physics I have sought to describe the instruments in current use, the results that have been obtained since the days of Secchi—that is, from the beginnings of 'astrophysics'—and the problems still in course of investigation.

It is superfluous to remark that the progress of observational work keeps constantly in step with that of theoretical research; in the last few years the latter has, moreover, made very remarkable advances.

I. HISTORICAL NOTES

Although there is evidence that sunspots had been seen before the invention of the telescope, their systematic observation and the earliest ideas concerning their nature nevertheless date from the time of Galileo. As is well known, the first telescope was constructed by him in 1610; in the following year he himself, J. Fabricius and Fr C. Scheiner independently announced their discovery.

This discovery aimed a severe blow both at the so-called perfection of the heavens and also at those who refused to accept the results of observation and experiment—so severe, in fact, that Galileo decided to proceed with caution until he was certain of the existence and the true nature of the sunspots. It was not until 1612 that, feeling fully confident, he wrote an account of them with his habitual precision and clarity to the Grand Duke Cosimo Medici, in his *Discorso intorno alle cose che stanno in sull'acqua*:

I S T O R I A
E DIMOSTRAZIONI
INTORNO ALLE MACCHIE SOLARI
E LORO ACCIDENTI
COMPRESE IN TRE LETTERE SCRITTE
ALL' ILLVSTRISSIMO SIGNOR
MARCO VELSERI LINCEO
DVVMVIRO D'AVGVSTA
CONSIGLIERO DI SVA MAESTA CESAREA
DAL SIGNOR
GALILEO GALILEI LINCEO
Nobil Fiorentino, Filofofo, e Matematico Primario del Serenifi.
D. COSIMO II. GRAN DVCA DI TOSCANA.

IN ROMA, Appreffo Giacomo Mafcardi. MDCXIII.

CON LICENZA DE' SVPERIORI.

Fig. 1. Titlepage of Galileo's three letters on sunspots, published by the Accademia dei Lincei in 1613.

'Having made repeated observations I am at last convinced that the spots are objects close to the surface of the solar globe, where they are continually being produced and then dissolved, some quickly and some slowly; also that they are carried round the Sun by its rotation, which is completed in a period of about one lunar month. This is an occurrence of the first importance in itself, and still greater in its implications.'

The matter can be briefly summarised: the Sun, like the Earth, rotates on its axis; from time to time spots of varying size and duration appear on its surface; these rotate with the Sun, and by their means the Sun's rotation period can be determined with a considerable degree of accuracy.

The diatribes and polemics of those who would not face up to the facts, or who preferred to think differently, proved futile; one such was Fr Scheiner, who in *Tres epistolae de maculis solaribus*, written under the pseudonym of *Apelles latens post tabulam*, denied that the spots could be fit objects for the Sun's surface. Galileo replied with his famous *Istoria e dimostrazioni intorno alle macchie solari e loro accidenti*, consisting of three letters to Marco Welser, in which he refuted Scheiner's conclusions and for the first time openly championed the Copernican doctrine—thus initiating the story of his misfortunes.

At the time of the discovery of sunspots the Sun was not far from a maximum of its 11-year cycle of activity; this maximum probably occurred in 1611 or 1612. A number of Galileo's drawings of the solar disc for the latter year still exist, and these show many large spots. Galileo did not carry his observations of solar activity any further than this, being occupied with other studies and observations, and it was not until many years later, in 1843, that Schwabe of Dessau announced a probable 11-year periodicity in the frequency of the spots.

The occurrence of spots on the Sun in no way detracted from its perfection: the Earth, after all, has its oceans, its continents and its mountains. Galileo realised this perfectly well; and, furthermore, he realised the fundamental importance of his discoveries in connexion with the interpretation of the motions of the Solar System, in opposition to the old and no longer tenable hypotheses. Thus he opened up the physical investigation of the constitution of the heavenly bodies, which in very recent times was to culminate in a most spectacular leap forward of astrophysical research.

2. IMPORTANCE OF SOLAR STUDIES

Once the laws of Kepler and Newton had been formulated, it was firmly established that the Sun is the ruler of the Solar System; it also became possible to determine the distances and dimensions of its planets. But it was still impossible to say anything about the constitution of the Sun, either as a thing in itself or in relation to the so-called 'fixed' stars. With the development of astrophysics, however, it became apparent that the Sun is simply a star, similar to many of those visible in the night sky—there being, indeed, many whose constitution is identical with the Sun's; then it was realised that great importance attaches to solar physical research

37

by virtue of its bearing upon the study of the universe and its evolution.

The Sun appears as a luminous disc projected against the sky. Its angular diameter is about 30', as is that of the Moon. It is therefore sufficiently large for a more or less powerful telescope—and still more, as we shall see, for a spectroscope—to reveal in detail the various happenings on its surface. The stars, on the other hand, are so distant from the Solar System that even the most powerful telescope shows them as nothing more than luminous points. It has only recently been possible to determine the diameters of a few of the largest and nearest stars, and that by an indirect method, i.e. by means of an interferometer attached to the telescope. Such diameters amount to barely five hundredths of a second of arc—36,000 times smaller than the Sun's angular diameter. It is therefore hopeless to expect that any surface detail of the stars will be visible; instead one is forced to investigate the total light they emit as luminous points. But if this light indicates that their constitution—or, at least, the constitution of some of them—is identical with the Sun's, then a great step forward will have been made in our understanding of the universe: for all that we discover about the Sun will be equally applicable to the evolution of the stars.

In the case of stars that are not only of similar constitution to the Sun but are also of comparable size, it is borne in upon us how immensely more remote from the Earth they must be than is the Sun. And it is correspondingly important to discover as much as possible about this relatively nearby and brilliantly self-luminous star on which our life depends. In addition to studying its physical constitution we shall be able to measure the vast quantity of energy that it radiates into space (and that portion, in particular, which falls upon the Earth), the manner in which this varies with time, and the effects that this radiation may have upon our planet.

3. DISTANCE AND DIMENSIONS OF THE SUN

Before anything else, we must form some idea of the Sun's distance from the Earth, and of its absolute and relative dimensions.

At mean distance from the Earth, the Sun's apparent disc measures 32', which is equivalent to a disc 6 inches in diameter viewed from a distance of 50 feet. More precisely, it should be said that this value varies according to the position of the Earth in its orbit, being 32' 32" at perihelion in January, and 31' 28" at aphelion in July. The solar parallax—i.e. the angle which the Earth's equatorial radius (3957 miles) subtends at the Sun's centre—is the fundamental datum which, once known, at once gives the Earth's distance from the Sun in miles. Several direct and indirect astronomical methods agree in giving the value 8″.80 for the parallax, whence the Earth–Sun distance, also termed the Astronomical Unit, is 92,948,000 miles. It may be asked if we can be sure of this figure, so important in all astronomical calculations, and if so, how sure. This depends upon the precision with which two data employed in its deduction—parallax and terrestrial radius—can be measured. Nowadays, particularly as a result of accurate measurements of the solar parallax, the Earth–Sun distance may be taken as known with an uncertainty of 10,000 miles. This is equivalent to an uncertainty of about 6 inches in a measured mile.

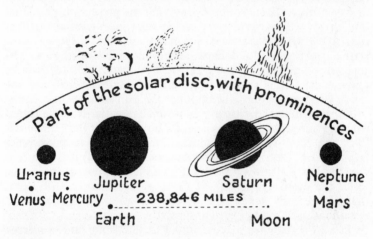

Fig. 2. Comparative sizes of the Sun and the major planets.

Since light covers 186,000 miles in one second of time, it follows that a light ray leaving the Sun will require 498 seconds to cover the Earth–Sun distance.

If we wish to form some idea of how much more distant the stars are than the Sun, we have to resort to the analogous concept of stellar parallax—or, more precisely, 'annual parallax': this is the angle subtended at the star by the radius of the Earth's orbit. In the case of α Centauri, the nearest known star to the Solar System, the annual parallax is 0″.76, whence it can be calculated that its light takes 4·3 years to reach us. The Sun, therefore, considered as a fixed star, is closer to the Earth than the nearest of the other stars in the same proportion as 4·3 years is to 498 seconds, i.e. more than 270,000 times.

39

Knowing the Sun's mean distance and mean apparent diameter we can at once calculate its radius, which turns out to be 432,500 miles, or 109 times the radius of the Earth; the volume of the Sun is therefore 1,306,000 times that of the Earth. Taking 1920″ as the Sun's mean diameter in seconds of arc, and 865,000 miles as its linear diameter, it follows that an object on the Sun's surface which subtends 1″ has a linear size of 450 miles. This measure will be useful in estimating the scale of the varied phenomena observed on the Sun.

To discover, further, if the Sun is made of denser or less dense materials than the Earth, we need to determine its mass. The law of universal gravitation tells us how to express the Sun's mass as a function of the quantities characterising the Earth's motion about it. Assuming, with sufficient accuracy for the present purpose, that the Earth's orbit is circular, we can equate the centrifugal acceleration to which the Earth is subjected and the attractive force acting between Sun and Earth according to Newton's law. The constant of universal gravitation being known, we find that the mass of the Sun is 333,420 times greater than the Earth's: if the Earth weighed one-tenth of an ounce the Sun would weigh 3 tons.

These figures show clearly how small the Earth is compared with the Sun; to redress the balance, however, the Earth is denser than the Sun, for if we compare the ratio of their volumes (1,306,000:1) with that of their masses (333,420:1) it is apparent that the Earth's density is some four times as great as the Sun's. Since the mean density of the Earth is 5·5 times that of water, that of the Sun (taking the density of water as unity) is 1·4. Already we are beginning to glimpse the fact that the Sun cannot be in a solid state, for its constituent materials are on the average much less dense than those solid materials of which the Earth is composed.

These data allow us, in addition, to calculate by how much the force of gravity at the Sun's surface exceeds that of the Earth. The ratio of the two forces may be approximately determined by dividing the ratio of the two masses by the square of the ratio of the two radii: the force of gravity on the Sun is about 28 times stronger than on Earth, whence it follows that a falling body, which travels 16 feet in the first second on Earth, would travel some 450 feet on the Sun.

Chapter I

HOW THE SUN IS OBSERVED

4. VISUAL AND PHOTOGRAPHIC TELESCOPES; SOLAR EYEPIECES

For the visual observation of the Sun any astronomical telescope is suitable, whether it be a refractor with a visually-corrected achromatic object glass or a reflector with a parabolic mirror.

The shorter the focal length of a telescope of given aperture, the smaller and brighter is the image formed in the focal plane of its object glass or mirror. In fact, the ratio between the diameter of the image and the real diameter of the Sun is equal to that between the focal length of the objective and the distance of the object; whence it can be calculated that, for example, an objective of 10 feet focal length will produce a solar image 1·13 inches in diameter an objective of 20 feet focal length an image 2·26 inches in diameter, and so on. This image may be observed directly with an ordinary ocular (which in turn forms an image—virtual, inverted and magnified—of the primary image) or it may be observed with the same ocular by projection. In direct observation, however, some means of reducing the intensity of the image is required if the eye is not to suffer injury; therefore to the ocular is attached a 'solar eyepiece' which in its simplest form consists of a plane parallel slip of tinted glass. Usually a black glass is preferred, which allows the passage of a small proportion of rays of such wavelengths as to give the Sun's image a whitish, slightly smoky appearance; alternatively, reflected or polarised light may be used, as in the solar eyepieces devised by Herschel and by Fr Cavalleri. Another type of solar eyepiece is that of Colzi, in which the intensity of the Sun's image is reduced in passing through a double prism consisting of a right-angled glass prism and a similar liquid prism. The pencil of rays, after reflection at the glass surface S (Figure 3) enters the glass prism P_1, and would be totally reflected were it not for the liquid prism P_2. But since P_2 is filled with vaseline oil, whose refractive index differs very little from that of glass, the reflection occurring at the hypotenuse is only partial, and the solar image reaching the observer's eye is suitably weakened.

It is possible by projection to observe the telescope's image on a screen, as was already the practice of Galileo and Fr Scheiner (Plate 4); this method is particularly convenient when it is desired to make drawings of the details of the solar surface. To do so it is only necessary to rack out the ocular from the focal plane of the objective until the image of the Sun comes into focus on the screen placed at a convenient distance behind the ocular. The diameter of the image on the screen depends upon the ratio of the distance of the screen from the ocular to the focal length of the ocular itself, multiplied by the diameter of the primary image formed by the object glass or mirror.

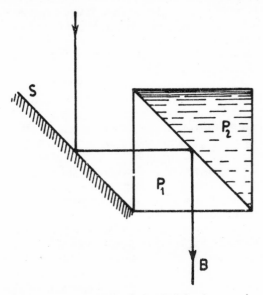

Fig. 3. Arrangement of the Colzi solar eyepiece.

If, alternatively, it is desired to photograph the Sun's image, all that is required is a photographic plate in the telescope's focal plane; in the case of a refractor, however, the object glass should be photographically corrected, so that the violet rays are brought to the same focus as the visual; if, on the other hand, a visually corrected object glass is used it is advisable to take the photograph through a filter which absorbs the shorter wavelengths. In any case, unless a telescope of long focal length is used the solar image at the principal focus will be small, and therefore it is desirable to enlarge it—as was done by projection in visual observation—by placing the photographic plate in the position of the projection screen. Telescopes constructed for this purpose are also termed 'heliographs'.

If a bright, but at the same time not too small, image of the Sun is required, so that its individual details may be distinguished, telescopes of long focal length must be employed, for the reasons given above. If, in addition, a high-dispersion spectrograph, also of considerable focal length, is to be attached to the telescope, the dimensions may be such as to prove inconvenient or even prohibitive, so far as a movable system consisting of telescope and spectrograph is concerned. For such purposes the idea of constructing long telescopes which are fixed in either a horizontal or a vertical position has been exploited; the Sun's image is reflected into the instrument throughout the hours of daylight by one or two plane mirrors oriented at the appropriate angles.

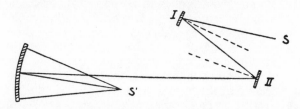

Fig. 4. Arrangement of the horizontal Snow telescope.

Examples of the horizontal type are the Snow telescope at Mt Wilson in California, a reflector, and various refractors at Meudon Observatory in France. The Snow telescope consists of a first plane mirror, also termed a 'coelostat' (Figure 4, I), a second plane mirror (II) and a concave mirror which forms an image of the Sun (S) at S'.

It is the task of the coelostat and the second mirror to reflect the Sun's light in a constant direction at all seasons and at all times of the day. The coelostat is therefore mounted on an axis which is parallel to that of the Earth and is turned by clockwork so as to follow the Sun in its apparent diurnal motion. The coelostat is movable on rails in an east-west direction, the second mirror similarly north-south; by this means it can be arranged that the concave mirror is fully illuminated at all hour angles and declinations of the Sun. The pencil of rays reflected from the plane mirrors is focused to an image by the concave mirror, whose aperture is 24 inches and focal length 59 feet. It is situated at the rear end of a shed consisting of an iron frame covered with white canvas, which is well ventilated so as to reduce undesirable heating.

The solar image at the focus S' of the concave mirror is about $6\frac{3}{4}$ inches in diameter, and may be directly photographed in that position by means of a spectrograph or spectroheliograph, as explained below.

The vertical type of fixed telescope was first constructed by G. E. Hale, and is known as the 'solar tower'. The refractor or reflector, fixed vertically, receives the Sun's light from a coelostat and second mirror mounted at the top of the tower. There are various solar towers in existence—for example, at the Mt Wilson, Arcetri (Florence), Potsdam, and McMath-Hulbert (Lake Angelus, Michigan) Observatories. Here the Arcetri instrument will be described.

The general arrangement of the different parts of this tower, which is of the refracting type, is shown in Figure 5. At the top, protected by a revolving dome, are the coelostat C and the second mirror D. Below the mirror is an astronomical object glass A, of about 12 inches aperture and 59 feet focal length, which forms a real image of the Sun, $6\frac{3}{4}$ inches in diameter, at B. B marks the end of the vertical telescope and the beginning of the instrument used to split up the Sun's light into its spectrum; this is housed in a pit dug in the ground on the axis of the tower.

The objective at the top of the tower can be adjusted in the vertical direction by an electrical mechanism controlled from the observing room at the base of the tower, so that the observer, by varying its distance from the plane B, can bring the image to a focus at the spectrograph slit situated there. The mirrors can also be rotated electrically, so as to bring any desired region of the Sun's image to the slit of the spectrograph.

The object glass A can be replaced by another, situated 23 feet (its focal length) above the plane B; this provides a solar image at the spectrograph slit about 2·75 inches in diameter. The one tower thus houses two telescopes, giving solar images of different sizes, which facilitates research of different types.

In order to eliminate the effect of wind the larger Mt Wilson tower is of double construction, consisting of one iron lattice-work structure inside another: the inner carries the mirrors, while the outer carries the dome and at the same time protects the inner. In the Potsdam tower the mirrors are supported by a wooden tower inside one of reinforced concrete. That at Arcetri is a simple lattice-work tower of reinforced concrete, and provides a vibration-less image in moderately strong winds.

At the McMath-Hulbert Observatory a cylindrical tower of sheet iron encloses and protects the steel lattice-work which carries the mirrors. It is of the reflecting type, the coelostat and

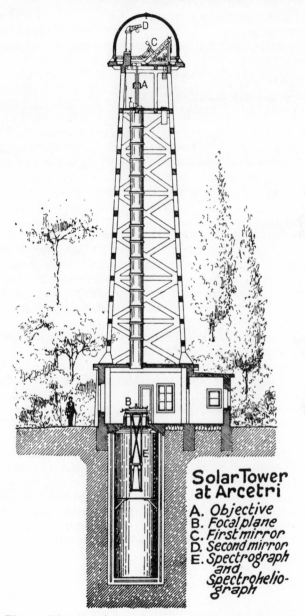

Solar Tower
at Arcetri
A. *Objective*
B. *Focal plane*
C. *First mirror*
D. *Second mirror*
E. *Spectrograph
   and
   Spectrohelio-
   graph*

Fig. 5. Diagram of the solar tower at Arcetri, Florence.

45

second mirror reflecting the Sun's light to a parabolic mirror mounted at the base of the tower; this in turn reflects it to a third plane mirror which transmits the solar image to the observing position.

5. SPECTROSCOPES, SPECTROGRAPHS, SPECTROHELIOGRAPHS, SPECTROHELIOSCOPES AND AUXILIARY INSTRUMENTS

These various names refer to instruments which are used for the visual or photographic observation of the Sun's spectrum and of its monochromatic radiations. If we split up a beam of sunlight with a prism we obtain its spectrum—an ordered series of colours from red to violet. If we wish to obtain a 'pure' spectrum—i.e. one showing the lines first observed by Fraunhofer in 1814, which bear his name—the pencil of solar rays must, before passing through the prism, be restricted by a narrow slit and also rendered parallel by means of a lens termed the collimator. After leaving the prism the coloured rays are collected by another lens, which forms an image of the spectrum; this is then observed, magnified, with an ocular. The slit, lenses and prism together constitute a spectroscope, so called because it is used for the visual observation of the spectrum.

If, on the other hand, it is desired to photograph the spectrum, the ocular must be replaced by a photographic plate. The width of the spectrum recorded on this plate will depend on the dispersive power of the prism and the focal length of the camera objective which forms the image on the plate; the intensity of the spectrum will vary according to the plate's sensitivity to the different colours. Such instruments are termed spectrographs.

Spectroheliographs and spectrohelioscopes are instruments used for the photographic or visual observation of the solar spectrum with a particular monochromatic radiation—that is to say, in the light of a single colour, or more precisely, with one of those Fraunhofer lines which we shall see later are of particular interest to the investigator. Once this line has been isolated from the rest of the spectrum it is possible with these instruments respectively to photograph it or examine it visually over the whole of the Sun's disc.

So far, in describing these various instruments, we have spoken of a single prism, but if we wish to increase the dispersion, thus obtaining a wider spectrum, it is necessary to use several prisms in succession. One such combination or train of prisms, in which careful choice of glasses of different refractive indices allows the spectrum to be observed in the same direction as the incident ray—

i.e. without deviation—is the so-called direct-vision prism invented by G. B. Amici in 1860. It consists of three prisms (Figure 6): *1* and *2* are of borosilicate crown, whose index of refraction is smaller than that of prism *3*, which is made of dense silicate flint. Since the refractive angles of *1* and *2* are opposed to that of *3*, as can be seen from the diagram, the dispersion of the crown prisms tends partially to cancel that of the flint, but the refractive angles and indices of refraction are so chosen that at the exit of the system there always remains a dispersion of the incident ray in the same direction as that from which it arrived at prism *1*.

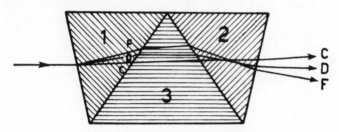

Fig. 6. G. B. Amici's direct-vision prism.

Instead of a prism or prisms, a diffraction grating may be used as the means of providing dispersion. Since the story of diffraction gratings—and particularly of their use in astrophysics—is both interesting and comparatively little known, we will give a brief account of it here, and at the same time explain how gratings are employed.

The discoverer of the phenomenon of diffraction was, as is well known, Fr Grimaldi, but the first gratings for obtaining the spectrum of a luminous source by means of diffraction were not made till many years later by Fraunhofer. It occurred to him to use a series of equally-spaced slits instead of the single pair of slits hitherto used for producing diffraction phenomena. His first grating, made in 1821, consisted of a silver wire wound round a brass frame. It was essential to take the greatest care that the intervals between the wires should be as equal as possible, this being an indispensable condition for the production of pure spectra. Fraunhofer later constructed gratings by engraving numerous parallel and equidistant lines on a glass plate; he finally succeeded in ruling up to 300 lines per millimetre.

If the prism of a spectroscope is replaced by an engraved glass plate of this sort and the view telescope is pointed perpendicularly to the plane of the grating, an image of the illuminated slit will be seen; if the telescope is shifted to various angles on either side of this position an ordered arrangement of spectra will be encountered, the violet end of each being nearest to the direct image of the slit and the red end furthest from it. These spectra are described as being of the first order, second order, third order, etc. In Figure 7, *O* represents the direct image of the slit, *VR* one of the first order spectra from violet to red, *V'R'* one of the second order spectra, etc.

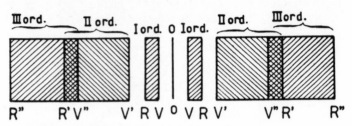

Fig. 7. Spectra of difference orders, produced by a diffraction grating.

Thus whereas a prism produces a single spectrum a grating produces a series of spectra. Despite the fact that the brightness of these spectra decreases as the order increases, gratings are preferable to prisms when, as in the case of the Sun, there is an abundance of light to illuminate the slit; for gratings have two advantages—great dispersion, and deviation which is proportional to wavelength.

Rutherfurd at New York was the first to produce 'reflection gratings' by silvering a glass plate; these are gratings which produce spectra by reflection instead of by transmission. He was also able to engrave such gratings on speculum metal, as well as on glass; this is an alloy of brass and tin, with a trace of arsenic to increase its brilliance, and has the advantage that, being softer than glass, it is easier to engrave and does not so rapidly blunt the diamond point used to rule the very numerous lines.

An American physicist, H. Rowland, attained a high degree of precision in making these gratings, using a machine of his own construction. He succeeded in engraving up to 4000 lines per millimetre both on plane metal plates and on concave mirrors which, possessing a definite focal length, obviated the necessity for additional lenses to focus the images of the spectra. The great precision obtained by Rowland resulted from his use of a perfect screw to shift the diamond point used to rule the lines, and the careful attention given to the shape of the diamond point and to

PLATE I. King Tut-ankh-Ammon and Queen Ankhesenpaaten illuminated
and protected by the god Ra (xviii Dynasty, *c.* 1600 B.C.).

PLATE 2. Sunrise as depicted on an Attic cup of the fifth century B.C.

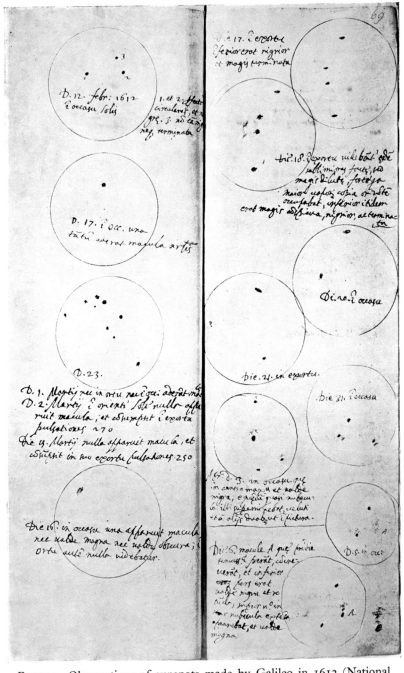

PLATE 3. Observations of sunspots made by Galileo in 1612 (National Library, Florence).

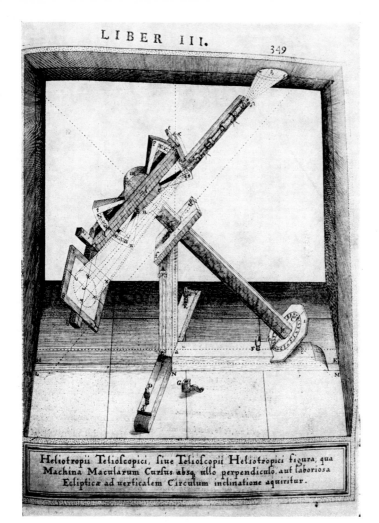

Heliotropii Teliofcopici, fiue Teliofcopii Heliotropici figura, qua Machina Macularum Curfus absq; ullo perpendiculo, aut laboriosa Eclipticæ ad uerticalem Circulum inclinatione aquiritur.

PLATE 4. Equatorial mounting used by Fr Scheiner for observing the Sun (from Book III of the *Rosa Ursina*).

PLATE. 5. Exterior of the horizontal Snow telescope, together with the two solar towers at Mt Wilson, California.

PLATE 6. The solar tower at Arcetri Observatory, Florence.

PLATE 7. Coelostat of the Arcetri solar tower (mirror C in Figure 5).

PLATE 8. The coelostat directed towards the Sun.

PLATE 9. Observing room of the Arcetri solar tower, showing the upper part of the spectrograph and the spectroheliograph; from the ceiling hangs the comparison arc.

the various parts of his dividing machine. His numerous gratings, widely used in astrophysical research, mostly have 600 lines per millimetre.

The technique of turning out good gratings is still rather difficult, and despite the progress that has been made in workshop practice few really good gratings have been made since Rowland's time. Good gratings, of remarkable size, have been made, and are still being made, in the workshop of Mt Wilson Observatory with a machine constructed by C. Jacomini (Plate 11); fine gratings have also been produced since 1953 by Bausch and Lomb, and great improvements have recently been achieved by H. W. Babcock.

The grating in use at Arcetri was ruled by Jacomini with a machine of this type. Its ruled surface measures about $4 \times 4\frac{1}{3}$ inches (10 × 11 cms), with 600 lines per millimetre, giving a total of 66,000 lines. The form of the lines ruled by the diamond is such as to concentrate the greater part of the light into one of the first order spectra, making it particularly suitable for use with the spectroheliograph.

Recently it has been found that aluminised glass (i.e. glass on which a thin layer of aluminium has been deposited by evaporation) provides greater brightness and allows greater accuracy in the ruling than does speculum metal. The lines can be ruled by a diamond on the aluminium film, or the glass surface itself can be engraved and then coated with a very thin and uniform layer of evaporated aluminium. At the Chicago University Institute of Physics gratings have been made with a ruled surface measuring about 8 inches (20 cms), and with 1200 lines per millimetre.

We will now describe the types of spectroscope, spectrograph, etc., most commonly used in observations of the Sun.

The types of spectroscope adopted by the early observers are still in use almost unchanged—particularly those for observing the prominences round the limb (Figure 8). The dispersive element is usually a train of Amici prisms, and the axis of the spectroscope, while remaining parallel to that of the telescope, is displaced laterally from the latter by an amount equal to the radius of the Sun's focal plane image; thus once the slit has been laid tangentially to the limb it will remain so when the spectroscope is rotated. The successive position-angles that the slit assumes relative to the Sun's limb, as the spectroscope is rotated, are read off an appropriately graduated circle. In this way the entire solar limb can be surveyed (Plate 12).

Spectrographs are for the most part of greater size, and are used with the vertical and horizontal Sun telescopes already described.

5—T.S.   49

The photographic method is an indispensable complement of the visual, over which it offers several advantages. With the spectrograph, for example, observations of the red and violet ends of the spectrum can be extended beyond the range visible to the eye; long exposures with very great dispersions can be made, recording on the plate the details of great numbers of Fraunhofer lines which can conveniently be measured later.

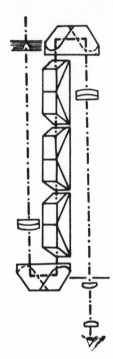

The dispersive element may be a prism, a grating, or a combination of the two. A frequently used arrangement employing a grating is that illustrated in Figure 9, in which a single lens, known as an autocollimator, acts both as collimator and as camera objective. The dispersion of a grating depends upon the order of the spectrum that is used, and on the number of rulings per millimetre; on the photographic plate the scale of the spectrum further depends upon the focal length of the spectrograph objective.

The focal length of the spectrograph in the large Mt Wilson solar tower is 75 feet, giving a scale of 5 mm per angstrom (the unit of wavelength, Å, equal to one ten-millionth of a millimetre) in the third order spectra: thus the two sodium lines, D_1 and D_2, are 3 cms apart.

Fig. 8. Layout of a prominence spectroscope. (Upper left, the slit; lower right, the eyepiece.)

As has already been said, the spectroheliograph is nothing more than a spectrograph which isolates the radiation of a given wavelength, such as a Fraunhofer line, and permits its examination over the whole solar disc.

Hale, following up this idea in the hope of being able to photograph the prominences, was the first to obtain positive results. In 1892 he succeeded in producing the first photograph of the chromosphere and the prominences that surround the solar disc, taken with one of the radiations of incandescent calcium vapour. His procedure was as follows.

Imagine an ordinary spectrograph to which a second slit has been added, immediately in front of the photographic plate; with this slit any desired region of the spectrum can be isolated—for example, one of its absorption lines. Thus only that solar radiation corresponding to this particular wavelength can record itself on the photographic plate, which is mounted almost in contact with the second slit. If, now, the whole instrument is shifted in such a way that its optical axis traverses the whole image of the Sun, all the successive positions of the slit being parallel to one another, an image will be built up on the plate which may be termed 'mono-chromatic'—or, rather, one corresponding to the radiations absorbed in the spectrum by the line under examination.

This image clearly represents an integration over the whole solar disc of the successive images of the first slit. To achieve this it is necessary for the motion of the solar image relative to the first slit (or vice versa) to be such that light from all regions of the disc should pass over the first slit in succession, whilst at the same time the photographic plate should partake of a corresponding motion relative to the second slit (or vice versa). The function of the second slit is to isolate the required line and nothing more; hence its width must be exactly that of the line itself, so that light from all other parts of the spectrum is excluded. The success of Hale's efforts was primarily due to the fact that he thought of using the H and K lines of calcium— the most intense solar lines, which, lying in the extreme violet, are of little use for visual observation, though they are very well adapted to photographic observation. Their exceptional intensity, the presence nearby of wide absorption bands which considerably reduce the brightness of the continuous spectrum, and the great sensitivity of the photographic emulsion to these short

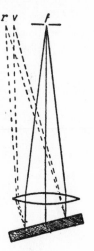

Fig. 9.
Arrangement of an auto-collimating spectrograph.

wavelengths, all combine to render these two lines admirably suited to the requirements of the spectroheliograph.

When, in consequence of the rapid progress of photography, it became possible to make use of red-sensitive plates, the red $H\alpha$ line of hydrogen was also successfully employed. Both on account of its intensity and of the large part played by hydrogen in the physics of the Sun, this development quickly led to important results.

We will now describe the type of spectroheliograph most commonly in use; although originally designed for photographing the prominences, it nowadays finds very much wider applications. The spectroheliograph can be used in conjunction with refractors or reflectors, or, if it is very large, with a fixed telescope of the vertical or horizontal type. Spectroheliographs differ among themselves in the matter of their moving parts: either the solar image and the photographic plate are fixed, and the whole spectroheliograph moves, or the spectroheliograph may be fixed, when the Sun's image is made to move across the first slit while at the same time the photographic plate moves past the second slit.

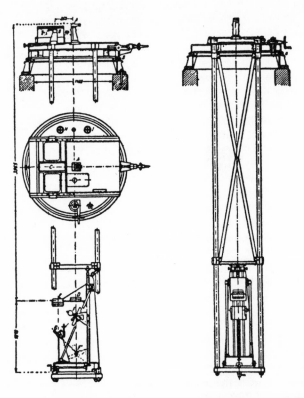

Figs. 10 and 11. Diagram of the combined spectrohelio-graph and spectrograph of the Arcetri tower telescope, seen from the side and from above.

The first spectroheliograph, Hale's now historic instrument which he built for his private observatory at Kenwood, near Chicago, was of the latter type. The spectroheliograph at the Arcetri solar tower—which is a combined spectroheliograph-spectrograph—belongs to the former. The two slits, A and B (Figures 10 and 11), are mounted on a platform which can be rotated about a vertical axis and also given a uniform horizontal motion equal in extent to the diameter of the Sun's image formed by the vertical telescope (about $6\frac{3}{4}$ inches).

The plate-carrier, C, is fixed to two supports which partake of the motion of the platform about its vertical axis but not of the motion of the two slits or of the lattice frame carrying the grating. At the lower end of this frame are mounted two objectives, D and E (6-inch aperture, 13 feet focal length), the mirror F and the diffraction grating G. The Sun's image is made to fall on the first slit, A, so that a parallel beam illuminates the mirror F, which in turn reflects it to the grating G. This disperses it and reflects it to the objective E, which forms an image of the spectrum in the plane of the photographic plate situated almost in contact with the second slit. This slit isolates any required line of the spectrum, and by moving the spectroheliograph across the solar image—which is kept stationary on the first slit by the coelostat clockwork—a photograph of the image in the light of this particular line is obtained. The mirror F can be moved down to F', thus varying the angle of incidence of the pencil of rays at the grating and allowing, within certain limits, a variation of its dispersion.

The displacement of the spectroheliograph is effected by a small electric motor mounted on the wall of the observing room, the transmission consisting of shaft and differential. This enables the spectroheliograph to be rotated about its vertical axis through an angle of 30° on either side of the east-west line, so that its displacement may at all seasons take place with the slit perpendicular to the Sun's equator.

A speedometer is coupled directly to the shaft of the motor; the reading of its dial gives the speed of the spectroheliograph's motion, which by appropriate choice of gear and motor speed can be varied from 0 to 25 mm (about 1 inch) per minute, so that exposures of different lengths can be made.

Mounted on a bar attached to the ceiling of the observing room is an electric arc, whose light is reflected into the spectrograph when it is required to have a comparison spectrum of a terrestrial source to compare with that of the Sun (Plate 9).

The same instrument can, if required, be used as a spectrograph, i.e. an instrument for photographing a section of the spectrum. All that is necessary is to replace the mounting of the photographic plate C (Figure 10) and the second slit B by another mounting, carrying a frame for a $3\frac{1}{2} \times 14$-inch plate; on this any region of the spectrum 14 inches long can be projected. The change-over from one instrument to the other is a matter of seconds; both have a focal length of 13 feet and a mean dispersion of approximately 4Å per millimetre.

The Rumford spectroheliograph, attached to the 40-inch equatorial at the Yerkes Observatory of the University of Chicago, is another example of the second type. In this instrument the solar image is moved across the first slit by displacing the telescope tube uniformly in declination, the photographic plate being simultaneously moved past the second slit by means of suitable electric motors.

The light from the first slit, having passed through a collimator, encounters a mirror from which it is reflected through two prisms; these, together with the mirror, turn the ray through 180° when the prisms are in the position of minimum deviation for the line under examination. The mirror can be replaced by a grating when greater dispersion is required.

The necessity for considerable dispersion shows itself clearly when the dark lines of the solar spectrum (excepting the broad H and K lines or bands of ionised calcium in the violet) are used. Since these lines only appear dark by comparison with the brilliant photosphere, and do in fact themselves emit light, it is possible with the spectroheliograph to obtain monochromatic images of the Sun by their means. But because these images portray the gas or vapour giving rise to the line it is absolutely essential that the dispersion should be sufficiently great to make the line wider than the second slit—for otherwise light from the continuous spectrum on either side of the absorption line would enter the camera and affect the plate.

Deslandres, at the Meudon Astrophysical Observatory near Paris, was constructing similar instruments for the examination of the Sun's monochromatic radiations at about the same time as Hale. At the outset he photographed the Sun with the second slit widened sufficiently to reveal a narrow strip of the solar spectrum on either side of the line under examination: thus if the line were displaced owing to movements of the gases in the line of sight (the Doppler effect) or for other reasons, these displacements would be recorded on the photograph. These images of the line were recorded across the whole solar disc, dividing it into so many zones which were photographed in turn, the spectrograph being moved on in a series of jerks. The spectroheliograph was a natural development from this type of instrument, which Deslandres named the *spectro-enregistreur des vitesses*. The spectroheliograph now at Meudon is used in conjunction with a horizontal telescope and various combinations of slits, grating and prisms.

This spectroheliograph is of the second type, the simultaneous movement of the object glass (1-inch aperture, 13 feet focal length) and the photographic plate being provided by two synchronised electric motors. The instrument is termed a multiple spectroheliograph because four alternative optical combinations are arranged round the same object glass and collimator. The function of these is to provide solar images of varying sizes and dispersions for a given line by quickly changing the optical parts and the dispersive element.

Although the practical application of photography to astronomical observation has developed with great rapidity—providing, until some years ago, the sole means available for the study of monochromatic images—it is nevertheless true that visual observation has certain advantages: among others, the speed with which the observations can be made, and the delicacy of the details that can be distinguished. For these reasons visual observations of the prominences at the limb are still made, and more recently Hale (following up a suggestion made long ago by Janssen, Lockyer and Young) constructed the first 'spectrohelioscope'—an instrument intended for the visual observation of solar phenomena in monochromatic light. The original idea was to oscillate or rotate the spectroscope slit in order to reveal the forms of the prominences; later, however, the widened-slit method, which will be described below, became generally used. It occurred to Hale to incorporate oscillating slits in the spectroheliograph: by giving both slits a rapid and synchronised movement, while the second slit was adjusted on, say, the $H\alpha$ line of hydrogen, not only would the images of the prominences be visible but also, by virtue of the persistence of vision, those of the bright and dark flocculi projected on the disc.

This was achieved by Hale at his solar observatory in Pasadena, California, with a horizontal telescope and a spectroheliograph of the type already described. The two slits of the spectroheliograph are mounted at the opposite ends of a horizontal bar; this is made to oscillate through about 0·2 inch about a support situated at the midpoint of the bar. Since the optical parts are arranged so that the second slit remains always superimposed on the chosen line, the synchronous oscillation of the two slits reveals a region of the Sun through a monochromatic window 0·2 inch wide; this is examined with an ocular magnifying 2 or 3 times. All one has to do is to regulate the speed of the motor supplying the bar's horizontal oscillation until a persistent image is seen.

The delicate structure of the solar details revealed by this means, and the possibility of observing on different parts (the red or violet side) of a given line, make the spectrohelioscope an invaluable complement to the spectroheliograph.

The principle of the spectrohelioscope's oscillating slit has been incorporated in the spectroheliograph of the McMath-Hulbert Observatory, so that with this instrument monochromatic photographs of the Sun can be taken without any movement of the solar image or photographic plate. In addition—as also with the Mt Wilson spectroheliographs—ciné-cameras have been installed, by whose means successive spectroheliograms can be taken on ordinary film at known intervals of time. This constitutes a notable advance, both on account of the continuous nature of the observations and also for the opportunity it affords of studying the development of the different solar phenomena.

Fig. 12. *Horizontal telescope and spectrohelioscope* (*G. E. Hale*).

From what has been said about spectroheliographs and spectrohelioscopes it will be apparent that these instruments are in effect nothing more than monochromators, since they permit the isolation of single radiations from the rest of the spectrum. Ordinary tinted glass filters are similarly monochromators, though they transmit a region of the spectrum that is always rather wide, embracing a considerable wavelength range in one colour or another.

But in recent times modern technology has solved the problem of constructing filters which transmit extremely narrow bands of the spectrum—even as small as 1 angstrom. With their aid, therefore, the whole solar disc can be observed in a given radiation without having recourse to instrumental movements or oscillating

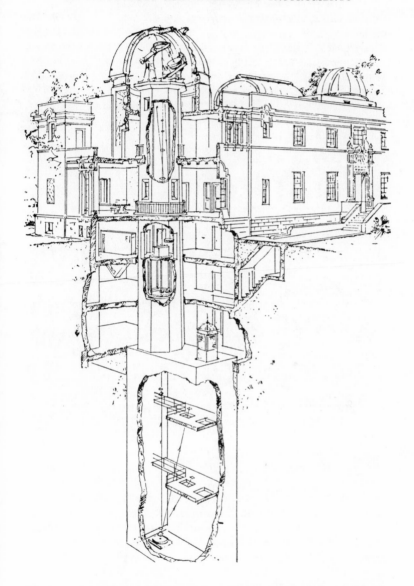

Fig. 13. *Astrophysical laboratory and solar tower of the California Institute of Technology (Caltech), Pasadena.*

slits, as is the case with the instruments described above. For the original idea of this type of filter we are indebted to the French astrophysicist, Bernard Lyot, and such filters have now been constructed and perfected both by him and by other workers. The principle on which they are based is the passage of the light to be filtered through a series of polarisers (P_1, P_2, P_3 . . . in Figure 14) with their planes of polarisation parallel to one another; these are

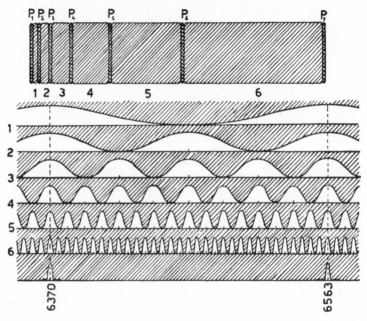

Fig. 14. Diagrammatic representation of the monochromatic polarising filter (B. Lyot).

separated by plates of quartz or iceland spar (1, 2, 3 . . .) whose thicknesses are calculated to produce interference fringes. The thicknesses and the number of these plates, at a correctly regulated temperature, allow the isolation of certain wavelengths, as can be seen in Figure 14. These wavelengths, as we shall see, are of particular interest in the study of the distribution of the gases in the chromosphere and corona.

Various instruments, whose names differ according to the function for which they are intended, are required for the examination and evaluation of the results of the visual and photographic observations. For the former there is the ordinary filar micrometer, which is attached to the eye-end of the telescope. But generally the measurements are made on photographs with the aid of comparators; these are fitted with micrometer screws and a graduated circle which permit the measurement of both rectangular and polar coordinates.

If one is going to measure the photograph of a spectrum one makes use of a spectrocomparator by means of whose micrometer screw wavelengths can be measured; alternatively it may provide means for projecting one spectrum alongside another—for example, a comparison spectrum and that of the Sun.

For the measurement of the intensities of different solar phenomena registered on photographic plates, microphotometers, either visual or recording, are employed. The plate under examination, suitably illuminated, transmits more or less light according as to whether the darkening of its different parts is less or more intense. The light thus transmitted by the plate is received by a thermopile or photocell which in turn causes the deflection, greater or smaller, of a galvanometer needle. The oscillations of this needle are recorded photographically and from the resultant trace the values of the intensity of the light which affected different parts of the photographic plate can be derived.

Chapter II

THE SUN UNDER DIRECT VISUAL AND PHOTOGRAPHIC OBSERVATION

6. *THE BRIGHTNESS OF THE SUN

Whilst considering the Sun as a star we saw how very much nearer the Earth it is than the nearest of the fixed stars; for this reason it is so much more brilliant than the stars.

The magnitudes of the stars, as is well known, are expressed in terms of a scale which was already established in ancient times for those stars that are visible to the naked eye: the brightest stars were assigned to the first magnitude, and to the sixth all those which could only just be glimpsed. The scale was later extended to include stars which are only visible with a telescope, and it was established by photometric means that from one magnitude to the next the brightness decreases by a factor of about 2·5. If the brightness of the Sun is to be expressed on this scale it is necessary to employ negative numbers to indicate its magnitude, the precise value being −26·72. On the same scale Sirius also has a negative magnitude, but in this case it is only −1·6. It can quickly be calculated, by means of the 2·5 ratio mentioned above, that the Sun appears to be eleven thousand million times brighter than Sirius. But this enormous difference in apparent brightness is entirely due to the respective distances of Sirius and the Sun from the Earth: for if the Sun were removed to the distance of Sirius it would appear as a star of the second magnitude, 3·6 magnitudes fainter than Sirius.

If the Sun is observed telescopically by any of the methods already described it will be seen that the disc is brightest at the centre and thence becomes steadily dimmer towards the limb; the luminous surface is termed the photosphere. Its uniform character is frequently marred by dark spots, and also by larger or smaller areas in the neighbourhood of the limb which are brighter than the photosphere; these were first observed by Galileo as 'piazzette più chiare del resto' and when describing them to Marco Welser in 1613 he gave them the Latin name of 'faculae'.

The photosphere, however, is not perfectly blank and featureless, but exhibits a sort of granulation which is more easily seen when the Sun's image is made to move fairly rapidly in the telescopic field, or on the screen when it is being observed by projection; when the atmospheric conditions are good it is also shown on photographs. In general appearance this granulation appears to consist of innumerable relatively bright grains (as of rice) projected on a less bright background; it is these granules that are effectively responsible for the brightness of the photosphere, for they stand out in marked contrast from a background which, although itself very bright, is considerably less so than the rice-grains. The granulation is well seen at the centre of the disc, but nearer the limb, where the intensity of the emergent rays is reduced owing to their oblique angle, the brightness of the rice-grain relative to the background is much reduced, along with the overall brightness.

The granules are normally circular in shape, though in the neighbourhood of spots they become elongated; their diameters do not exceed 1″. The granulation is thus not uniform, and is furthermore so dependent on atmospheric conditions that the study of its variations, and especially of the movements of the individual grains, is extremely difficult, whether by visual or by photographic methods.

Photographs taken under good seeing conditions also reveal what Janssen termed the solar *reseau*: the granular photospheric background is not uniform in all regions but displays a pattern consisting of a greater or smaller number of separate zones. While the granules in the spaces between these zones are certainly of a different size they are still clearly and distinctly visible; those within the zones, however, are distorted and partially invisible, often vanishing altogether and being replaced by streaks. These distorted areas are more or less circular, though they sometimes also assume a polygonal appearance. The diameter of the zones varies, but often exceeds 1′ arc.

The displacements suffered by the Sun's rays in passing through the terrestrial atmosphere provide a likely explanation of these phenomena. The outline of the Sun's limb always appears more or less wavy, owing to the constant movements of the atmospheric layers, and the same deformations that affect the limb naturally affect the rest of the disc also. It has also been suggested that the darker and lighter zones are a result of the different intensities of the gaseous condensations that form the photosphere—actual columns of ascending and descending gases.

Recently several workers have undertaken the investigation of the characteristics of the granulation, i.e. the dimensions, motions and intensities of the individual grains. Their diameters are for the

the most part of the order of $1''$ or $2''$, larger diameters than this probably being due to the distortion of the images by our own atmosphere. The determination of the differences of intensity between individual granules likewise depends upon the quality of the images, but for grains of $5''$ diameter it has been found that (expressing the difference in stellar magnitudes) $\Delta m = \pm 0.07$; this corresponds to a temperature difference of $110°$ between the dark and the bright regions, assuming that the temperature of the solar surface is $5700°K$. Under exceptionally good seeing conditions photographs taken in the visible region of the spectrum show rice-grains with a diameter of about 600 miles. The mean distance between adjacent granules is about 900 miles, so that they cover about 35% of the whole solar surface. Their intensities are from 15% to 20% greater than that of the intergrain surface, indicating a temperature difference of about $200°$ to $300°$.

All this refers to undisturbed regions of the Sun. Extremely disturbed regions are often encountered, and in these the rice-grains may be replaced by a tiny black spot. Such dark specks grow simultaneously larger and darker until they appear to be completely black against the bright photospheric background. They are then termed 'pores', and are nothing more than minute sunspots.

7. THE SPOTS

When the pores grow to a considerable size they are termed sunspots. The birth and typical development of a spot, as discovered by observation, may be described as follows.

Two large spots are in general formed from single pores or small spots; the preceding member of this pair, also called the leader (relative to the direction of the Sun's rotation, i.e. that which will reach the western limb first), is in the majority of cases the more compact and has a faster motion in longitude. Between these two a string of small spots gradually develops; this, however, soon disappears, and with it the following spot. The remaining spot— i.e. the leader—thereafter assumes a circular shape, becomes progressively smaller, and finally disintegrates into a number of small spots or pores from which a new spot formation is frequently generated.

Both the durations and the sizes of sunspots vary between wide limits. Sometimes the whole sequence of events is unfolded in a few days; often, however, it lasts for months, occupying several successive solar rotations.

The majority of pores never develop into spots, while there are some spots whose diameters are many times greater than that of the Earth. Pores and small or medium-sized spots are for the most part more or less circular. Large spots, on the other hand, are characteristically of extremely complicated structure, and often occur in groups which include many smaller spots and pores.

In all fully developed spots two regions can be distinguished: the umbra, or central region, whose surface is uniformly dark, and the penumbra which surrounds the umbra. Pores appear to lack a penumbra, or at best to have a very inconsiderable one. In the vicinity of a spot the density of the granulation differs from that of regions remote from any spot: the granules appear to be larger or more closely packed, so that the granulation itself is hardly distinguishable, the less luminous background being almost completely hidden. The boundary separating the bright photosphere from the penumbra is extremely sharp: the background becomes very dark, the granules assume an elongated form and group themselves radially about the spot, and are separated from one another by relatively wide intervals. This radial arrangement of the granules ceases as abruptly as it began, and within it is the uniformly dark umbra. The umbra only appears to be dark by comparison with the photosphere, however; in reality it is always extremely brilliant.

Galileo, controverting Fr Scheiner's observations, had already noted this fact in the first of his letters to Welser: '. . . I believe, on the contrary, that the spots visible on the Sun are not only less dark than the dusky markings on the Moon, but that they are not inferior to the brightest regions of the Moon when directly illuminated by the Sun . . .'. That this is so can easily be observed when one of the inner planets, Venus or Mercury, passes in front of the Sun's disc. The hemisphere of the planet that is turned towards the Earth is completely dark, its apparent luminosity deriving from sunlight reflected on to it from our own atmosphere. For this reason the planet's apparent brightness is not negligible; nevertheless it is considerably darker than the self-luminous umbra of any spot with which it can be compared. The numerous estimates of the brightness of a typical umbra that have been made differ widely among themselves; as a mean value, 0·4 times that of the photosphere may be taken.

Spots, besides being divided into umbra and penumbra, often contain brilliantly luminous material which divides up the umbra in the manner of bridges (Plates 24 and 25); large spots may contain several such bridges. We shall see later how results obtained with the spectroheliograph have accounted for the development and life-history of these bridges.

At times of great solar activity enormously large spots may be observed, with umbrae measuring more than 2' (roughly 55,000 miles) in diameter, or seven times that of the Earth. Dimensions of this order are somewhat rare, and a spot whose overall diameter (including the penumbra) reaches even 30,000 miles is exceptional. When a spot attains to a diameter of 25,000 miles it becomes visible to the naked eye; at the maxima of solar activity spots of this size are frequently observed.

Almost 16,000 spot groups have been recorded since 1874, the year in which the Greenwich Observatory began its catalogue of spots observed daily by means of photography. Many spots are visible only for a day or two before they vanish, some develop to medium size, and a few attain to the dimensions mentioned above.

The daily area of each group is given in the Greenwich publications, the unit of area being taken as one-millionth of the Sun's hemisphere, or 1,174,000 square miles. Of the 16,000 groups that have been observed since 1874, only 27 have achieved an area of 2500 millionths, equivalent to about 3000 million square miles. Among outstandingly large groups, those that appeared during the last solar cycle in 1946 and 1947 are worth mention: they were the largest of all the spot groups which have been measured regularly since 1874, and probably also the largest that have been observed since the time of Galileo. The great group of April 1947—the largest ever observed—developed from some small spots which were already formed when observed at the Sun's east limb in latitude 23° south on February 5. These spots grew rapidly till February 7, when they formed a large enough group to be seen with the naked eye. When the group reappeared at the east limb on March 3, after one solar rotation, it had already changed markedly, having become much larger and more compact than in February. In March the group consisted primarily of one enormous spot which apparently developed from the leading—i.e. western—components of the February group, while the following components had disappeared. When it reappeared on March 30 for its third passage across the disc the great group, though more diffuse, was spread over a still wider area. At its maximum development the group covered 1% of the solar disc, its area being 5400 millionths of a hemisphere, or about 6200 million square miles; at its fourth and last passage it had shrunk considerably. The great spot of March 1947 broke all records as regards size, its area reaching 4300 millionths, or about 5000 million square miles.

Previously to 1874 the observatories recorded, not overall area, but the length and breadth of a group. From these data it is impossible to arrive at the area since the group might have consisted of many separate spots. A group observed during

PLATE 10. Observing the solar spectrum with the Arcetri solar tower.

PLATE 11. Machine at Mt Wilson Observatory for ruling diffraction gratings; constructed by C. Jacomini. On the machine can be seen a grating of 20 cm diameter in the process of being engraved.

PLATE 12. Prominence spectroscope employed with Amici's equatorial at Arcetri Observatory. The Sun is observed by projection with the finder.

PLATE 13. Interior of the well of the Arcetri solar tower, seen from above and showing the lower part of the combined spectroheliograph-spectrograph.

PLATE 14. Lower part of the spectroheliograph-spectrograph. Below the objective on the left (E in Figure 10) can be seen the diffraction grating.

PLATE 15. The Rumford spectroheliograph attached to the Yerkes Observatory 40-inch refractor.

PLATE 16. Lower part of the Rumford spectroheliograph showing the prisms and grating.

PLATE 18. The multiple spectroheliograph at Meudon Observatory.

PLATE 17. Coelostat and second mirror of the horizontal telescope at Meudon Observatory.

PLATE 19. Anterior part of the Meudon spectroheliograph, showing the arrangement for spectrohelioscopic observation.

PLATE 20. Spectrocomparator at Arcetri Observatory.

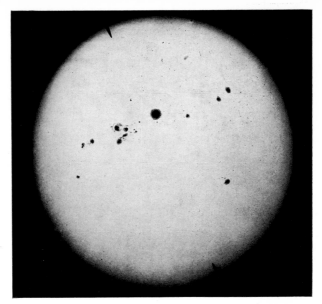

PLATE 21. Direct photograph of the Sun (Mt Wilson, 1929 November 30).

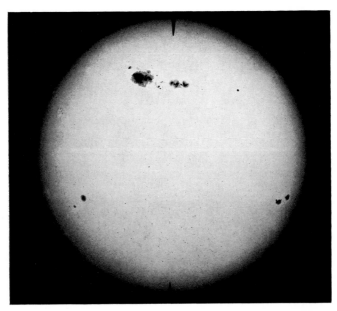

PLATE 22. The great spot group of the winter of 1946 (Mt Wilson, 1946 February 4).

September and October 1858, which was much extended in longitude, is quoted in several descriptive works as the largest that has ever been observed. But the derived value of the area would be erroneous if the group consisted of a long train of spots, and its overall extension were assumed to be the diameter of a large circular group; in fact, the group covered only 1000 millionths of the solar hemisphere.

Large spot groups commonly survive longer than one solar rotation (about 25 days). Groups of the largest area, although they may be observed upon the visible part of the Sun's surface, are usually born on the invisible hemisphere, whilst those born on the visible hemisphere disappear before attaining the maximum area. Only four out of 27 of the larger groups were formed on the

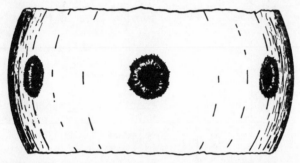

Fig. 15. Appearance of a spot at the centre of the disc and at the limbs (Wilson effect).

visible hemisphere; three of these lasted for as long as 90–100 days. Other groups of smaller dimensions survived for still longer periods. Sometimes it is not a single spot or group of long duration that one is observing, for the same region of the Sun's surface may remain active for months, producing a succession of new spots. These do, in fact, often reappear in a position whose co-ordinates are the same as those of an earlier group, sometimes even before the old group has disappeared.

When one wishes to consider the true shape of the spots one must bear in mind that they are located on the surface of a sphere and therefore appear under different perspectives according as to whether they are nearer to or further from the limb. Furthermore, since the spots are presumably disturbances in the photosphere they will not develop only on the surface but also at levels above or below it. Hence the problem arises of determining not only their form but also the level of the photospheric surface on which they appear.

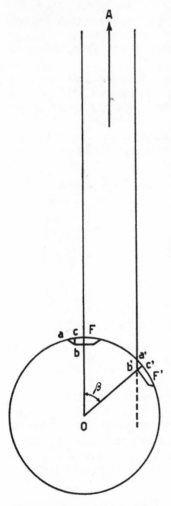

Fig. 16. *Measuring the depth of a sunspot.*

It was A. Wilson of Glasgow who in 1774 first noted, as a result of direct observations, that a spot whose umbra and penumbra are circular and concentric when it is at the centre of the disc seems to undergo a progressive change of shape as it approaches the western limb. The umbra shrinks steadily, and the eastern half of the penumbra likewise; at the same time the western part, nearest to the limb, contracts more slowly. Finally, close to the limb itself, the umbra disappears altogether, the whole spot now being reduced to a narrow dark line which is the western part of the penumbra. Should the spot survive long enough to reappear at the eastern limb 13 days later, the same sequence of events will be observed in reverse order as the spot moves gradually towards the centre of the disc.

Wilson quickly arrived at a simple explanation of this phenomenon: the spot is a funnel-shaped depression, the centre of which lies at a lower level than that of the photosphere. This level—i.e. the depth of the spot—can be determined by measuring the width of the penumbra when the spot is near the centre of the disc, and the angle between the centre of the disc and the spot's umbra at the time when the eastern side of the penumbra disappears from sight. Assuming that the shape of the spot, and therefore the width of the penumbra, remains sufficiently constant during the spot's passage from the centre to the limb, the depth of the spot can easily be calculated.

In this way Wilson found that the average depth of sunspots was about equal to one-third of the Earth's radius, a result confirmed subsequently by Herschel, Secchi, Tacchini and Fr Chevalier, although a number of spots have been observed whose appearance is different from that described by Wilson. Warren de la Rue, discussing observations made at Kew, found that out of 89 sunspots 72 were of the normal Wilson type, while 17 behaved abnormally. As a result of a long series of observations made at Zô-sè in China, Fr Chevalier confirmed that spots are in general depressions of various depths in the photosphere, but he derived a smaller mean depth than that of Wilson—not exceeding 1″, or about 450 miles.

If it is true that the majority of spots are cavities, then they should be seen on the limb as notches, deeper or shallower according to their sizes and depths. This effect had, in fact, already been observed by Cassini in 1719, and later by other observers. As has already been said, however, some spots do not behave in the manner described by Wilson, but in the opposite manner, so that it cannot be laid down as a general rule that the spots are at a lower level than the photosphere.

The hypothesis has also been put forward that although the spots are depressions within the penumbra, the umbra is nevertheless at a higher level than the photosphere. We shall see in the next chapter that these different levels can be determined with greater precision by spectroscopic methods.

8. *THE FACULAE

Faculae are regions of great brightness, usually greater than that of the photosphere, which straggle in irregular fashion for many thousands of miles across the Sun's surface. They are only to be seen in the neighbourhood of the limb, where they stand out in marked contrast to the reduced brightness of the photosphere. They appear as blotches or as branched structures, and their shape sometimes changes in the course of a few hours although they may remain for weeks in the same region of the Sun. When very close to the limb they occasionally appear to project from it, suggesting that they are elevated above the photosphere. If they are indeed at a higher level than the photosphere this would at once explain the fact that they appear so bright in the vicinity of the limb. The reduced brightness of the photosphere in this region is, indeed, probably due to the existence of a solar atmosphere whose capacity to absorb radiation would increase sharply towards the Sun's surface owing to its increasing density.

If a heavenly body is surrounded by an atmosphere of a given thickness it is obvious that those rays emerging perpendicularly from the surface of the body will pass through a thinner layer of atmosphere than those leaving it obliquely. Hence the light reaching us from the limb regions will pass through a more heavily absorbing thickness of atmosphere and will accordingly appear less bright than that emanating from the centre of the disc.

We shall see later that this marked absorption varies according to the wavelength of the solar radiation involved. If the faculae are elevated above the photosphere their light will have traversed a higher and less dense layer, therefore losing but little of its intensity, while the rays coming from the lower levels of the photosphere will be more heavily absorbed.

The faculae may therefore be regarded as raised areas—mountains of gas rising above the mean level of the photosphere. They are usually found in association with sunspots; this is not invariable, however, for faculae at times occur in regions devoid of spots. In general they appear long before the formation of a spot and survive long after it has disappeared; they may accordingly be thought of as regions of deep-seated disturbance in the Sun's atmosphere. Little can be said regarding their height above the photospheric surface except that it is probably not greater than several hundred miles; their crests are usually brighter than the intervening valleys and must therefore be hotter than the latter. The relative intensity of the faculae and the photosphere varies according as to whether they are nearer to or further from the limb, the respective figures being about 1·15 and 1·05.

9. *DISTRIBUTION AND PERIODICITY OF THE SPOTS AND FACULAE

If we are to investigate the distribution of the spots and faculae on the surface of the solar globe it is first necessary to determine their coordinates, just as is done for points on the Earth's surface.

It had already been noticed by the early observers that the spots and faculae move from east to west along paths parallel to the solar equator; if they are born on the invisible hemisphere they first appear at the eastern limb, to disappear at the western. They may last long enough to be seen for a whole rotation, or even several rotations, of the Sun. From these motions it has been deduced that the solar sphere, as seen from the Earth, rotates in a period of 27 days.

The points where the axis of rotation cuts the Sun's surface are its two poles: the north pole being the one which, as seen from the

Earth, is nearer to the north pole of the star sphere, the other being the south pole. As in the case of the Earth, every plane passing through the solar axis is termed a meridian plane, and the great circle where such a plane cuts the Sun's surface is termed a meridian. The meridian which at an agreed moment divides the visible hemisphere into two halves is chosen as the zero meridian, and from it heliographic longitude (analogous to geographical longitude on the Earth) is reckoned east and west. Since there are no fixed reference points on the Sun it is necessary to select a new zero meridian for each series of observations.

If now we imagine a series of planes arranged perpendicularly to the Sun's axis, these will trace out a number of small circles on the Sun's surface, which represent parallels of latitude; that which is determined by the plane which passes through the Sun's centre, perpendicular to its axis, is termed the equator. From the equator heliographic latitude is measured north and south, as on the Earth.

Filippo Salviati, the interlocutor in Galileo's *Dialogo dei Massimi Sistemi*, had the following to say on the third day of the discussion: 'Whilst at my Villa delle Selve, encouraged both by the presence of a solitary spot upon the Sun, very large and dark, and also by a long spell of very clear and fine weather, I asked that observations of the spot should be made throughout its entire transit; from day to day, at the hour of the Sun's crossing of the meridian, its position was carefully marked on a chart; thus it was revealed that its path was not a straight line, but on the contrary was somewhat curved. This put us in mind to make other observations from time to time. In this we were strongly encouraged by a theory that had suddenly entered my guest's mind, and which he explained to me in the following words: "Filippo, it seems to me that the way to an important conclusion lies open before us. For if the axis about which the Sun rotates is not perpendicular to the plane of the ecliptic, but is slightly inclined to this plane—as is suggested by the curved path which we have lately observed—then we shall have a firmer and more conclusive conception of the relationship of the Sun to the Earth than has been provided by any previous theory".'

The solar equator is, in fact, inclined to the ecliptic—i.e. the plane of the Earth's orbit—at an angle of about $7°$, whilst that of the Earth makes an angle of $23°\!.5$ with the ecliptic. Because of this inclination of the solar equator to the plane of the ecliptic, and therefore to our line of sight, the spots in crossing the disc do not usually describe straight lines, but ellipses which represent the orthographic projection of the parallels of solar latitude as seen from the Earth. Only when the Earth is at the two opposite points on its orbit where the Sun's equatorial plane cuts that of the ecliptic do the spots appear to follow straight paths, the solar equator then being a diameter of the apparent disc.

When the Earth is at these two positions it is also in the plane of the Sun's equator, and the line of sight from the Earth to the Sun is perpendicular to the latter's axis of rotation, which therefore lies in a plane perpendicular to the line of sight, i.e. in the plane of the apparent disc. For all other positions of the Earth in its orbit the Sun's axis is inclined to the plane of the apparent disc at angles varying from 0° to 7°. This inclination is the same as the angle

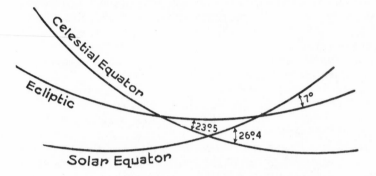

Fig. 17. Inclination of the solar equator to the ecliptic and to the celestial or terrestrial equator.

which the solar radius directed at the Earth makes with the Sun's equator, and may therefore be termed the heliographic latitude of the centre of the disc. This angle is clearly not of itself sufficient for determining the position of the Sun's axis as seen from the Earth; in order to do this the position angle of the axis must also be known—i.e. the angle which the projection of the axis on the apparent disc makes with a predetermined direction.

Now the Sun's apparent diurnal motion in the sky is in an east-west direction, and hence by noting the displacement of a well-defined point on the solar disc the north–south direction can be discovered, being perpendicular to the former; this direction is defined in the sky by the celestial meridians, and it is with reference to it that the position angle of the Sun's axis of rotation is referred. This angle varies from 0° to 26° 25′.

The inclination of the axis, and its position angle as defined above, depend not only on the position of the Earth in its orbit, but also on the inclination of the solar equator to the plane of the ecliptic (7°.2), the inclination of the Earth's equator to the same plane (23°.5), and the orientation in space of these three planes (the longitude of the ascending node of the solar equator on the ecliptic is 73°.7). It has already been said that at the two epochs when the Earth crosses the Sun's equatorial plane (early June and early December) the solar axis lies in the plane of the apparent disc, and the two poles are situated on the limb itself. In these circumstances the position angle of the axis attains a value of −14° (in June) or +14° (in December), whilst the minimum and maximum values (±26°.4) are attained on April 10 and October 10 respectively.

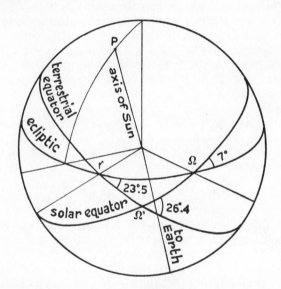

Fig. 18. *Orientation of the Sun with respect to the ecliptic and the terrestrial equator.*

From January to July the north pole lies to the west of the north–south line, and from July to January to the east of it. The occasions when the position angle of the solar axis is nil, its projection therefore coinciding with the north–south line, occur in early January and July. From June to December the Sun's north pole is turned towards the Earth, reaching its maximum inclination of 7°.2 in September, whilst from December to June the south pole is turned towards the Earth, maximum negative inclination occurring in March.

In the *Nautical Almanac*, the *American Ephemeris* and the

Handbook of the British Astronomical Association for each year can be found an ephemeris for physical observations of the Sun; this quotes for every day of the year, in addition to the two data referring to the solar axis (position angle and inclination, or heliographic latitude of the centre of the disc), the heliographic longitude of the centre of the disc reckoned from the solar meridian which passed the ascending node of the equator on the ecliptic on 1854 January 1.

It has already been said that the average period required by a spot to return to the same position on the disc relative to the Earth is 27 days. This is not the true period of the Sun's rotation, but what is termed the synodic rotation period, because in the time occupied by the Sun in rotating once the Earth has also moved on along its orbit. In order to derive the true or sidereal rotation period from the synodic period it is necessary to correct the latter for the distance covered by the Earth during one synodic rotation.

Since the spots are not fixed points on the solar surface, but often have proper motions of their own, it will be understood that they are incapable of yielding a very exact value for the rotation period —this, as we shall see later, can be derived by means of the spectroscope. We shall, furthermore, learn that the Sun rotates at different speeds in different latitudes, though the mean value of the sidereal rotation period may be given as 25·35 days at the equator.

The position of the Sun's equator in space, relative to the plane of the ecliptic, is expressed by means of two elements: inclination, which is simply the angle between the two planes, and longitude of the node, which is the angle on the ecliptic enclosed by the straight line marking the intersection of the two planes and a predetermined reference direction. The nodes are the two points at which the Sun's equator cuts the plane of the ecliptic: the ascending node is that at which a point on the Sun's equator passes (by virtue of its rotation) from beneath to above the ecliptic, the term descending node being reserved for the other. The longitude of the node always refers to the ascending node.

The problem of determining these two elements has been solved by various observers from Fr Scheiner onwards; values accepted nowadays are 7° 15′ for the inclination of the solar equator to the ecliptic, and 73° 40′ for the longitude of the node in 1850. It is necessary to state the epoch of the latter datum since its value is not constant, precession causing an annual increase of about 0.8; its present value is thus about 75°. Conversely, when these elements are known, the simple formulae of spherical trigonometry allow the coordinates of a spot, or of any other of the phenomena exhibited by the Sun, to be calculated; their positions are referred, either visually or photographically, to the centre of the Sun by reference to the limb.

The systematic observation of the spots and the determination of their positions on the Sun have shown that they do not occur indifferently over the whole surface of the Sun, nor always with the same frequency. There are, indeed, periods when the Sun is completely devoid of spots, and others when spots are present in considerable numbers. They are usually confined to two zones of the solar globe, bounded by the 5° and 40° parallels of latitude in each hemisphere. They rarely appear at the equator and have very seldom been observed in higher latitudes than 45°. Moreover, it has been found that their mean latitude at any time is closely related to their frequency. An investigation of the numbers and sizes of the spots will reveal that both vary considerably with time —not only from day to day, but also from month to month and from year to year. It had long been suspected that these variations were of a periodic nature, but it was reserved for Schwabe, as has already been noted, to discover that the maxima of sunspot activity recur every 11 years. The number of spots, though varying from day to day, exhibits a regular long-period trend, with a maximum during which it is possible to count up to 25 or 30 spots (including both large and small ones) and a minimum during which not a single spot may be seen on the Sun for several days or even weeks. R. Wolf succeeded in collating all the sunspot observations since the time of Galileo and in establishing a mean period of 11·1 years for their frequency, though this value is subject to considerable variations.

In order to assess this variable frequency he counted the spots in terms of his 'relative numbers' (R), which are still employed at the present day. These take into account the number of spot groups (g) visible on a given day, and also the number of single spots (f). While each spot counts as 1, each group counts as 10; hence the relative number for the day in question is the number of spot groups multiplied by 10 and added to the number of individual spots. In addition, to allow the observations of different observers, using telescopes of various sizes, to be treated as homogeneous, Wolf reduced them to a common basis by means of appropriately calculated factors (k), the factor 1 being assigned to his own observations at Zurich, made with a telescope of 10 cms aperture and a magnification of ×64. The relative number is then given by

$$R = k(10g + f).$$

73

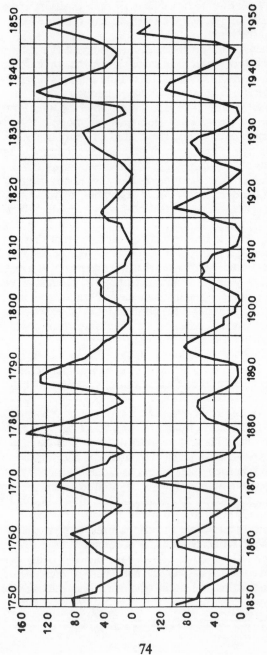

Fig. 19. The 11-year cycles of solar activity from 1750 to 1950. Ordinates: relative numbers, or Wolf numbers.

74

Wolf published his results in the *Astronomische Mitteilungen* of Zurich Observatory, where they were at first continued by his successors, A. Wolfer and W. Brunner, and currently by M. Waldmeier with international cooperation.

Because of the importance of the relative numbers in solar physical investigations, as well as in the relationships between solar and terrestrial events, the figures for every year from 1749 to 1954 are given in the Table on page 80.

A more precise use of spots as criteria of solar activity consists in measuring the total area that they occupy (both umbrae and penumbrae); this is regularly carried out at, for instance, Greenwich Observatory. There the area occupied by spots, expressed in millionths of the Sun's visible hemisphere, is measured daily on photographs by means of a grid engraved on glass, due allowance for the effect of perspective being made in the case of spots far from the central meridian. Thus at the 1859 maximum, for example, an average of about 1400 millionths was spot-covered each day, whilst at the subsequent minimum in 1867 the figure was only 200 millionths. At the 1913 minimum the mean daily area of the umbrae was only one-millionth, that of the entire spots (umbrae and penumbrae) 7, and that of the faculae 95; at the 1917 maximum, on the other hand, the figures were 247 for umbrae, 1537 for the whole spots, and 2305 for the faculae.

The relative numbers for the same years can be found in the Table; from it, moreover, the deviations of the various cycles from the mean figure of 11·1 years can be deduced. These deviations can also be clearly seen in Figure 19, as well as the different spot frequencies from cycle to cycle; it appears that a group of cycles showing strong activity is followed by a group of low activity. The same diagram—or, better, the upper half of Figure 20—furthermore shows that the rise from minimum to maximum is more rapid than the fall from maximum to minimum; it has, in fact, been deduced from the mean of the cycles so far observed that the interval from maximum to minimum amounts to about 6·5 years, while that between minimum and the succeeding maximum is only about 4·5 years.

We shall see later that considerations arising from the investigation of the magnetic fields in sunspots suggest that the duration of the complete solar cycle is 22 or 23 years rather than 11, and that the different intensities in different cycles is due to the superimposition on the 11-year cycle of other longer and shorter cycles. Schuster, investigating a series of cycles by harmonic analysis, unearthed at least four superimposed cycles, though these were not able to reproduce the observed variations with sufficient accuracy. Oppenheim, using an analogous theoretical method, established two cycles: one of 11·25 years and a super-cycle of 450

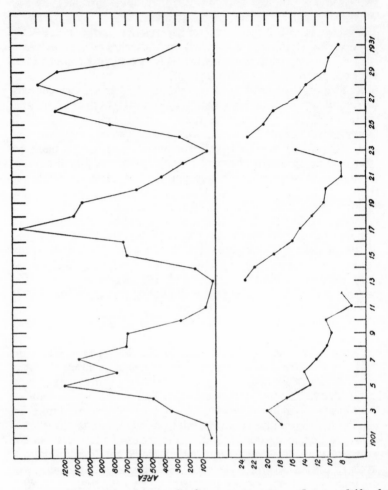

Fig. 20. *Upper: the three cycles from* 1901 *to* 1931. *Lower: drift of mean northern and southern latitude of the spots during the three cycles.*

years, by the combination of which he was able to reproduce Wolf's relative numbers reasonably well.

If we superimpose the maxima of the various cycles we find that the form of the spot-frequency curve is in general determined by

76

the maximum monthly relative number of a given cycle (R_m). M. Waldmeier has found that the duration of the rise from minimum to maximum (T) can be represented, for even cycles, by

$$\log R_m = 2 \cdot 69 - 0 \cdot 17T$$

and for odd cycles by

$$\log R_m = 2 \cdot 48 - 0 \cdot 10T$$

i.e. the number of years, T, decreases as the intensity of the maximum increases. The curves of four representative cycles are shown in Figure 21. This result is important, because when the com-

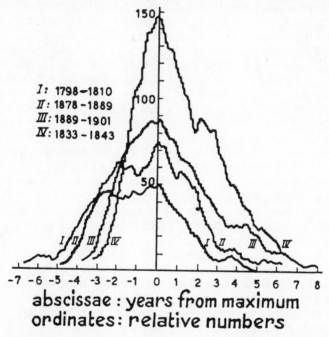

abscissae : years from maximum
ordinates: relative numbers

Fig. 21. Characteristic curves of different 11-year cycles (Waldmeier).

mencement and early trend of a cycle are known it allows the epochs of maximum and minimum to be predicted. Longer-range forecasts than this are not practicable, because the law governing the succession of high and low maxima is still unknown. It appears that the value of R_m increases and decreases in a period of about 7 cycles. A maximum for R_m occurred in 1778, another in 1860, and a third in 1937; the next and last, which was of abnormal height, was observed in 1947. It also seems that these long-period variations, repeating in a period of about 78 years, are displayed in the distribution of the spots in the north and south hemispheres.

The true trend of solar activity is much more irregular than that indicated by monthly or annual averages, as is proved by series of regular and uninterrupted observations. Thus a very high relative number may be found close to a very low one. These variations may persist for several days or even months, but exhibit no regularity or periodicity. The latter, however, is to be noticed in the rotation of the Sun, and may be studied by various methods; this, given the duration of the spot, is possible only assuming that the spots are often reborn in the same region of longitude.

It has already been said that the spots, besides varying in number with time, vary also in latitude. Spörer was the first to investigate this phenomenon, which is of considerable theoretical importance in connexion with the Sun's constitution and also with the magnetic period of the spots. They occur only in two zones, situated on either side of and parallel to the equator, which are effectively contained between latitudes $\pm 5°$ and $\pm 40°$. Following a minimum of solar activity the first spots of the new cycle appear around latitude $\pm 30°$. As the cycle proceeds the zones occupied by the spots move in towards the equator, so that by the time maximum is reached they are in $\pm 15°$; the zones continue to be displaced towards the equator until the end of the cycle, when they are at about $\pm 8°$. The first spots of a new cycle often make their appearance before the last of the old cycle have vanished; indeed, two or three years before the final disappearance of the spots in lower latitudes, those of the new cycle may be seen in high latitudes.

At sunspot minimum there are, therefore, four distinct zones of disturbance; two near the equator, approaching extinction, and two in high latitudes, pertaining to the new cycle, which begin to be active before the preceding cycle has come to an end. In Figure 22 are marked the centres of the spot groups that appeared during the 1934–44 cycle, and the beginning of the following one. The diagram clearly illustrates the characteristic features of the spots: the repetitions of the cycle, the restricted zones in which spots appear, and the shift of latitude during the course of a single cycle.

It is possible to envisage the formation on the Sun of a sort of giant wave of disturbance produced by the drift of the spots towards the lower latitudes, probably indicating a pulsating atmosphere such as is observed in the class of variable stars called Cepheids. In Figure 23 the various monthly relative spot numbers for the 1933–44 cycle are plotted in order to show the short-period variations that occur during the course of a cycle.

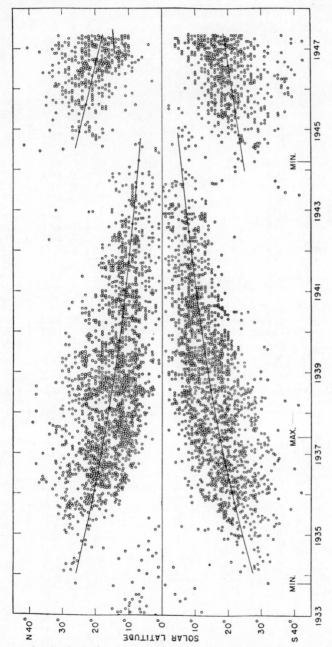

Fig. 22. *Latitude drift of spots from* 1933 *to* 1947. *Ordinates: solar latitude.*

79

Year	R	Year	R	Year	R	Year	R
1749	80·9	1799	6·8	1849	95·9	1899	12·1
1750	83·4	1800	14·5	1850	66·5	1900	9·5
1751	47·7	1801	34·0	1851	64·5	1901	2·7
1752	47·8	1802	45·0	1852	54·2	1902	5·0
1753	30·7	1803	43·1	1853	39·0	1903	24·4
1754	12·2	1804	47·5	1854	20·6	1904	42·0
1755	9·6	1805	42·2	1855	6·7	1905	63·5
1756	10·2	1806	28·1	1856	4·3	1906	53·8
1757	32·4	1807	10·1	1857	22·8	1907	62·0
1758	47·6	1808	8·1	1858	54·8	1908	48·5
1759	54·0	1809	2·5	1859	93·8	1909	43·9
1760	62·9	1810	0·0	1860	95·7	1910	18·6
1761	85·9	1811	1·4	1861	77·2	1911	5·7
1762	61·2	1812	5·0	1862	59·1	1912	3·6
1763	45·1	1813	12·2	1863	44·0	1913	1·4
1764	36·4	1814	13·9	1864	47·0	1914	9·6
1765	20·9	1815	35·4	1865	30·5	1915	47·4
1766	11·4	1816	45·8	1866	16·3	1916	57·1
1767	37·8	1817	41·1	1867	7·3	1917	103·9
1768	69·8	1818	30·4	1868	37·3	1918	80·6
1769	106·1	1819	23·9	1869	73·9	1919	63·6
1770	100·8	1820	15·7	1870	139·1	1920	37·6
1771	81·6	1821	6·6	1871	111·2	1921	26·1
1772	66·5	1822	4·0	1872	101·7	1922	14·2
1773	34·8	1823	1·8	1873	66·3	1923	5·8
1774	30·6	1824	8·5	1874	44·7	1924	16·7
1775	7·0	1825	16·6	1875	17·1	1925	44·3
1776	19·8	1826	36·3	1876	11·3	1926	63·9
1777	92·5	1827	49·7	1877	12·3	1927	69·0
1778	154·4	1828	62·5	1878	3·4	1928	77·8
1779	125·9	1829	67·0	1879	6·0	1929	65·0
1780	84·8	1830	71·0	1880	32·3	1930	35·7
1781	68·1	1831	47·8	1881	54·3	1931	21·2
1782	38·5	1832	27·5	1882	59·7	1932	11·1
1783	22·8	1833	8·5	1883	63·7	1933	5·7
1784	10·2	1834	13·2	1884	63·5	1934	8·7
1785	24·1	1835	56·9	1885	52·2	1935	36·1
1786	82·9	1836	121·5	1886	25·4	1936	79·7
1787	132·0	1837	138·3	1887	13·1	1937	114·4
1788	130·9	1838	103·2	1888	6·8	1938	109·6
1789	118·1	1839	85·8	1889	6·3	1939	88·8
1790	89·9	1840	63·2	1890	7·1	1940	67·8
1791	66·6	1841	36·8	1891	35·6	1941	47·5
1792	60·0	1842	24·2	1892	73·0	1942	30·6
1793	46·9	1843	10·7	1893	84·9	1943	16·3
1794	41·0	1844	15·0	1894	78·0	1944	9·6
1795	21·3	1845	40·1	1895	64·0	1945	33·2
1796	16·0	1846	61·5	1896	41·8	1946	92·6
1797	6·4	1847	98·5	1897	26·2	1947	151·6
1798	4·1	1848	124·3	1898	26·7	1948	136·3
						1949	134·7
						1950	83·9
						1951	69·4
						1952	31·5
						1953	13·9
						1954	4·4

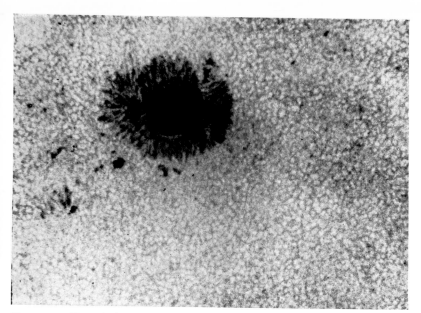

PLATE 23. Granulation photographed near the centre of the disc by Lyot at the Pic du Midi Observatory (Pyrenees), 1943 May 17.

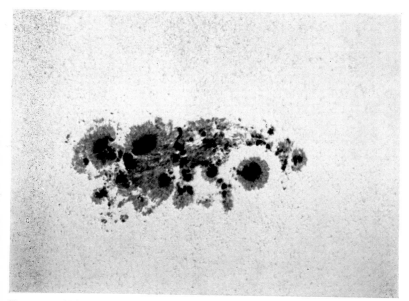

PLATE 24. Direct photograph of the great spot group of the summer of 1946. Dimensions, 156,000 × 78,000 miles (Mt Wilson, July 26^d 14^h 7^m).

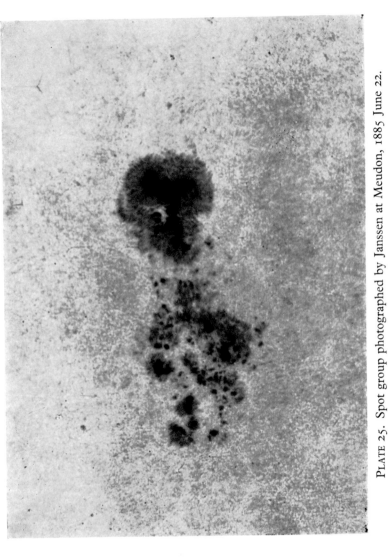

PLATE 25. Spot group photographed by Janssen at Meudon, 1885 June 22.

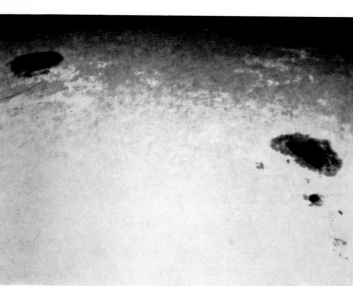

PLATE 27. Spots and faculae photographed at the Sun's limb (Meudon, 1908 September 14).

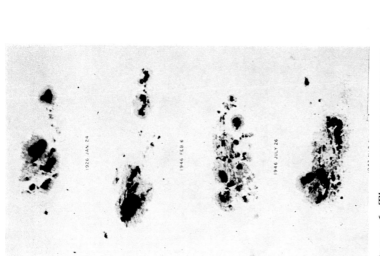

1926 JAN 24

1946 FEB 6

1946 JULY 26

PLATE 26. The greatest sun-spot groups observed.

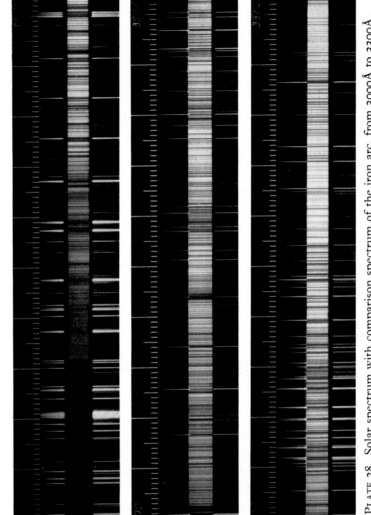

PLATE 28. Solar spectrum with comparison spectrum of the iron arc, from 3000Å to 3300Å.

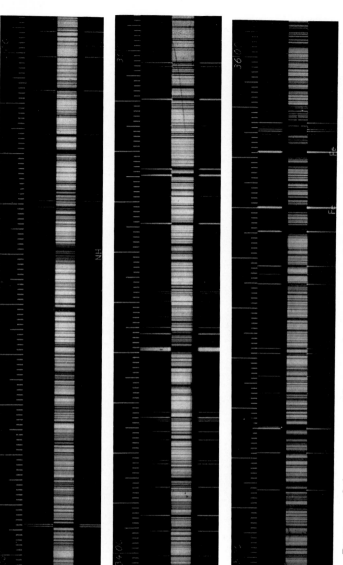

PLATE 29. Solar spectrum with comparison spectrum of the iron arc, from 3300Å to 3600Å.

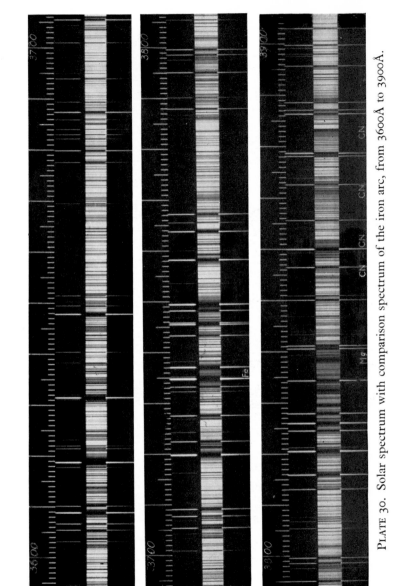

PLATE 30. Solar spectrum with comparison spectrum of the iron arc, from 3600Å to 3900Å.

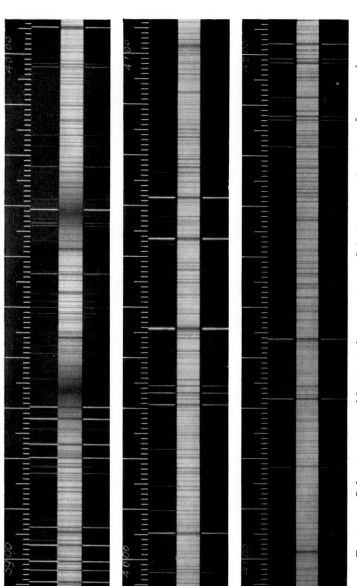

PLATE 31. Solar spectrum with comparison spectrum of the iron arc, from 3900Å to 4200Å.

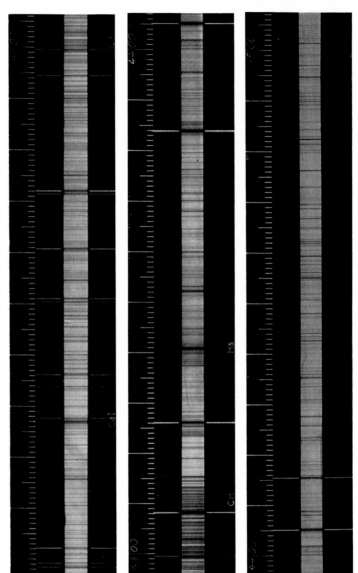

PLATE 32. Solar spectrum with comparison spectrum of the iron arc, from 4200Å to 4500Å.

There appears to be no obvious law, like that of the latitudes of the spots, for their distribution in heliographic longitude. Spot activity is generally unequally intense in different longitudes, being concentrated in certain zones of longitude which persist for longer or shorter periods, and may last for as long as several years. Spots are born in them from time to time, particularly in the form of long spot-chains which may extend for 90° in longitude. Furthermore the formation of spots in the two hemispheres is not independent, since there is some probability that a group in one hemisphere will have a corresponding group at the same longitude in the other, so that the regions occupied by spots in the two hemispheres appear to be connected. The frequency of spots decreases in proportion as their length of life increases. The majority of them last only for several days, their length of life depending on their latitude.

Spots usually appear first as pores, about 2″ in diameter; these may develop into spots or else disappear again. In the former case a group may

9—T.S.

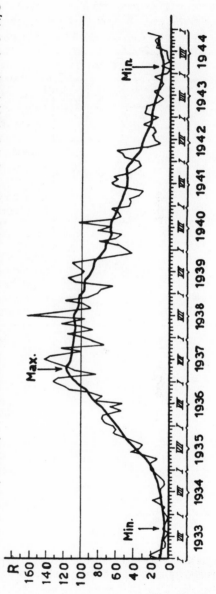

Fig. 23. *Relative spot numbers (monthly averages for the 1933–1944 cycle).*

81

be formed—consisting of a small collection of minute spots concentrated in a limited area—or alternatively a single spot. The majority of groups do not get past this stage, and disappear during the following few days. In the case of large groups the following development is usually observed: on the second day after its birth the group assumes an elongated form; the individual spots congregate at the preceding and following ends of the group, in both of which positions a larger spot than the others develops. These are the principal spots of the group and are known as the leader (i.e. the preceding one, in the direction of the Sun's rotation), *p*, and the trailer, or following one, *f*. The principal spots are furnished with penumbrae, and small spots are scattered over the space between them. The group attains its maximum area in about 10 days. During the following days the smaller spots disappear, leaving the main pair; then the *f* spot shrinks and likewise disappears, while the shape of the *p* spot becomes circular. The spot may persist for weeks at this stage before becoming smaller and finally disappearing. We shall later consider the manner in which this type of development is related to the magnetic fields present in the spots.

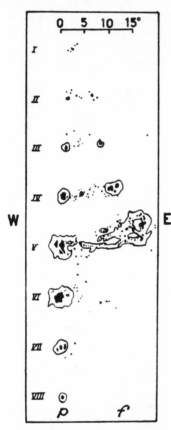

Fig. 24. Zurich classification of spot groups.

The Zurich astronomers have suggested an eight-stage classification of the development of spot groups (Figure 24). Class I comprises small pores, V represents the maximum development, with two large spots separated by an area covered with small ones, and VIII shows a single spot.* Some groups develop no further than

* The series of numerals from I to VIII has since been replaced by the letters A, B, C, . . . H.

class I, others develop to II and then relapse to I (I–II–I). The greatest development is represented by class V, the group occupying an elongated area whose major axis is oriented approximately parallel to the solar equator. The axis of the group—i.e. the line joining the two principal spots—is always inclined to the parallel of latitude passing through it, in such a way that the latitude of the p spot is smaller than that of the f spot. According to W. Brunner's measurements this inclination is $2°$ between latitudes $0°$ and $\pm 10°$; $7°5$ between $\pm 10°$ and $\pm 25°$; and $16°7$ between $\pm 25°$ and $\pm 35°$. The inclination of the axis depends upon the stage of development reached by the group: for a class II group its mean value is $7°8$; for classes III and IV, $6°5$; and a group of maximum development (class V), $4°6$. This decrease of inclination with increasing development results from the proper motions of the spots.

Regarding the faculae it may be said that their activity parallels that of the spots inasmuch as they are found close to or in the neighbourhood of the spots; in addition, however, they are encountered in high latitudes—according to the investigations of Mascari, between $75°$ and $80°$. The origin of these faculae appears to differ from that of the low-latitude faculae—or at any rate they do not acquire the same energy as the latter.

There are thus two facular regions: the first comprises the wide facular belts whose centres of activity vary with the 11-year cycle, moving inward from $\pm 30°$ towards the equator; the second comprises those facular zones which lie near the poles and which are of a more or less stationary character. We shall discover an analogous feature when dealing with the prominences, though it cannot be said that the two phenomena are identical.

It is interesting to consider the characteristics of the different cycles, examining both their 11-year trend and also their behaviour in particular years. Maxima which may be described as exceptional occurred in 1778, 1837, 1870 and 1947; these were separated by markedly lower maxima. This, as has already been said, may be due to the superimposition of other periods of different lengths. Among the maxima of the last hundred years, those of 1829, 1894, 1906 and 1928, which were of moderate or low intensity, exhibited a regular series of secondary maxima. The maximum of 1829 consisted of four secondary maxima separated by equal intervals of 11 months; the 1894 maximum had three secondary maxima, 12 months and 11 months apart; that of 1906, five at intervals of 7 and 11 months; and the 1928 maximum, three, separated by intervals of 15 and 17 months.

10. THE SUN'S ROTATION PERIOD AS DETERMINED BY THE SPOTS AND FACULAE

We have said that the Sun's rotation period, as determined by the motions of the spots, is 25·35 days, but that this is only a mean value, applicable to spots near the equator; for other spots, in higher latitudes, higher values are obtained. Spörer and Carrington, from their long series of systematic observations, derived values that agreed fairly well with one another, but the discrepancies between these and the values obtained by other observers were not explained till later, when Carrington himself demonstrated that the Sun does not rotate as a solid body; its rotation period varies as a function of latitude. It is minimal at the equator, and increases gradually towards the poles; the approximate values are as follows:

Latitude	Rotation period (days)
0°	25·0
10°	25·2
20°	25·7
30°	26·5
40°	27·4

The last value is uncertain, because of the small number of spots appearing at this latitude and the consequent scarcity of observations. We shall see later how these data may be extended to higher latitudes by means of the spectroscope.

The rotations in different latitudes are illustrated in Figure 25. It is based on the assumption that on a given date there are spots at 10° intervals of latitude along the central meridian (left-hand diagram). Each spot is carried westward by the Sun's rotation with a mean velocity appropriate to its latitude; the result is that at the end of one solar rotation their relative positions are as shown in the right-hand diagram.

Several attempts have been made to represent analytically the dependence of rotational speed on heliographic latitude by means of an empirical formula. Various formulae have been derived by different observers, but they are all of the same general form, containing a constant term and a term which varies with latitude. If we put ξ for the diurnal angular rotation—i.e. the angular distance covered by the spot in one day—it is clear that if the Sun rotated as a solid body ξ would have a constant value; instead, we have, for example, such formulae as the following, due to Spörer and Maunder respectively:

$$\xi = 8°.55 + 5°.80 \cos \phi$$
$$\xi = 12°.43 + 2°.01 \cos^2 \phi$$

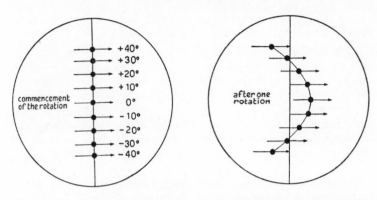

Fig. 25. *Apparent longitude drift of spots in different latitudes during one rotation of the Sun (Maunder).*

Taking the mean of the most reliable measures, we have:

Latitude	ξ (spots)
±0°	14°.40
±5	14·38
±10	14·31
±15	14·20
±20	14·06
±25	13·89
±30	13·69
±35	13·47

giving a difference of 1° in the Sun's angular velocity between the equator and the 35° parallel. These figures are derived from a very great number of sunspot observations, but as regards their accuracy it should be noted that individual results are extremely discordant owing to the proper motions of the spots across the Sun's surface.

A determination of the rotation period has been undertaken at

Greenwich Observatory, using only long-lived spots—i.e. those lasting at least 25 days; these are generally regular in outline, approximately circular, and the leaders of spot-groups. Such spots, by virtue both of their regular shape and their long duration, are very well adapted to the determination of the rotation. The diurnal angular sidereal motion, determined by 449 spots of the four cycles (1878–1923), was found to be

$$\xi = 14^{\circ}\!.37 - 2^{\circ}\!.60 \sin^2 \phi$$

Spots have proper motions in both longitude and latitude, and these may be either erratic or systematic. The systematic proper motions of long-lived spots have been investigated at Greenwich, where it was discovered that the motions in latitude are extremely small, amounting to no more than $0^{\circ}\!.1$ per rotation. Moreover, the general drift of the spot zone towards the equator during the course of the solar cycle—which should average $0^{\circ}\!.14$ per sidereal rotation—cannot be detected in the motions of individual spots.

The systematic motions in longitude, on the other hand, are of much greater importance. As long ago as 1913 Maunder had shown that these are related to the age of the spots. At the birth of a group it is generally possible to distinguish two principal spots, as already described: the leader (or preceding one, as defined by the direction of the Sun's rotation) is the furthest west of the two, and the trailer, or following spot, furthest east. During the first two days of its existence the leader advances rapidly in longitude by about $1^{\circ}\!.0$ per day. During the next two days its velocity drops to $0^{\circ}\!.4$ per day, and continues to decrease till the fifteenth day, after which its mean motion is that proper to its latitude. Around the twentieth day the spot has a slow retrograde motion of about $0^{\circ}\!.06$ per day. Corresponding changes take place in the size of the spot, which grows rapidly at first, reaching a maximum on about the ninth day and thereafter shrinking. Maximum size is attained at roughly the same time in the case of spots lasting about 60 days and of those with shorter durations.

Figure 26 illustrates this behaviour of the preceding spot. In the upper curve the ordinates are displacement in longitude: the rising section of the curve represents motion towards the west, i.e. in the direction of the Sun's rotation. In the lower curve the ordinates represent areas expressed in millionths of the visible hemisphere. The abscissae of both curves are the spot's age in days.

The motion of the following member of a pair is always slower than the mean velocity appropriate to its latitude; this is most noticeable at the time of its birth, when its mean value is 0°3 eastward. The corresponding variations in area are a rapid growth to a maximum on the third or fourth day, followed by a gradual decline.

The evidence of spectroscopic observations makes it impossible to doubt that the angular velocity of rotation of the different levels of the solar atmosphere increases with increasing altitude above the solar surface. If, therefore, the variations of rotational velocity shown by the leaders of groups are due to changes of level, it follows that the spots are situated at a greater height at the time of their formation, and that they sink rapidly to lower levels, decreasing in size as they do so.

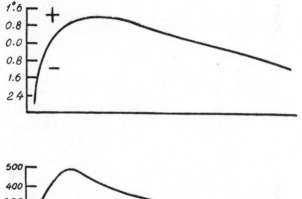

Fig. 26. Mean displacement in longitude, and variation of area, of the leaders of long-lived groups.

It may be that, as d'Azambuja observes, the forces acting at the time of a group's formation tend violently to separate the leader and trailer, and that when this initial impulse has died down the motions of the spots are arrested by the viscosity of the medium. The subsequent motion of separation, observed particularly in the case of the leader, will correspond to the true velocity of the stratum containing it, and will therefore be slightly smaller than that derived from the above formula based on long-lived spots.

Probably these proper motions in longitude are connected with the inclination of the axis of the group to the equator. The forward motion of the *p* spot in the first stage of the development of groups, and the decreasing inclination of their axes as the development continues, are different aspects of the same phenomenon, both being dependent on a single unknown cause.

Apparent displacements of the spots, both in longitude and latitude, due to the presence of a solar atmosphere and dependent on the spot's level in the photosphere, have been noted by different observers. Indeed, when a spot is near the limb it is observed obliquely through the Sun's atmosphere, so that from the Earth it will continue to be visible after it has passed round the limb, owing to solar refraction analogous to that of the Earth's atmosphere. Hence observations of spots in this particular position will

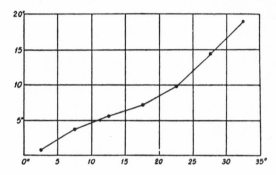

Fig. 27. *Change of mean inclination of the axes of spot groups as a function of heliographic latitude.* (*Abscissae, heliographic latitude; ordinates, mean inclination.*)

lead to an erroneous determination of the speed of the Sun's rotation. And if spots are cavities in the Sun's surface it will be necessary to take their depth into account if we wish to derive their rotation period relative to the surface of the photosphere.

The determination of the Sun's rotation period from observations of the faculae is difficult and not particularly accurate, since they differ from the general run of sunspots in providing no well-defined reference points; furthermore, they are only visible in the neighbourhood of the limb. On the other hand they offer the advantage, as compared with spots, of having in general longer lives. The most comprehensive determinations are those made by Maunder from the Greenwich photographs for the years 1888–93. Small isolated areas visible among the faculae were identified by Maunder at intervals of one complete rotation, and by means of these he arrived at the following figures:

Zone of each hemisphere	Mean sidereal rotation	ξ
0°–10°	24^{d}88	14°47
10 –20	25·08	14·35
20 –30	25·60	14·06
30 –40	26·59	13·54
45	28·06	12·83

From these he derived the following empirical expression:

$$\xi = 14°54 - 2°81 \sin^2 \phi$$

The various rotation periods deduced from different solar phenomena will be compared later, when the results obtained by spectrohelioscopic and spectroscopic methods have been described.

The proper motions of the faculae have also been studied at Greenwich by comparing their mean latitude at successive rotations. In this way a proper motion away from the equator amounting to 0°8 per sidereal rotation has been established for faculae lying between 0° and 40°; those in higher latitudes appear to have larger proper motions.

11. THE FORM OF THE SUN AND ITS SUPPOSED VARIATION

As long ago as 1750 Bradley was making systematic measures of the solar diameter in various latitudes; and, quite apart from the problem of a possible secular contraction, attention was soon being devoted to the sphericity of the solar globe and the variation of its diameters, perhaps in step with the different phases of solar activity. Measures of the Sun's diameter were, and still are, made with meridian circles which give the horizontal diameter by the transit times of the west and east limbs, and the vertical diameter by the difference in declination of the north and south limbs. The diameter may also be determined by means of heliometers and by photography.

Fr Secchi and Fr Rosa, of the Observatory of the Collegio Romano, have discussed the problem of the variations of the Sun's diameter, making use of all the observations then available; Fr Rosa, in a detailed study, concluded that at times when the numbers of spots and prominences are minimal the Sun's equatorial diameter is maximal. Similarly R. Wolf, having discussed the meridian circle observations of Hilfiker, found that the great spot maximum of 1870 was in agreement with what he termed the Secchi-Rosa law.

In 1873 Respighi began a series of systematic measures of the Sun's horizontal diameter at the Campidoglio Observatory; these are being continued at the present time at the Rome Observatory's station on Monte Mario.

It is difficult to be sure to what extent the supposed variability of the diameter is a real characteristic of the Sun and to what extent it is due to other causes. The problem is probably complicated by the fact that the two diameters, equatorial and polar, are slightly different, this difference itself varying with the 11-year cycle. According to Lane Poor, who investigated the findings of different observers using different methods, the ratio of the two diameters varies in a periodic manner. The length of this period is still uncertain, but appears to be roughly the same as that of the sunspot cycle. The amplitude of the variation is about 0″.2, the difference between the maximum positive and negative values being about 0″.5.

The Sun's diameter is measured regularly at Greenwich Observatory with the meridian circle, and a discussion of the observations of the period 1915–25 has indicated that the vertical diameter exceeds the horizontal by 0″.3; this difference can be attributed, at least in part, to the different methods of observation: as has already been said, the horizontal diameter is derived with a recording micrometer and the vertical by measuring with the circles the difference between the zenith distances of the north and south limbs.

Attempts to correlate the observed diameters with the sunspot cycle have produced inconclusive results. On the other hand, if the differences between the calculated diameters given in the *Nautical Almanac* and the observed diameters are tabulated for every month of the spot cycle, variations of up to 1″ are found, the diameter being largest in summer and smallest in winter.

A discussion of the various causes that might give rise to such an effect leads to the conclusion that it may be due to irradiation, whose effect varies during the course of the year. It has indeed been suggested that irradiation may be linked to the different atmospheric absorption at different altitudes above the horizon, and also to the variations of contrast between the bright solar disc and the background of the sky. Cullen, as a result of discussing the Greenwich observations, found that the variations of the Sun's diameter are proportional to the secant of its zenith distance, attaining a value of precisely 1″. On the other hand the total effect of irradiation on the Sun's diameter (whose mean value is 1920″) seems to be 3″. It would appear, therefore, that the annual variations of the solar diameter caused by irradiation are quite considerable, and it is no matter for surprise that it is difficult to disentangle this apparent variation from a possible real variation of the solar globe.

M. Cimino, who based an investigation of the mean annual values of the equatorial region of the Sun upon the regular observations made at the Campidoglio Observatory from 1876 to 1937, has brought to light two persistent and semi-periodic variations. The first and fundamental variation has a mean period of 22·5 years, while that of the secondary variation is 7·5 years. The fundamental period coincides with that exhibited by solar magnetic fields (p. 183).

Considering the necessarily limited precision of limb transit observations, it cannot be said that the problem of the variability of the Sun's diameter has been solved. It would seem necessary to devise observational methods capable of providing more reliable results, and to carry out the observations from places where the variations due to terrestrial factors are as small as possible. That the equatorial and polar diameters of the Sun may be unequal, and that this difference may be variable, is possibly confirmed by the fact that the external atmospheric envelope known as the chromosphere appears to be variable, and still more by the very marked periodic variations occurring in the corona—the outermost envelope of the Sun's atmosphere, only completely seen during eclipses.

It had already been noticed by Respighi that the depth of the chromosphere varies at different latitudes; we shall see later (p. 122) that the observations made regularly at Arcetri have shown the depth of the chromosphere to be greater at the poles than at the equator at the time of minimum solar activity, while it is approximately the same all round the limb at times of maximum activity.

Chapter III

THE SUN UNDER SPECTROSCOPIC OBSERVATION

12. *SPECTRUM OF THE PHOTOSPHERE

When the image of the Sun is thrown on to the slit of an ordinary spectroscope, a continuous spectrum crossed by numerous dark lines is obtained; these lines were discovered by Wollaston in 1802 and independently by Fraunhofer in 1814. Fraunhofer made a detailed investigation of them, designating the principal ones progressively from the red to the violet by letters of the alphabet, and thus for the first time charting the solar spectrum. These absorption lines, which are named after him, later assumed great importance when the discoveries of Kirchhoff and Bunsen revealed the manner of their formation and the identities of the elements responsible for them.

The spectrum of the bright solar disc is produced by the photosphere, and its general characteristics—such as the number, positions and intensities of the lines—are always the same, provided that the spectroscope slit lies over a region at or near the centre of the disc which is not disturbed by spots or eruptions. Visually, the spectrum with its sequence of colours can be traced from the violet (about 4000Å) to the deep red (about 7000Å), though these limits cannot be precisely stated since they depend on the colour sensitivity of the individual eye and the brightness of the spectrum. They can be considerably extended by photography, beyond both the violet and the red, and still further if special observational methods are resorted to, such as quartz spectrographs for the ultraviolet region and spectrographs with rock-salt prisms for the infrared.

From Fraunhofer's time up to the advent of photography increasingly precise and detailed maps of the solar spectrum were drawn. The most extensive and accurate map was that made photographically by Rowland, using a concave grating of high dispersion. The overall length of the spectrum in Rowland's map is more than 40 feet, and it includes 20,000 lines between 2975Å and 7331Å. A graduated scale on the map allows the wavelengths of the different lines to be estimated to 0·01Å, each scale division being equal to 3·3 mm. Moreover, the map is accompanied by what Rowland himself termed the 'Preliminary Table of Solar Spectrum Wavelengths', published in the early volumes of the *Astrophysical Journal* (1895–97); this lists, for all the lines, the wavelengths to 0·001Å, the identifications with terrestrial elements (where known), and the intensities estimated by eye on an empirical scale. On this scale the two most intense lines in the solar spectrum, the *H* and *K* lines of calcium in the violet, have the values 1000 and 700 respectively, while the intensities of the faintest lines visible on Rowland's photographs are indicated by 0000.

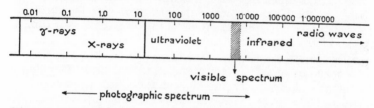

Fig. 28. *The spectrum of radiations from* 0·01Å *to* 1,000,000Å.

Rowland's wavelengths are based upon a single datum, that of the D_1 line of sodium, and on relative correspondences in the spectra of different orders. However, the wavelength of this line, as determined by more recent measurements, differs by about 0·2Å from the value used by Rowland, and, moreover, it has been discovered that for various reasons the wavelengths of the solar lines are different from those of the same lines produced *in vacuo*. It therefore became desirable that an international system of wavelengths should be adopted, based entirely on terrestrial sources. The wavelength of the red line of cadmium was selected as the primary standard; this can be measured directly in terms of the standard metre to an accuracy of 0·001Å. Secondary and tertiary standards are provided by lines in the iron arc, whose wavelengths are linked with that of the red cadmium line by very precise interferometric methods.

Using these fundamental lines and the powerful instrumental resources of Mt Wilson Observatory (e.g. the 160-foot solar tower and the 75-foot spectrograph), St John and his collaborators repeated Rowland's measures and in 1928 published the *Revision of Rowland's Preliminary Table*. This contains the revised wavelengths of the Fraunhofer lines from 2975Å to 7331Å, using the new international system, and in addition those of about 2000 lines in the infrared between 7331Å and 10,219Å, together with many new identifications and with intensities of lines in sunspots as well as those of the disc. The faint lines, which Rowland indicated by the symbols o to oooo, are in the *Revision* indicated by negative numbers from o to −3.

In 1940 Minnaert and his collaborators published a *Photometric Atlas of the Solar Spectrum*. Original photographs of the Sun's spectrum from 3332Å to 8771Å, taken at Mt Wilson, were scanned with a recording microphotometer, which converts the varying intensities into large-scale traces (Plate 39). These show the outline of the continuous spectrum with absorptions of different depths representing the various Fraunhofer lines. The scale of the diagrams is 2 mm per angstrom, allowing wavelengths to be read to o·o1Å on the abscissae, while the ordinates give the intensities from o to 100 (the latter being that of the continuous spectrum) on a scale of 10 cms.

Spectroscopy has advanced so rapidly of recent years that our understanding of the spectra of the terrestrial elements, obtained in the laboratory under varied conditions, has increased enormously; and, furthermore, we are beginning to understand the mechanism whereby spectra are produced. As a result, both the number of the identifications that have been established between lines in laboratory spectra and those of the Fraunhofer spectrum, and also our knowledge of the corresponding energy states of the elements, have been very considerably advanced.

Besides numerous new identifications the *Revision* contains details of the conditions of temperature and pressure under which many of the lines are produced. Different spectral lines will be produced according as to whether the electrons revolving round the nucleus of an atom vibrate with more or less energy. When the excitation of the atom increases, one or more electrons may escape from the attraction of the nucleus, with the production of an atom ionised one or more times, in place of the original neutral atom; new lines, easily recognised, are thereby produced, and, so far as the limitations of laboratory methods permit, these lines can be reproduced on the earth by employing increasingly advanced states of excitation—as, for example, the ordinary flame, the electric arc, or the electric spark. The work required to ionise an atom is called its ionisation potential; the unit of energy commonly employed is the electron-volt, defined as the energy acquired by an electron accelerated by a difference of potential of 1 volt; its value is $1·59 \times 10^{-12}$ ergs.

In the *Revision* neutral atoms are indicated by the element's chemical symbol—for example, Ca for calcium—singly ionised atoms by Ca^+, doubly ionised atoms by Ca^{++}, etc. A more recent convention is to denote singly and doubly ionised atoms by Ca II and Ca III respectively, retaining the symbols Ca or Ca I for the neutral atom.

The Fraunhofer lines are for the most part due to the neutral atoms of elements having high ionisation potentials, and to the ionised atoms of elements with low potentials. Leaving for later discussion the different theories that have been advanced concerning the quantities of the various elements composing the Sun, we will here list the atomic numbers and names of those elements which, according to C. E. Moore, have been shown to be present or absent from the Sun.

Fifty-six elements are certainly present:

1 Hydrogen	26 Iron	56 Barium
2 Helium	27 Cobalt	57 Lanthanum
4 Beryllium	28 Nickel	58 Cerium
6 Carbon	29 Copper	59 Praseodymium
7 Nitrogen	30 Zinc	60 Neodymium
8 Oxygen	31 Gallium	62 Samarium
11 Sodium	32 Germanium	63 Europium
12 Magnesium	38 Strontium	64 Gadolinium
13 Aluminium	39 Yttrium	66 Dysprosium
14 Silicon	40 Zirconium	69 Thulium
15 Phosphorus	41 Niobium	70 Ytterbium
16 Sulphur	42 Molybdenum	71 Lutecium
19 Potassium	44 Ruthenium	72 Hafnium
20 Calcium	45 Rhodium	74 Tungsten
21 Scandium	46 Palladium	76 Osmium
22 Titanium	47 Silver	77 Iridium
23 Vanadium	50 Tin	78 Platinum
24 Chromium	51 Antimony	82 Lead
25 Manganese	55 Caesium	

Three elements identified in sunspots:

3 Lithium   37 Rubidium   49 Indium

Two elements present only in compounds (BH, MgF, SrF):

5 Boron   9 Fluorine

Four elements represented by a single line:

18 Argon   48 Cadmium   79 Gold   90 Thorium

Three elements of doubtful occurrence:

65 Terbium   68 Erbium   73 Tantalum

Nineteen elements absent, or uncertain owing to insufficient laboratory data:

10 Neon	43 Technetium	80 Mercury
17 Chlorine	52 Tellurium	81 Thallium
18 Argon	53 Iodine	83 Bismuth
33 Arsenic	54 Xenon	88 Radium
34 Selenium	61 Promethium	92 Uranium
35 Bromine	67 Holmium	
36 Krypton	75 Rhenium	

Twelve elements whose occurrence is improbable:

84 Polonium	89 Actinium	95 Americium
85 Astatine	91 Protoactinium	96 Curium
86 Radon	93 Neptunium	97 Berkelium
87 Francium	94 Plutonium	98 Californium

Of the 22,000 lines listed in the *Revision*, only 12,000, or 57%, have been identified. There thus remains much work to be done before the origins of the solar spectrum are fully understood; nevertheless it is true to say that all the most intense Fraunhofer lines have been identified. But even when all the lines have been identified this in itself will not establish the presence on the Sun of every one of the known terrestrial elements, both because of the limited regions accessible to spectroscopic investigation and because of the small quantities of the particular elements that may be present.

The spectra of the various regions of the photosphere contain, in addition to single lines, dense groups of lines which on account of their characteristic appearance are termed 'bands' by spectroscopists. They are due to the vibrations of molecules, and their presence proves that the conditions of temperature and pressure in these regions are such as allow compounds to exist without being dissociated into their constituent atoms.

According to the identifications adopted at present, the principal bands are caused by cyanogen (CN), molecular carbon (C_2—the Swan bands), the hydrides CH, NH and OH, the hydrides of aluminium, magnesium, calcium and silicon, and the oxides of boron, aluminium, titanium, iron and zirconium; other and much more intense bands are, as we shall see, encountered in the spectra of sunspots.

In Rowland's map the most conspicuous line, after the two lines of ionised calcium in the violet, is the red $H\alpha$ line of hydrogen, which is the first of the Balmer series; the $H\beta$, $H\gamma$ and $H\delta$ lines of this series in the violet are also well marked. Only less conspicuous

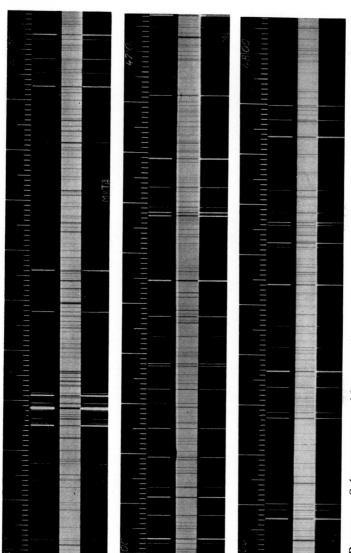

PLATE 33. Solar spectrum with comparison spectrum of the iron arc, from 4500Å to 4800Å.

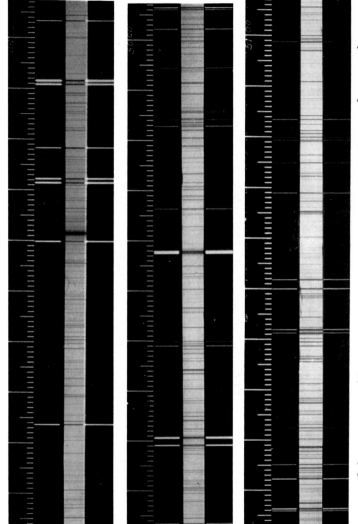

PLATE 34. Solar spectrum with comparison spectrum of the iron arc, from 4800Å to 5100Å.

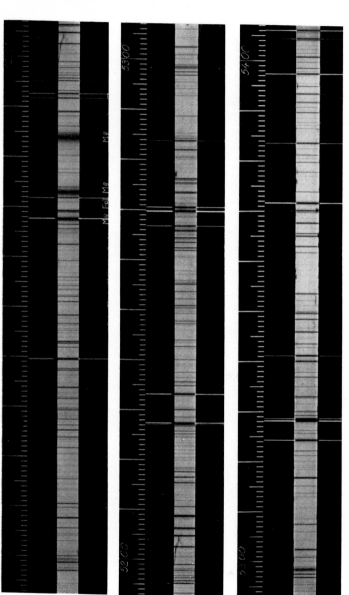

PLATE 35. Solar spectrum with comparison spectrum of the iron arc, from 5100Å to 5400Å.

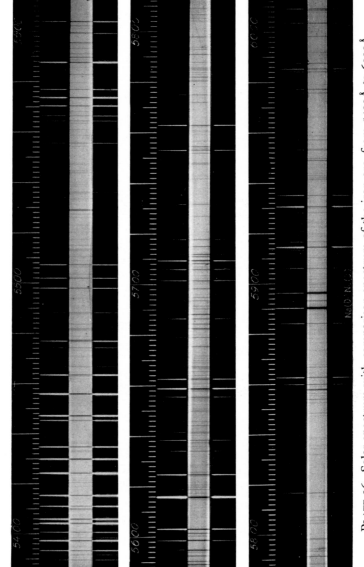

PLATE 36. Solar spectrum with comparison spectrum of the iron arc, from 5400Å to 6000Å.

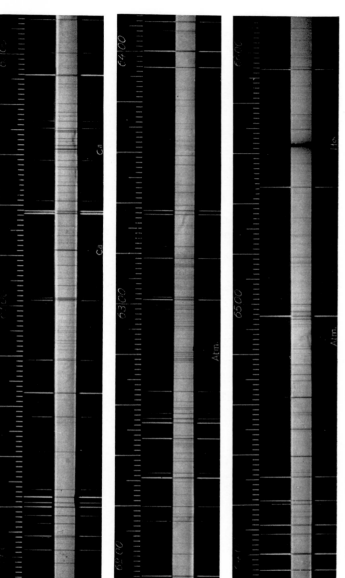

PLATE 37. Solar spectrum with comparison spectrum of the iron arc, from 6000Å to 6600Å.

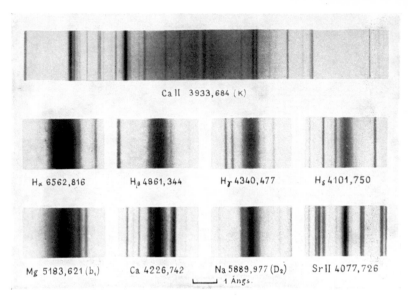

Ca II 3933,684 (K)

Hₐ 6562,816   H₃ 4861,344   Hᵧ 4340,477   H₅ 4101,750

Mg 5183,621 (b,)   Ca 4226,742   Na 5889,977 (D₂)   Sr II 4077,726

⊢——⊣ 1 Ångs.

PLATE 38. The more intense Fraunhofer lines of the solar spectrum. The double reversal of the K line of Ca II will be noticed.

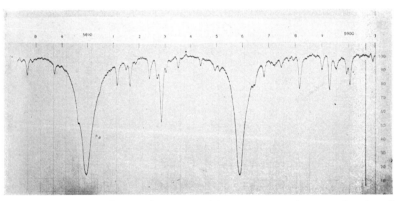

PLATE 39. Section of the Minnaert-Mulders-Houtgast photometric atlas of the solar spectrum, showing the D_2 and D_1 lines of neutral sodium at 5890Å and 5896Å respectively. (Cf. Plate 36.)

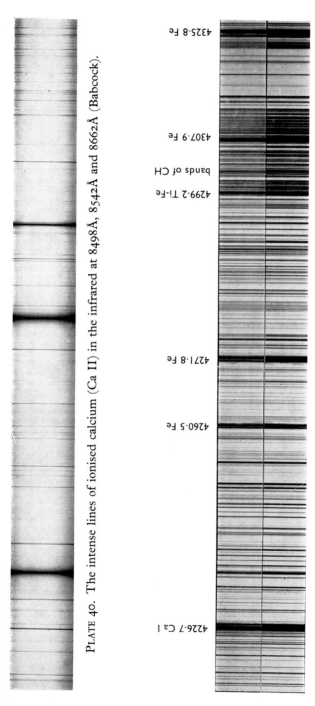

PLATE 40. The intense lines of ionised calcium (Ca II) in the infrared at 8498Å, 8542Å and 8662Å (Babcock).

4325.8 Fe

4307.9 Fe

bands of CH

4299.2 Ti-Fe

4271.8 Fe

4260.5 Fe

4226.7 Ca I

PLATE 41. Violet region of the Sun's spectrum at the centre (above) and at the limb (below) from 4220Å to 4325Å (Arcetri).

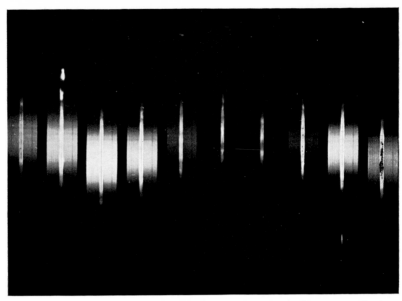

PLATE 42. Reversal of the $H\alpha$ line at the Sun's limb and over prominences (Arcetri).

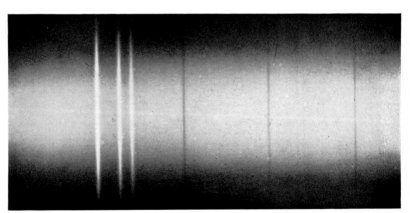

PLATE 43. Reversed oxygen lines at the Sun's limb: 7771Å, 7774Å and 7775Å in the infrared (H. W. Babcock).

are the sodium lines in the yellow and those of magnesium in the green.

All the Sun's ultraviolet radiations of shorter wavelength than 2850Å are absorbed by a thin stratum of ozone in the Earth's atmosphere, which absorbs strongly between 3000Å and 2000Å. At the latter wavelength absorption by oxygen begins, and continues down to wavelengths of a few angstroms. Since 1947 it has been possible to investigate the ultraviolet spectrum as far as 1650Å by means of grating spectrographs installed in rockets of the V2 type used in the last world war; these have reached heights exceeding 60 miles. The two resonance lines of Mg II at 2795·5Å and 2802·7Å have been detected; they are remarkable for their intensities, which are comparable with that of the Ca II lines. The absorption of these two lines covers a band 50Å wide, and they have extensive wings. Two fine emission lines are to be seen at the centre of the absorption. These appear in all the spectrograms taken at different times, and have approximately the theoretical intensity ratio of 2:1. It seems probable that these radiations are emitted under the conditions of high temperature and low pressure obtaining in the Sun's upper atmosphere, and are thus not due to any specific and isolated chromospheric activity as is the case with the reversed lines of Ca II.

In 1952 the first photographs of the Lyman α line of hydrogen at 1216Å were obtained—again by means of ultraviolet spectrographs carried to an altitude of 50 miles by means of rockets. Below 2100Å the continuous spectrum is weak, and the emission α line shows up clearly against the diffused light. At the time this photograph was obtained the Sun was fairly active; future observations will be able to show whether this line is subject to variations associated with the state of the Sun's activity.

With the aid of thermo-luminous phosphorus and photon-counters, rockets have also made possible the recording of X-rays of wavelengths shorter than 7 or 8Å; their presence appears to depend upon the condition of the solar activity. It thus appears to be established that the Sun emits soft X-radiation and that this must be absorbed in the regions of the Earth's atmosphere which constitute the E layer.

In the red beyond the Hα line, Fraunhofer's A and B bands, which are well resolved into lines, are noticeable; they are recognised to be due to oxygen in the terrestrial atmosphere. Our atmosphere acts as a filter which absorbs these radiations to an extent dependent upon the thickness of the oxygen layer that they traverse; hence these bands are much more intense when the Sun is near the horizon. At least 6500 of the 22,000 lines at present catalogued originate in our atmosphere. They are known as telluric bands, and besides the oxygen bands those of water vapour, ozone and perhaps carbon dioxide have been identified.

Not all the elements listed in the foregoing Table are represented in every photospheric spectrum; hence it cannot be said that this is the same in all regions of the disc. Indeed, when the slit lies over a region of the Sun that is disturbed by spots or faculae, over the vicinity of the limb, or over the region immediately outside the limb, noticeable differences are exhibited by the Fraunhofer lines and by the energy distribution of the continuous spectrum.

13. SPECTRA OF THE LIMB, SPOTS, REVERSING LAYER AND CHROMOSPHERE

If the slit of a spectroscope is displaced progressively from the centre of the Sun's disc towards the limb, a gradual modification of the spectrum is observed. This manifests itself in three characteristics when the limb region is reached:

(i) Some of the lines which are most intense at the centre of the disc—such as the H and K lines of calcium—do not present clear-cut edges, but a gradual falling off of intensity towards the continuous spectrum, constituting what are termed the wings of the line. These wings become gradually weakened as the limb is approached, and in some cases disappear completely.

(ii) Many lines become wider, their contrast with the continuous spectrum weakening.

(iii) Some lines become more intense at the limb, others less so, according to their origin—i.e. the energy-level at which they are produced. This phenomenon is analogous to that occurring in sunspots.

The relative differences in intensity of the lines from the edge to the centre of the disc are most marked in the blue, violet and ultraviolet regions of the spectrum, and less so in the green, yellow and red, except in the case of those lines having well-developed wings at the centre of the disc (such as the D_1 and D_2 lines of sodium, and the b_1, b_2 and b_4 lines of magnesium: Plate 41). In the region between 3815Å and 3840Å the appearance of the spectrum is greatly altered owing to the almost complete disappearance of the wings that characterise the most intense lines at the centre of the disc. These effects are probably due to the different thickness of the atmospheric layers that the rays from the centre and from the edge of the disc have to traverse before leaving the Sun; they are very noticeable in the blue and violet, and even more so in the ultraviolet. Temperature and pressure gradients produce variations in the relative intensities of the lines, as occurs in reverse order in spot spectra. Analogous differences are found in the sequence of stellar spectra.

The characteristics shown by the spectra of the sunspots differentiate them clearly from the photospheric spectrum of the centre of the disc, and by their means the differences of temperature and pressure between the spots and the photosphere may be determined. The most important of these characteristics are the following: the hydrogen lines are weaker than in the photospheric spectrum, and the neutral calcium line at 4227Å is markedly more intense; also spot spectra contain a continuous hydrocarbon band from 4299Å to 4315Å, while the violet region of the continuous spectrum decreases in intensity more rapidly than that of the photospheric spectrum.

The relative intensities of very many of the lines are changed: some become darker, others weaker, according to the elements producing them, though in certain cases some of the lines of a particular element will be darkened while others of the same element are less intense as compared with the photosphere. Besides this, the spectra of spots exhibit innumerable new lines, many of which are grouped into bands. Many lines are widened, and in some cases doubled or trebled. These characteristics may be accounted for by comparing the spot spectra with others obtained in the laboratory, and still more by comparing the energy distribution of their continuous spectra with that of the photosphere's.

The strengthening of some lines and the weakening of others is a result of the lower temperatures of the spots, compared with the photosphere; this is confirmed by the presence of bands which, in so far as they can be identified, are mainly due to titanium oxide and the hydrides of magnesium and calcium. Hale has shown that the widening and doubling of certain lines is an example of the 'Zeeman effect', which indicates the existence of intense magnetic fields in the spots (see p. 169).

To facilitate the study of spot spectra a photographic chart extending from 4600Å to 7200Å has been made at Mt Wilson; a second chart relates particularly to the study of the magnetic fields. These charts show clearly that most of the lines of certain elements are more intense in spots than in the photosphere—those, for example, of calcium, sodium, chromium, titanium and vanadium; for other elements, such as hydrogen and silicon, the majority of the lines are weakened; and for others again (as, for instance, iron, cobalt and nickel) some lines are intensified and others are weakened.

Laboratory work has demonstrated that all those lines whose intensities are weakened in spot spectra belong to the category known as 'enhanced', i.e. they originate in atoms which are at a relatively high energy-level or are even ionised. Lines which are more intense in the spots, on the other hand, are due to atoms at low-excitation levels. The theory of ionisation will provide a fuller explanation of these phenomena.

Almost 5000 lines in the region covered by the Mt Wilson chart have been identified as belonging to titanium oxide bands, and it has been found that their intensities increase in the direction of longer wavelengths, as also occurs in the spectrum of the titanium flame. About 600 lines of calcium hydride and 500 of magnesium hydride have also been identified in spot spectra. It may be said that about 80% of the lines not yet identified individually in spot spectra can be attributed to these three compounds.

Since, as we shall see, about 90% of the solar atmosphere is hydrogen, the dissociation of all the hydrides must be impeded by mass action or by the great excess of hydrogen present. The presence of calcium hydride is particularly significant, and satisfactorily confirms the law of mass action under these conditions, for the energy of formation of the CaH molecule is very small (23,000 calories) compared with that of the other molecules occurring in the spots.

As regards oxygenated compounds, the excess of hydrogen present results in very strong reduction of the oxides of those elements which are capable of forming both oxides and hydrides, owing to the peculiar play of equilibrium between oxides, hydrides and hydroxides; the reduction of the oxides of elements incapable of forming hydrides, however, is much less marked.

Coming now to the spectroscopic examination of the higher levels of the Sun's atmosphere, spectra of the reversing layer, the chromosphere, the prominences and the corona can be individually distinguished. Here we will deal with the first two, leaving the prominences and corona till later.

When the slit of a spectroscope of sufficient dispersion is laid tangentially to the solar limb and one of the more intense lines (such as $H\alpha$) is observed, it will be noticed that the wings which flank the dark line of the photospheric spectrum have disappeared, to be replaced by two bright lines—or, more precisely, by two bright components of the same line; these are more brilliant than the continuous spectrum, whose intensity is, in any case, much reduced at the limb (Plates 42 and 44). In brief, with the slit in such a position the dark hydrogen line is still visible, though its intensity is slightly reduced, and it is accompanied on either side by an emission component (cf. Figure 30). If the slit is moved further out from the limb than the tangential position, the continuous spectrum and the dark lines fade out, while the two bright components merge into one (cf. Plate 43). This phenomenon is displayed by all the lines, but owing to diffused light from the solar disc and to atmospheric turbulence it is only to be observed in the case of the brighter lines and under good seeing conditions.

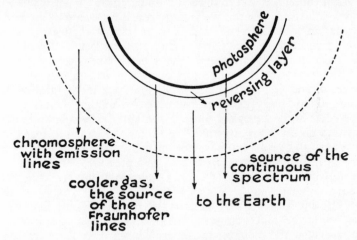

Fig. 29. Sources of the continuous, absorption and emission spectra in the solar atmosphere.

At the slit position where the bright components begin to appear (which phenomenon is termed double reversal by analogy with the behaviour of laboratory spectra) it may be considered that we have reached the spectrum of the so-called reversing layer, more properly thought of as the lower chromosphere. This is much more satisfactorily observed during total eclipse of the Sun immediately before second contact or immediately after third contact— i.e. some seconds before the body of the Moon completely covers that of the Sun, and some seconds after it uncovers it again. Since the Sun's disc is then covered by an opaque body situated outside our atmosphere—namely, the Moon—all the light emitted by the photosphere is occluded, leaving visible only the outer region consisting of the Sun's atmosphere. The lower levels of this region are composed of those same elements whose absorption lines appear in the spectrum of the photosphere. Under these particular observational conditions the photospheric light is absent from this stratum, and hence, by Kirchhoff's law, its atoms emit the same radiations that they are capable of absorbing, and we see emission lines, on the centres of which are superimposed the absorption components, giving rise to the phenomenon of double reversal (cf. p. 106).

This can also be clearly observed under laboratory conditions in, for example, the electric arc, where the density and distribution of the vapour which emits and absorbs radiation occur under diverse physical conditions and in different strata which are analogous to those on the Sun. The process is more clearly explained by modern theories, to which reference will be made later; in the meantime it may be said that the spectrum of the reversing layer—also called the 'flash spectrum' because of the speed with which it appears and disappears when the spectroscope slit is laid tangentially to the limb, and also during eclipses—is nothing more than (with minor differences) a reversed reproduction of the photospheric spectrum. Each absorption line of the latter corresponds to an emission line in the spectrum of the reversing layer; but since the reversing process is complicated by the different heights, and consequently different temperatures and pressures, of the gases, the relative intensities of the lines vary from one spectrum to another.

If the slit is moved still further out from the Sun's limb the majority of the fainter emission lines gradually disappear, leaving only a few of the most intense lines. We are then observing the spectrum of the highest levels of the solar atmosphere, known as the chromosphere.

The dividing line between the reversing layer and the chromosphere may be taken as lying in the zone where the majority of the Fraunhofer lines vanish; its calculated mean height above the surface is some 375 miles. The high chromosphere, above this level, consists only of those gases which are more abundant in the solar atmosphere, and these attain a mean altitude of 6000–10,000 miles or more; such heights are reached by the prominences, which may be considered as part of the chromosphere. It should not, of course, be imagined that sharp boundaries separate the photosphere, reversing layer and chromosphere. The lower levels of the chromosphere give rise to a continuous spectrum of the sort that Kirchhoff thought characterised a solid body; from this level there is a gradual and continuous transition to the upper and less dense atmosphere. The nomenclature used here, which was based on the observed phenomena, has been retained for its convenience.

In the chromosphere the lines of the Balmer series of hydrogen are extremely conspicuous, particularly the $H\alpha$ line which gives the chromosphere its brilliant red colour. Also present are the H and K lines of ionised calcium, which are very intense photographically but less so visually, and which characterise the highest levels. The yellow D_3 line of helium is also among the brighter lines; it is already present in the flash spectrum but is not observed as an absorption line in the spectrum of the photosphere. It is well known that helium was discovered on the Sun at the 1868 eclipse, and that it was not until 27 years later that Ramsay isolated it from gases extracted from the mineral cleveite. At the present time about 30 lines of helium have been identified in the spectra of the chromosphere and prominences; they all belong to the arc spectrum of this element except the faint line at 4686Å, which belongs to the spark spectrum.

As might be expected, the best conditions for studying the spectra of the upper and lower chromosphere are those provided by the brief moments of total eclipse, and since the introduction of the camera and the diffraction grating much work has been done. We shall return to this subject in the chapter on eclipses, but it may be said at this point that these spectra can also be observed in full sunlight with the aid of solar towers and special arrangements to cut out as far as possible the diffused light round the Sun's disc.

Hale and Adams, using the 60-foot tower telescope at Mt Wilson, were the first to succeed in photographing the spectrum of the reversing layer in full sunlight by this method, and to establish the differences in the relative intensities and wavelengths of the lines in the spectra of the reversing layer and of the photosphere. As already said, the majority of the lines are doubly reversed, the components sometimes being symmetrical with respect to the central dark component, and sometimes asymmetrical; the cause of this phenomenon is probably to be sought in anomalous dispersion.

The enhanced lines are all found to be of exceptional intensity, and it is therefore they that are first and most easily seen reversed. They belong for the most part to the spectra of zirconium, caesium, lanthanum, praseodymium and neodymium, all singly ionised. The fact that these high excitation lines (which under the conditions prevailing in the chromosphere appear as emission lines) are the first to appear enhanced depends on the temperature and pressure conditions of the particular level of the solar atmosphere at which their atoms happen to be situated. This has recently been demonstrated by the theory of ionisation and by the investigation of the equilibrium of the chromosphere under the action of the various forces to which it is subjected.

14. *MONOCHROMATIC PHOTOGRAPHS OF THE SUN, BRIGHT FLOCCULI, FLARES, AND DARK FLOCCULI OR FILAMENTS

We have already described (p. 50) how monochromatic photographs of the Sun, using various radiations, may be obtained by means of the spectroheliograph. It has also been pointed out that when the $H\alpha$ line is observed at the limb with a spectroscope of sufficient dispersion the phenomenon of double reversal is observed, whilst the line is singly reversed when the slit is displaced a few " arc outside the limb. In very active and disturbed regions also—such as those near spots or covered with faculae—the $H\alpha$ line may appear singly or doubly reversed, as was first noted by Donati and Young. The same phenomenon is exhibited by other intense spectral lines, such as the H and K lines of calcium, whose position in the extreme violet makes their observation more convenient by photography.

If the Sun is photographed with Deslandres' *spectro-enregistreur des vitesses* (p. 54)—which in essentials is a spectroheliograph whose second slit is opened sufficiently to include a narrow strip of the continuous spectrum on either side of, say, the K line, and which is given a discontinuous movement across the Sun's disc— a picture of the solar surface similar to that in Plate 45 is obtained. Here can be seen in each of the adjacent exposures, separated from their neighbours by black lines, the K line which in different regions of the Sun's disc is more or less bright (reversal) than the continuous spectrum.

From this representation of the Sun we pass at once to that obtained with the spectroheliograph, by narrowing the second slit so that it can transmit only the radiation emitted by the line under examination, and by imparting a continuous movement to the spectroheliograph relative to the whole solar disc. Spectroheliograms are thus obtained—usually with the H and K lines of calcium and the $H\alpha$ hydrogen line, though other lines can be used provided they are wide enough to ensure that no radiation other than that of the line itself can affect the photographic plate.

The Sun's surface in these spectroheliograms is seen to be covered by small clouds, called flocculi; they may be either bright or dark, consisting for instance of calcium or hydrogen, measuring about 1" in diameter, and resembling the granulation of the photosphere.

According to Langley's theory, the granules into which the photosphere can be resolved under favourable terrestrial atmospheric conditions are the extremities of columns of gas rising from lower levels of the Sun. They seem to characterise regions where convection currents proceeding from the Sun's interior carry the hot gases to an altitude where the temperature has fallen sufficiently to allow them to condense.

Hale believes that in the upper regions of these condensed columns other gases, which do not condense so easily, will continue to rise, and that the granulation visible with the spectroheliograph may represent ascending columns of calcium. It is furthermore conceivable that the higher and more extensive calcium clouds consist of such gaseous columns rising above the chromosphere in the form of jets and streamers which are termed prominences when observed at the limb; these, as we shall see, are composed largely of calcium and hydrogen.

Reference has already been made to the faculae—bright regions visible near the limb, which lie at a higher altitude than the general level of the photosphere. It was originally thought that the calcium clouds were identical with the faculae, but when it subsequently became clear that there were conspicuous differences between them it was necessary to find a distinctive nomenclature. On account of their cloud-like appearance Hale named them 'flocculi', and as such they are now universally known.

The spectroheliograph provides a method of analysing the flocculi and, as described below, of determining their structure at different heights above the photosphere. It must be assumed that at the base of a flocculus the calcium vapour from the Sun's interior is comparatively dense, whilst at greater heights it expands and its density accordingly decreases. Moreover it is known from laboratory experiments that very dense calcium vapour produces very wide spectral lines, and that as the density of the vapour decreases, so the lines become finer and more sharply defined.

An examination of the solar H and K lines of ionised calcium shows that this vapour occurs on the Sun under widely varying conditions of density. The discussion will be limited to the K line, since the H line is very close to the $H\epsilon$ line of hydrogen, and can be separated from it only by employing considerable dispersion. But all that is said of the K line applies equally to H and to the other intense solar lines such as $H\alpha$ (cf. Figure 30), $H\beta$, etc.

The whole of the wide K absorption line is commonly designated by the symbol K_1; within it a violet section, K_{1v}, and a red section, K_{1r}, can be distinguished. As already stated, the whole of this line is due to relatively dense calcium vapour at a low altitude.

If we examine this line at the Sun's limb or over flocculi—or, generally, over any disturbed region—we encounter a single or double reversal. In a single reversal the central bright line is denoted by K_2; in a double reversal the two components K_{2v} and K_{2r},

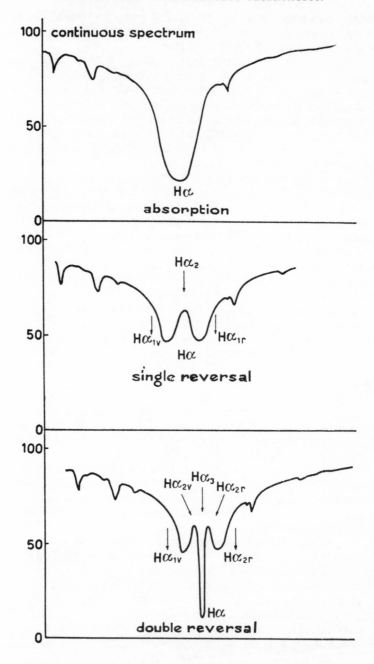

Fig. 30. *Components of the H line in the solar spectrum.*

and the central absorption line K_3, are distinguished. In truth the line, or the K_2 components, occur also in undisturbed regions of the Sun, though they are then very weak. Now it will at once be obvious that the vapour responsible for the K_2 components is higher and less dense than that causing the K_1 line, and that the vapour giving rise to the K_3 line is still higher and rarer than that producing the K_2 lines.

The spectroheliograph provides a means of separating and photographing these various levels of calcium vapour. It is only necessary to adjust the second slit near the edge of the wide K_1 line, and to photograph the Sun with it, in order to obtain the distribution of that part of the vapour which is dense enough to produce a line of such width. Under these conditions no light from the higher and more rarefied vapour can enter the slit, since it is incapable of producing a line of such a width that it can enter the second slit when it is adjusted to this particular position. The flocculi photographed in this manner are almost indistinguishable from faculae.

As the second slit is adjusted nearer and nearer to the centre of the K line, passing in succession over the K_{2v}, the K_{2r} and the K_3 lines, so increasingly higher levels will be photographed; this can be seen in the examples reproduced in Plates 48, 50–52, 63. The flocculi increasingly acquire a physiognomy quite peculiar to themselves and differing progressively from that of the faculae. It can be seen that at the higher levels the flocculi always cover the greater part of the spot groups, and if, in addition, the *spectroenregistreur des vitesses* is used in conjunction with the spectroheliograph, it will be possible to derive the velocities of the vapours and their circulation over the spots themselves.

The intensities of the flocculi may be more or less marked, according to the degree of excitation of the vapour producing them. Sometimes, in very disturbed regions, their intensity is very great indeed; in some cases the vapour is being erupted from the interior of the Sun at high velocities, and rapid changes are clearly visible with the spectrohelioscope. Ordinary flocculi of only average intensity, however, change slowly and indicate less disturbed conditions on the Sun's surface.

At times these eruptions are also visible by direct observation. On 1859 September 1, Carrington and Hodgson noticed an eruption above a large group of spots. This was characterised by the sudden appearance of two very brilliant granules, even more intense than the surrounding photosphere. An extraordinary light, which appeared to be in motion, lasted for about five minutes and then vanished for a time. Simultaneously with this rare phenomenon a terrestrial magnetic disturbance developed, increasing into a magnetic storm of exceptional intensity; this was accompanied by a bright aurora borealis which was visible down to low latitudes. This remarkable coincidence was the first observed example of a direct influence of solar events upon the Earth; in fact, as we shall see later, the magnetic storm and the aurora occurred a certain time after the solar storm. Many other exceptional eruptions have since been observed, particularly since the employment of new instruments. In 1892 Hale obtained the first spectroheliograms of an eruption; these eruptions, as might be expected, are most frequent at epochs of maximum solar activity. Thus, for example, on 1926 January 24 a brilliant one was observed over and around a large spot group, whose shape changed rapidly with considerable displacement of the $H\alpha$ line, indicating that the hydrogen in the region was in rapid motion (the Doppler effect). The eruption continued for the greater part of the following morning with extraordinary brilliance; the D_1 and D_2 lines of sodium were reversed, showing as emissions over a large spot. In some places the D_3 line appeared dark and much displaced towards the red, indicating a velocity of recession from the Earth. On the morning of the 26th the eruption appeared to be over, but towards midday another small and brilliant eruption broke out for a few minutes whilst a bridge formed across the spot. On the 27th another small but active eruption developed near a large spot.

During the sunspot maximum of 1938–9 Abetti and Colacevich, working with the Arcetri tower telescope, undertook an investigation of the eruptions at the limb, noting the deformations and intensity variations of the $H\alpha$ emission line. These intensities were in the main between 0·4 and 1·4 times that of the continuous spectrum, but on one occasion (1938 November 15) a maximum intensity of 4 times this value was attained. Radial velocity measurements of this line revealed velocities of approach up to a maximum of 250 miles per second (1939 March 20). Fr Secchi in his book, Le Soleil, had already referred to these characteristic configurations of the $H\alpha$ line, and explained them in terms of explosions occurring in the hydrogen atmosphere, whence masses of gas are projected upwards and then fall back again to the surface of the Sun.

By means of the spectrohelioscope and ciné-films it is possible to study and follow the course of these eruptions, whose importance derives not only from their significance in solar physics but also from the effects which they produce on Earth. On account of the rapidity with which they flare up and then vanish again, and also because of their intensity, they have been given the name of 'flares'.*

Flares may be described as follows:

Their intensities increase suddenly, and they are of short duration; they are visible in monochromatic light—especially that of the $H\alpha$, H and K lines—in restricted regions of the chromosphere or in the vicinity of active spot groups. They may appear as well-defined bright points in spectroheliograms taken in the light of these lines; occasionally they cover as much as 5000 millionths of the solar hemisphere. With rare exceptions they occur within about 60,000 miles (one-seventh of the solar radius) of regions occupied by spots. Although they are confined to the chromosphere, considerable variations of level are shown by individual flares. Usually they develop with very great rapidity—often reminiscent of a lightning flash—on already formed bright hydrogen or calcium flocculi; the subsequent fading is slower. The duration of maximum intensity rarely exceeds 5 minutes, but it may burst out again at the same point or at nearby points, so that the flare may last several hours altogether.

Their spectra show bright reversals of the absorption lines of the Balmer series, those of neutral helium and of ionised calcium, iron, silicon and a few other metallic atoms (Ti II, Sr II, Sc II, etc.). At the limb, as we shall see when dealing with the prominences, they appear as small pointed flames which later sink back into the chromosphere, suggesting the existence of columns of gas reaching to the highest levels of the chromosphere.

The intensities of the flares can be measured by visual or photographic photometric techniques, and provide one of the criteria of their importance; another index is the area of the solar surface that they occupy. According to the observations of M. A. Ellison and other investigators, the curves of growth obtained by plotting the effective width of the $H\alpha$ emission line against time give a good measure of the intensity variations of the flare and provide a quantitative basis for their classification.

Photometric measures of the hydrogen and ionised calcium flares have been undertaken using the spectroheliograms obtained at the Arcetri tower telescope by M. C. Ballario. Use was made of the international designations (as given, for example, in the *Quarterly Bulletin on Solar Activity*, published by the Zurich Federal Observatory), whereby the importance of the different flares is expressed on a scale from 1 to 3, their combined intensities and areas being taken into account. In the Arcetri measures the

* Italian, *brillamenti;* French, *éruptions chromosphériques;* Spanish, *fulguraciones.*

photographic density of the densest part of the flocculus, which constitutes the flare, is compared with that of the nearby undisturbed regions. From the density is derived the intensity, and it was found that in the case of $H\alpha$ flares an importance of 1 corresponds to a mean intensity of 1·6 times the $H\alpha$ intensity in an undisturbed area; an importance of 2 to an intensity ratio of 1·8 :1; and an importance of 3 to an intensity ratio of 2·0 :1.

The intensities of the K_{23} flares are as follows: for those of importance 1, a mean intensity 3·4 times that of the chromospheric K_{23} in an undisturbed region near the flocculus under examination; importance 2, intensity 4·3 times; importance 3, intensity 4·8 times. Instead of taking the intensity of the non-disturbed spectral line as unity, reference is made to the known intensity of the continuous spectrum; but since this diminishes from the centre to the limb, the resultant values vary with the heliographic coordinates of the flare at the time of observation. In any case one may say of exceptionally brilliant flares that their intensity is as great as 3 or 4 times that of the continuous spectrum.

Mean durations of flares (Ellison and Waldmeier)

Class	Duration (mins)	Maximum and minimum values
1	20	4–43 mins
2	30	10–90 mins
3	60	20–155 mins
3+	180	1–7 hrs

The incidence of flares varies in step with the spot activity. If R is the relative spot number and E the daily number of flares, then $E \cong 0·05R$; at a time of pronounced activity ($R=200$) there are thus on the average 10 flares per day, for the most part of low intensity. Since there is a strict relationship between flares and spots they obey the same laws of longitude and latitude distribution. During the lifetime of a single spot group 50 or more flares may develop in it, their intensity and activity being strictly related to the type of the group. Figure 31, opposite, shows how these characteristics are tied to the development of the spots, flares being restricted almost exclusively to the first third of their development. The stationary spots of classes VII and VIII are virtually free from eruptions. In classes III, IV and V more numerous as well as more intense eruptions occur. These may appear in any part of the bright flocculus whatsoever, but they show some preference for positions just outside the penumbra, either at the border of the umbra or between the various umbrae of the group. Flares show a

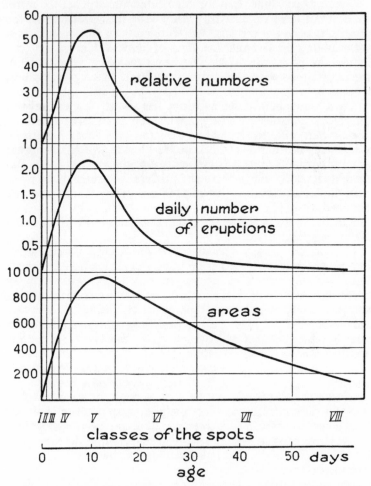

Fig. 31. *Trends of spot numbers and areas (in millionths of the visible hemisphere) and daily number of eruptions during the development of spot groups (Waldmeier).*

tendency to reappear in the same positions in a group after an interval of hours or days. L. and M. d'Azambuja found that the maximum number of flares appear, according to the development

III

of the bright flocculi, towards the fifteenth day after the first appearance of the floccular area. At the return of this region after one rotation only a few flares will be observed.

One must conclude from the augmented ionisation of the terrestrial atmosphere produced by flares that their radiation in the ultraviolet region of the solar spectrum must be phenomenal, notwithstanding the fact that the areas of flares seldom exceed one-thousandth of the solar disc. They must therefore be very rich in the radiation between wavelengths 600Å and 1800Å which causes ionisation.

The examination of their spectra has shown that the relative intensities of certain lines vary considerably from flare to flare and also between different regions of the same flare. The $H\alpha$ emission is markedly conspicuous whilst the He I line at 5876Å may appear as an absorption or as a strong emission in class 3+ flares. But there does not appear to be a standard flare spectrum which covers examples of all classes. A list of 116 lines in the spectra of flares, obtained with high dispersions, has been compiled by Allen, who found that in flares all the low-excitation lines of Fe II and Fe I are strongly enhanced.

Flocculi are closely related to, if not identical with, those objects which are observed as prominences jutting from the Sun's limb. An even closer connexion appears to exist between the latter and the type of flocculi which, on account of their appearance, are termed 'dark' or, more appropriately, 'filaments'. These are only to be observed when the spectroheliograph is so adjusted that no light other than that emanating from the exact centre of the line (such as $H\alpha_3$ or K_3) can pass the second slit. Since these sections of the lines are very narrow compared with the other components, a spectroheliograph of extremely high dispersion is required, for otherwise the line would not be wide enough for the slit still to transmit sufficient light to affect the photographic plate. This has been achieved with, in particular, the multiple spectroheliographs in use at Meudon, in which wide dispersion and at the same time the elimination of diffused light are obtained by means of successive dispersive elements.

The monochromatic images in the light of the K_3 line exhibit, in addition to the appearances described, long, black and very narrow lines which are more or less inclined to the solar parallels; these are the dark flocculi or filaments. When these are carried to the limb by the Sun's rotation a prominence is almost always to be observed at the point where the filament begins or ends, from which it must be concluded that the filaments are nothing more than prominences seen in projection on the disc.

PLATE 44. Reversal of the *Hα* line at the Sun's limbs: upper and lower, spectra of the east and west limbs; centre, spectrum of the centre of the disc (Arcetri).

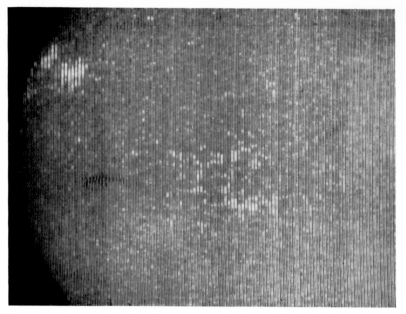

PLATE 45. Part of the solar disc photographed with H. Deslandres' *spectro-enregistreur des vitesses*, focused on the *K* line, 1910 April 11. To the left can be seen a filament with a high radial velocity (Meudon).

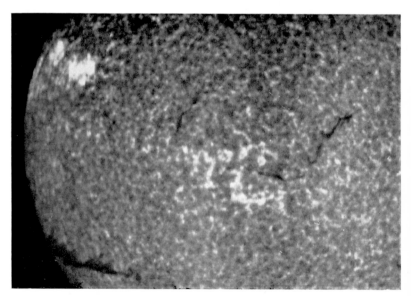

PLATE 46. The same part of the solar disc photographed at the same time as the preceding Plate, with the spectroheliograph focused on the K_3 line. The filament with the high radial velocity is now visible (Meudon).

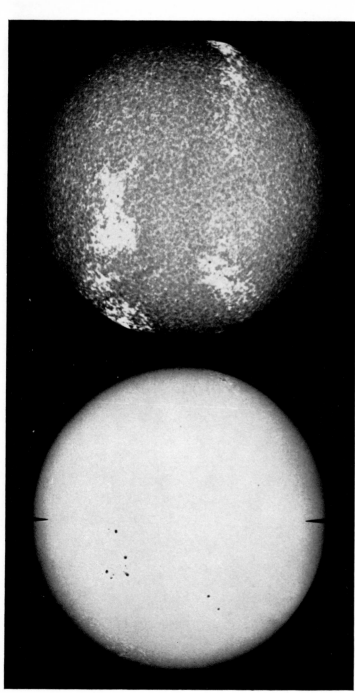

PLATE 47. Direct photograph of the Sun and synchronous spectroheliogram in calcium light ($K_{2,3}$ line); Mt Wilson, 1926 January 11.

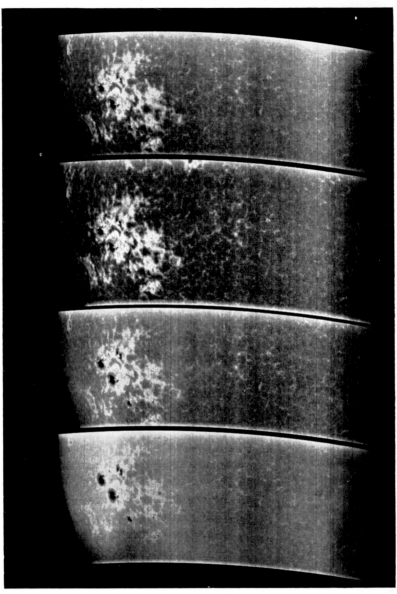

PLATE 48. Spectroheliograms taken at Yerkes Observatory, 1919 August 22. From bottom to top of the series the slit was shifted progressively nearer the centre (K_3) of the K line.

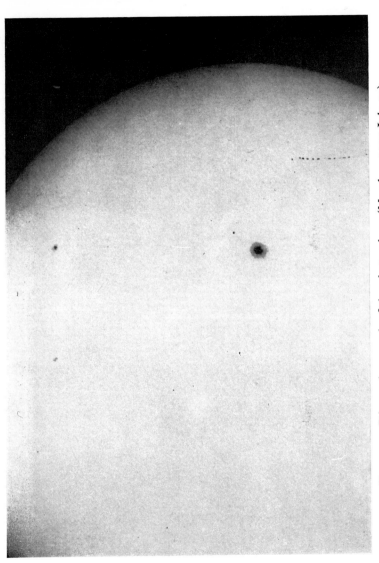

PLATE 49. Direct photograph of the photosphere (Meudon, 1927 July 29).

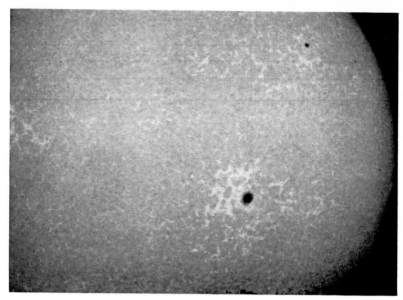

PLATE 50. Spectroheliogram of low level ionised calcium (K_1) in the chromosphere (Meudon, 1927 July 29).

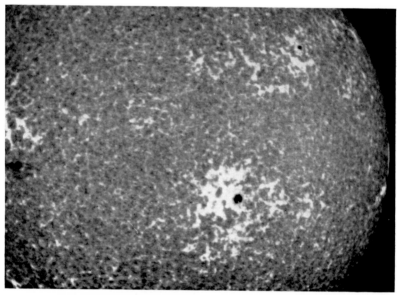

PLATE 51. Spectroheliogram of medium level ionised calcium (K_2) in the chromosphere (Meudon, 1927 July 29).

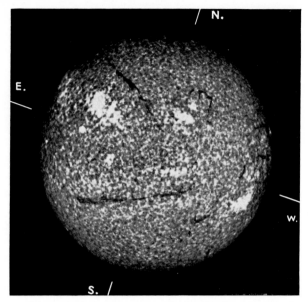

PLATE 52. Spectroheliogram taken with the K_3 line of ionised calcium
(Meudon, 1930 May 26).

PLATE 53. Spectroheliogram taken with the $H\alpha_3$ line of hydrogen
(Meudon, 1930 May 26).

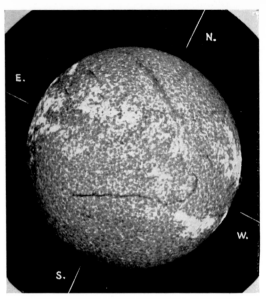

PLATE 54. Spectroheliogram taken with the K_3 line of ionised calcium
(Meudon, 1949 March 25).

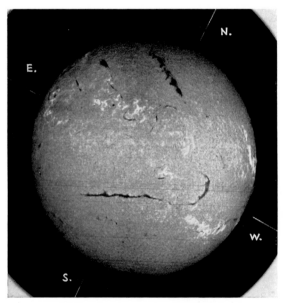

PLATE 55. Spectroheliogram taken with the $H\alpha_{2,3}$ line of hydrogen
(Meudon, 1949 March 25).

The same may be said—at least for disturbances caused by the adjacent hydrogen line, H_ϵ—of the H line, which is also due to ionised calcium. If the spectroheliograph is adjusted on the hydrogen lines a different set of appearances is observed, especially in the case of the $H\alpha$ line (which must, of course, be recorded with red-sensitive panchromatic plates). Spectroheliograms made with these lines again show bright and dark flocculi, but the general structure of the floccular network and of the flocculi themselves is considerably altered, as can be seen from Plates 52 *et seq.*

Spectroheliograms taken with the $H\alpha$ line reveal the finest and most detailed structure of the high level of the Sun's atmosphere which is isolated with this line. According to what part of the line is used, so (as in the case of the K line) images of different levels are obtained. With the slit adjusted on the central part, H_3, flocculi are shown which differ noticeably from those shown by the edges of the line; in this case, also, dark filaments are shown. The differences between the K_3 calcium flocculi and the $H\alpha$ hydrogen flocculi are shown in Plates 52–55, 59; the disturbed zones are in general the same, but the structure, relative intensity and details of form of the flocculi are markedly different.

Another feature which is characteristic of $H\alpha$ spectroheliograms is that to which Hale first drew attention, namely, the cyclonic or vortical structure of those flocculi lying in the vicinity of sunspots; it was this appearance which led to the discovery of the magnetic fields in the spots themselves. These solar vortices may be observed over a single spot, when they show a very regular distribution, or they may be associated with spot groups, in which case their structure is more complex. The appearance of the single and well-defined vortices is such as to indicate a right-handed (i.e. clockwise) rotation of the gases in the southern hemisphere and left-handed rotation in the northern; this assumes that the direction of their motion is towards the interior of the spot. However, this cannot be stated as an invariable law, corresponding to that of terrestrial cyclones, since there are many instances of spots lying close together in the same hemisphere, and often belonging to the same group, whose vortices rotate in opposite directions.

In some cases these vortices appear to exert a strong attraction on the surrounding gases. Thus, for example, St John has obtained a spectroheliogram of a long dark filament in the vicinity of a well-defined vortex centred over a spot. The nucleus of the spot split in two and within a few hours successive spectroheliograms showed the filament not only stretching out towards the spot but dividing into two branches, each of which reached one of the umbrae, as though these constituted centres of attraction. The mean velocity of the filament towards the spot exceeded 60 miles per second.

For observations of this type the following application of the spectrohelioscope invented by Hale is particularly useful. When a flocculus or filament has a large line-of-sight velocity it is no longer possible to observe it in the normal wavelength of the $H\alpha$ line, on account of the Doppler effect; if its velocity of approach or recession exceeds about 20 miles per second this line will no longer fall on the second slit of the spectrohelioscope and will therefore be unobservable. The $H\alpha$ line can be brought back to the slit by interposing a plane parallel glass plate in the path of the rays in front of the slit, and inclining it in such a manner as to shift the spectrum in its plane. The amount of the shift is measured by the angle through which the plate had to be rotated relative to the pencil of rays from the grating or prisms, and from this angular measurement the filament's radial velocity is derived.

This method thus gives the same results as those of Deslandres' *spectro-enregistreur des vitesses*, with the advantage that the various phases of a particular development can be followed more rapidly. In this way Hale studied various hydrogen eruptions, usually in the neighbourhood of very active spots, and found that in the bright masses of hydrogen the $H\alpha$ line is shifted towards the violet end of the spectrum; this indicates motion towards the observer, and hence the hydrogen is rising. The dark filaments, on the other hand, are observed on the red side of the $H\alpha$ line, and are produced by absorption in hydrogen masses moving away from the observer, i.e. towards the Sun's centre.

The small filaments which are encountered in the immediate vicinity of spots may be thought of as chromospheric bridges: they generally stretch from a sunspot to a small dark speck on the outer border of the penumbra. The movement of gases along the filament always occurs in the direction of the spot, often with a considerable radial velocity amounting to from 15 to 70 miles per second. The shape and rapid motions of these filaments lead one to think that they are nothing other than eruptive prominences (see p. 126) projected on the disc.

Other lines than those of calcium and hydrogen already mentioned have been systematically used with the spectroheliograph, notably by d'Azambuja at Meudon. These lines number about ten, and belong to five different elements; iron, calcium, magnesium, neutral sodium and ionised strontium. As with ionised calcium, so these lines produce spectroheliograms almost identical with the direct image of the Sun when the slit is adjusted to their edges; and as the slit is moved nearer and nearer the centre of the line so the regions of the faculae and of the flocculi appear. After a maximum of visibility has been attained these regions and the bright flocculi disappear, and a uniform granular structure covering the whole disc becomes prominent. When the second slit is laid over the centre of the line the images reveal, in addition to a faint granulation, zones of faculae and bright flocculi which seem to be identical with those obtained with K_1 line, except for their relative faintness.

The granulation revealed by these lines is the same as that seen with hydrogen light and gives the same impression of being composed of dark granules on a bright background; the mean diameter of the granules is about 5 times that of the photospheric rice-grain. There is, however, no trace at all of vortices in the regions of spots.

These results reveal the existence of a connexion between the structures of the high- and low-level gases. The momentary disappearance of the facular zone and that of the bright flocculi indicates that, despite the similarity of appearance, the details obtained with the central part of the line have a different origin from those revealed by its other parts. The fact is a conclusive argument in favour of the hypothesis that these are indeed the same faculae photographed by means of their continuous spectrum. Nothing but the respective levels intervenes to modify the granular structure, and it is thus, given the different altitude of the hydrogen, that the structure is able to assume a different appearance.

The vortices would be caused by mechanical agencies analogous to our terrestrial cyclones, and the less dense and less viscous upper levels would be more susceptible to them than the lower levels. These investigations provide the final confirmation that the granulation constitutes the essential structure of all the chromospheric gases.

It may in general be said of the birth and duration of the floccular zones that they endure longer than the spots and usually start from a small regular flocculus in a given region. The flocculus then becomes elongated, showing a tendency towards a certain definite orientation, and completely covers a more or less extensive zone in which one or more spots appear. These early phases follow rapidly on one another in the course of a few days, and at the same time the zone continues to spread without losing its compact nature. Having reached maximum development it remains stationary for some time; it then begins to disperse, its area still increasing, and the spots disappear. The brighter parts gradually fade, and in the end the disturbed region assumes the ordinary appearance of the granulated chromosphere.

The orientation of the floccular zones when they have attained their normal elongation is not random. In each hemisphere they are inclined to the equator in such a way that their western end is nearer to it than their eastern. The inclinations vary from 0° to 40° without showing any definite relation to heliographic latitude. It will be remembered that spot groups exhibit analogous inclinations, though these are much smaller (not exceeding about 19°) and increase regularly with latitude (pp. 83, 88).

The variations of the floccular zones follow those of the spots: at the start of a new cycle they begin to appear in high latitudes, and subsequently they accompany the spots in their shift towards the equator. Their areas and intensities reach a maximum simultaneously with that of the spots, after which their activity falls off to nil, or nearly so, during the minimum. The presence of flocculi is thus another important index of solar activity, and for this reason their variations are followed by spectroheliographs and spectrohelioscopes at observatories all over the world, where their intensities and areas at different phases of the cycle are measured. For example, the annals of the Meudon Observatory contain synoptic charts (*Cartes synoptiques de la chromosphère et des taches*) which show the position and extent of the spot groups, flocculi and filaments for each solar rotation (Plate 69). Analogous data are also published each month in the *Sonnen-Zirkular* of the Fraunhofer Institute at Freiburg in Germany, and by the Coimbra and Ebro-Tortosa Observatories, which quote the positions and areas of the flocculi.

To provide a more rapid information service regarding solar activity the Zurich *Bulletins*, published from 1917 to 1944 by international arrangement, gave the so-called 'character figures' which were based on an empirical scale from 0 to 5; 0 represented the complete absence of flocculi, and 5 a maximum of area and intensity, the latter naturally being most commonly realised at sunspot maxima. These character figures were estimated from an examination of hydrogen and calcium spectroheliograms obtained at a number of different observatories.

15. ROTATION PERIOD OF THE FLOCCULI

Flocculi, of course, participate in the Sun's rotation, and it is of interest to enquire whether the speed of this rotation and the law governing it are the same as those of the spots. Various observers have made these measures, attempting to identify the same points in a particular flocculus during the course of its rotation. But it will be recognised that because of the difficulty of identifying these points and also because of the proper motions of the individual flocculi, the results of these determinations are neither accurate nor reliable. All the same, satisfactory agreement has been obtained between different sets of measurements.

An extensive programme of measures was undertaken by Fox with the Rumford spectroheliograph attached to the Yerkes Observatory 40-inch equatorial. The diurnal sidereal motion was deduced from 4000 points selected in calcium flocculi (K_{23} line) on 285 plates, and in the great majority of cases two plates, exposed on consecutive days, were used. Fox expressed the results thus obtained by means of an empirical formula similar to that derived for the spots. Putting ξ for the angle through which a flocculus travels in one day, he obtained

$$\xi = 11°58 + 2°98 \cos^2 \phi$$

From an examination of the proper motions of flocculi situated around spots Fox also revealed the existence of cyclonic motions such as are shown by $H\alpha$ flocculi.

The mean results of the determinations of the solar rotation period in different latitudes by means of the calcium flocculi are as follows:

ϕ	ξ	ϕ	ξ
0°	14°53	25°	14°07
5	14·48	30	13·89
10	14·40	35	13·79
15	14·31	40	13·61
20	14·21	45	13·23

A comparison of these results with those derived from the faculae and the spots shows that, as would be expected, the velocities of faculae and calcium flocculi are almost identical; the spots, on the other hand, yield a rotation period in all latitudes which is shorter, on the average, by about 0°1 in ξ. Thus we can discover the first indications (at any rate as far as these two phenomena are concerned) of a tendency which is consonant with the hypothesis that the highest levels of the Sun's atmosphere have the highest velocities.

Determinations of the rotation periods of the dark hydrogen and calcium filaments have been made at the Kodaikanal and Meudon Observatories. The former were based on observations of filaments during their passage from the eastern limb to the western.

Filaments being no more than prominences projected on the disc, the level at which the measurement is made depends upon the respective mean altitudes above the chromosphere of the points chosen. The angular diurnal sidereal velocities obtained at Kodaìkanal with $H\alpha$ filaments are as follows:

ϕ	ξ	ϕ	ξ
$0°$	$14°.40$	$25°$	$14°.13$
5	14.40	30	14.06
10	14.34	35	13.93
15	14.30	40	13.90
20	14.21		

It will be noticed that the rotational velocities of these filaments are practically the same as those of spots in equatorial regions, but become progressively greater in higher latitudes, up to a maximum difference of about $0°.5$ in latitude $40°$.

The Meudon determinations were based on K_3 spectroheliograms showing filaments with very sharply defined outlines. A different procedure from that employed at Kodaìkanal was followed by L. and M. d'Azambuja, who derived the rotation periods from the times at which the filaments transited the Sun's central meridian at each rotation. To avoid as much as possible the effect of parallax—due to the filaments' high altitudes in the Sun's atmosphere—the epochs at which the plane containing the filament passed through the observer were taken; these epochs may precede the transits of the central meridian by several days, owing to the habitual orientation of the filaments and their systematic tendency to incline towards the west.

The results of these measures, involving many filaments observed between 1919 and 1930 in a wide range of latitudes, are as follows:

ϕ	ξ	ϕ	ξ
$0°$	$14°.39$	$35°$	$13°.80$
5	14.41	40	13.66
10	14.37	44	13.4
15	14.33	52	12.9
20	14.23	57	12.8
25	14.14	66	12.5
30	13.99		

These may be approximately represented by the formula

$$\xi = 14°48 - 2°16 \sin^2 \phi$$

As with the hydrogen filaments, the angular velocity of the calcium filaments at the equator is sensibly equal to that of the spots, but exceeds the latter in higher latitudes, although to a smaller extent than the hydrogen filaments; this difference can be accounted for by the different methods of making the measures employed at the two observatories. The polar filaments show a general tendency to elongate with time, at a mean rate of about 4° per rotation.

16. *THE CHROMOSPHERE AND PROMINENCES: THEIR CONSTITUTION AND CLASSIFICATION

When the Moon's disc completely covers the photosphere during eclipses the chromosphere can be seen with the naked eye as a vivid red atmospheric ring surrounding the solar globe. With the aid of the spectroscope, also, it is always possible to observe the chromosphere in full sunlight as a rim of unequal thickness around the disc. In order to view its structure satisfactorily it is desirable to widen the spectroscope slit slightly, while keeping it tangential to the limb. With the slit in this position (or, better, a few seconds of arc outside the limb) and observing with one of the stronger lines such as $H\alpha$, the bright, indented and constantly agitated edge of the chromosphere is seen; this agitation is an effect due partly to terrestrial atmospheric turbulence, but partly also to real motions of the chromosphere.

Fr Secchi very expressively likened it to a 'prairie fire'. At the base, immediately in contact with the Sun's surface, its colour is more striking than in its upper levels, so that when the spectroscope slit is placed perpendicularly to the limb the most intense lines are seen to end in bright points, giving them the appearance of spears whose length depends upon the intensity of the line, the power of the telescope, and the state of the atmosphere. When the most intense lines are used, the chromosphere can generally be traced to a height of from 10″ to 15″ in full sunlight, though to much greater heights during eclipse.

The fine points comprising the edge of the chromosphere, which may plausibly be likened to flames, may be inclined in the same or in opposite directions. Sometimes the change of direction is very clearly marked at the poles, where a series of straight, vertical flames, higher than the others, may be observed; these are somewhat reminiscent of the coronal tufts. In calm regions of the chromosphere the points of the flames may all lean in the same direction along considerable stretches of the limb—sometimes for more than a quarter of the whole circumference—beyond which they change their inclination. In the neighbourhood of the equator, and in disturbed regions generally, they have the appearance of flames which actually flicker from one moment to the next.

It seems impossible to assume the existence of a regular circulation system in the solar atmosphere which at the level of the chromosphere could manifest itself in one particular direction of these luminous points. According to Secchi, their inclinations are more constant and regular at epochs of maximum solar activity, when, also, they are directed towards the poles. At periods of minimum activity they show less regularity, or at least no general regularity.

Often, and particularly in regions occupied by spots, the chromosphere assumes the appearance of a very elaborate *reseau* whose complex surface seems to be composed of bright clouds analogous to flocculi: some of these clouds swell and expand so as to form small elevations, diffuse at their edges. These elevations exhibit a variety of shapes and sizes before developing into real prominences, so that no sharp and precise distinction can be drawn between the chromosphere and the prominences. It is, however, convenient to restrict the name 'prominence' to those elevations whose height above the mean chromospheric level exceeds 30″.

The depth of the chromosphere is not uniform round the whole limb. Respighi, as long ago as 1869, between a minimum and a maximum of solar activity, derived a height of about 12″ with the $H\alpha$ line, but noted that it appeared to be greater near the poles than near the equator. In 1875, near a sunspot minimum, Secchi made the same observation, and also noted that during periods of more or less general calm on the Sun, very considerable activity was nevertheless evident in the polar regions, where it manifested itself in abnormal brightness and size of the flames composing the chromosphere.

These early observations of Respighi and Secchi suggested that it would be of interest to make regular measurements of the depth of the atmosphere, and to follow its variations during the course of the solar cycle. Such determinations are important because, according to the theoretical investigation of Milne into the chromospheric equilibrium between gravity and radiation pressure, variations in the depth of the chromosphere are a probable consequence of the maintenance of such an equilibrium. An atmosphere sustained by radiation pressure would immediately fall into collapse if the amount of radiation from the interior of the

Sun decreased, and although it would adapt itself to the new conditions the density at high altitudes would in the meantime suffer very considerable fluctuations. A decrease in the intensity of the Sun's radiation so slight as to be quite unobservable by existing methods could, according to Milne, produce a temporary diminution of the density at a height of some thousand miles above the surface of the photosphere. Measurements made with the spectroscope slit perpendicular to the Sun's limb—the length of the reversed $H\alpha$ line being measured with a micrometer from the end of the absorption line to the point where the emission line merges into the background of the sky—cannot be very precise owing to the mobility and form of the chromosphere. Nevertheless, if the terrestrial atmosphere is sufficiently transparent and the images well defined, measures made at a variety of latitudes are able to indicate where the chromosphere is relatively deep and where relatively shallow.

Fig. 32. Reversal of the $H\alpha$ line observed with the slit set radially to the Sun's limb (Secchi, Le Soleil).

Determinations of this type are undertaken as part of an international programme of solar observations at a number of different observatories, among them Arcetri, Catania, Madrid, Prague and Tashkent.

A series of measures of the height of the chromosphere was initiated in 1921 at Arcetri, the Amici equatorial (14·6-inch aperture, 18 feet focal length) being used in conjunction with a Zeiss spectroscope (Figure 8 and Plate 12); this gave a dispersion of 15° from $H\beta$ to $H\alpha$. Measurements were made round the disc at 30° intervals, starting at the north pole, and have been reduced to the year 1946.

The results of this series of 25 years' observations may be summarised as follows:

The mean height of the $H\alpha$ reversal, when the spectroscope slit is set at right angles to the Sun's limb, was 10″5±0″5 for the whole of the period under consideration. Small variations, observed from year to year, which were within the limits of the mean error, were also confirmed by analogous observations made at Catania and Madrid; it is therefore probable that there is a variation in the mean altitude of the chromosphere throughout the 11-year cycle.

Another fact firmly established by the Arcetri observations is that at different stages of the 11-year cycle the chromosphere may be uniformly distributed round the solar limb or may be deeper at the poles than the equator. Relating the observed heights at different heliographic latitudes to those measured at the Sun's north pole, M. G. Fracastoro has calculated the percentage values as a function of latitude for every 30° and for every year. The resultant curves show a sinusoidal trend which is well defined around minima, but weak and irregular around maxima.

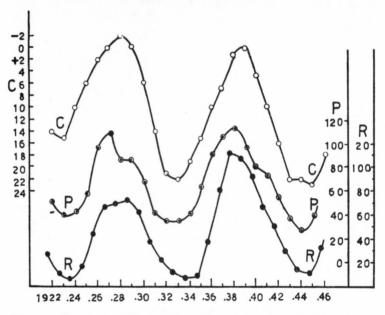

Fig. 33. Correlation between the height of the chromosphere (C), the number of prominences observed (P), and relative spot numbers (R) from 1922 to 1946 (Arcetri).

Defining empirically an 'index of sinuosity' as the absolute value of the sum of the four differences (a) north pole−equator, (b) equator−south pole, (c) south pole−equator, (d) equator−north pole, Fracastoro derived the annual values of these indices, which agree with the Wolf relative numbers (R) and the numbers of prominences (P). Curve C in Figure 33 therefore represents the distribution and form of the hydrogen chromosphere throughout the 11-year cycle, as compared with other aspects of solar activity. It does not appear to be possible to deduce the existence of a relationship between the height of the chromosphere and the frequency of the prominences in different latitudes, although, as Respighi had already noted, it is true that in the neighbourhood of a prominence the chromosphere is often deeper than normal.

Other methods of determining the height of the chromosphere in various wavelengths have been devised—for example, that of Fox. Two diametrically opposed points on the solar disc are reflected on to the spectroscope slit by means of prisms whose distance apart can be adjusted by means of micrometer screws. The double altitude of the chromosphere for the line under examination is then given by the difference between the maximum and minimum separations of the prisms when the light from the two limbs shows the reversal of the lines. Some observations made with the Yerkes 40-inch refractor have yielded a mean altitude greater than $10''$ with the $H\alpha$ line, and greater than $8''$ with the D_3 line of helium.

D'Azambuja at Meudon has employed the spectroheliograph to compare the diameters of the images formed successively by the radiation of a chromospheric line and of the continuous spectrum. Pettit has made use of the spectrohelioscope, finding for $H\alpha$ a depth of about $8''$. It is to be expected that different values will be obtained with telescopes of different powers and spectroscopes of different dispersions, used in various localities under diverse conditions of atmospheric transparency.

All the values obtained by these methods are considerably lower than those determined for the reversing layer and chromosphere during solar eclipses, owing to the great quantity of diffused light always present in full sunlight; eclipse observations therefore yield more reliable values of absolute height.

The prominences—more or less brilliant, and reaching to greater or smaller heights around the Sun's limb—are also visible with the naked eye during total eclipses, but they have only been observable in full sunlight since the combination of telescope and spectroscope was effected in 1868. It had already been suspected by Sir Norman Lockyer in 1866 that the prominences, being composed of incandescent gases, could be observed with the spectroscope, but it was not until October 1868 that he had a suitable instrument at his disposal for their observation in full sunlight. Meanwhile, a few months before this, J. Janssen—who had gone to India to observe the total eclipse of 18 August—had been struck by the great brilliance of the prominences, which yielded intense emission lines. Immediately after the eclipse he showed, with considerable ingenuity, that the prominences could also be seen in full sunlight. Both Janssen and Lockyer, independently and simultaneously, communicated their discovery to the French Academy, and from that date began the regular observation of the prominences which has continued to the present day.

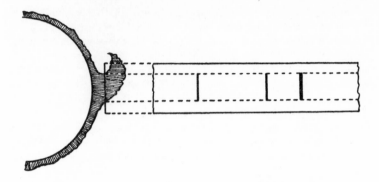

Fig. 34. Observation of the emission spectrum of the prominences with the spectroscope slit set tangentially to the solar limb.

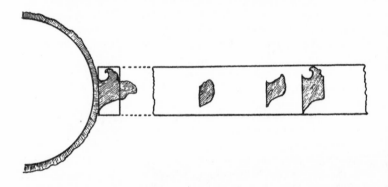

Fig. 35. Observation of the spectrum and form of the prominences with a widened slit.

If the slit of a spectroscope attached to a telescope is adjusted to a point on the limb where a prominence is situated, a spectrum of emission lines will be seen; their intensity and number will depend on the intensity and quality of the particular prominence. As the slit is moved gradually further from the limb the lines will continue to be seen for a length of time determined by the size and shape of the prominence, the distance from the limb at which they finally vanish corresponding to the height of the prominence.

In order to have a better view of the complex forms of the prominences it is preferable to open the spectroscope slit—as first realised by W. Huggins in 1869—so that, instead of the lines, so many monochromatic images of the prominence itself are seen. Widening the slit naturally results in loss of definition, but the prominences are in general so intense that a suitable widening of the slit (which depends upon the dispersion available) allows the complex forms of the prominences to be well seen, either wholly or partially according as to whether or not they can be contained completely by the slit width.

Fr Secchi and Respighi at Rome were among the first to undertake the regular observation of the prominences, and the former was able to establish the fact that, unlike the spots, they are to be found in all latitudes from the equator to the poles, and that they are extremely numerous: in the one year 1871 he counted no fewer than 2767.

Prominences may assume a great variety of shapes, resembling clouds, jets of smoke or vapour, trees, feathers or fountains, as can be seen from Secchi's very fine drawings or from modern photographs. These shapes may endure for some time, or they may change very rapidly. Secchi distinguished two categories of prominence, according to their relative stability—quiescent and eruptive.

The spectrum of prominences consists, as has been said, of emission lines belonging to the Balmer series of hydrogen, to ionised calcium (H and K) and to helium (D_3). These principal lines are always seen, but many others (belonging to neutral and ionised metals) are visible during total eclipses and even in full sunlight in the case of the more intense and active (eruptive) prominences. These show numerous lines due to ionised atoms, such as Fe II, Ti II, Sr II and Mn II, and also such neutral atoms as He, Fe, Mg, Na, etc. In conclusion it may be said that prominence spectra contain the more intense lines of the flash spectrum, and that their visibility and intensity are determined by the temperature and pressure conditions in each individual prominence.

The occasional appearance of the continuous spectrum indicates a condition of abnormal pressure. Given long enough exposures and good enough seeing conditions the spectrum of the prominences would probably be identical with the flash spectrum, except that some lines (such as those of helium) would be more intense in the former, while those of elements like barium would be weaker. This would suggest that the forces which eject the prominences from the chromosphere act in such a way as to separate out the heavier elements, of which barium is one.

The following classification of prominences, more detailed than that of Secchi, has been suggested by Pettit (see Plate 77):

(i) Active prominences, which appear to be under the influence of an area of attraction or of a nearby spot.

(ii) Eruptive prominences, which shoot up rapidly in a direction more or less vertical to the solar surface.

(iii) Spot prominences, in the form of closed rings or jets, reminiscent of the fan-like jets of a fountain.

(iv) Vortical prominences in the form of spirals, or resembling stranded rope.

(v) Quiescent prominences, whose shapes change more slowly than any of the foregoing.

In reality all prominences are active, it being only their degree of activity that varies. Classes (i) and (ii) are intimately connected, since a single prominence may exhibit the two phases simultaneously, or pass from one to the other. Although a spot may or may not be associated with a prominence of these two classes, both classes may nevertheless be associated with class (iii).

The name 'prominence' is generally confined to elevations rising more than 30″ above the level of the chromosphere; this is the minimum altitude, however, and prominences are often observed up to 2′ or 3′, while in exceptional cases they may extend for more than one solar diameter. Similarly the bases of the prominences may be very narrow, measuring only a few tenths of a degree of the solar limb, or they may extend for several degrees, and in exceptional cases for as much as 20° or 30°, i.e. 20, 30 or even more times the Earth's diameter.

The prominences are not, of course, only extended in the two dimensions in which they are seen at the Sun's limb, and their third dimension may be determined by comparing their shape while projected on the disc with their shape at the limb. As we have already seen (p. 112), prominences projected on the disc generally appear as filaments, or, in the case of those showing exceptional activity, as bright flocculi. Filaments are frequently curved, and when they are observed radially or are situated near the centre of the disc their true thickness can be measured.

Measurements made by Pettit have shown that this thickness is extraordinarily small, a large number of determinations giving values ranging from 3750 to 7500 miles. Their lengths vary over a wide range; few prominences are shorter than about 40,000 miles, while a length of 375,000 miles is exceptional; however, there are cases on record of a line of prominences (though not a continuous line) stretching for more than one quarter of the solar circumference.

Their heights also vary widely, especially those of the first four classes. The highest so far observed attained an altitude of 1·22 solar diameters, penetrating the region of the outer corona.

The three-dimensional shape of a prominence should therefore be thought of as that of a thin tongue of flame, composed of incandescent gases, which rises for some thousands of miles from the chromosphere to which it is joined by columns of gas as a tree is attached to the ground by its roots. The following dimensions may be taken as representative of the prominences: thickness, 6000 miles; length, 125,000 miles; height, 30,000 miles; giving a volume about 90 times that of the Earth.

A notable prominence was that observed on 1919 May 29 as a great vortex connecting two points on the limb and possibly continuing into the Sun's interior. It appeared on March 22 at the eastern limb in latitude −35°, and increased gradually in both intensity and height at each successive appearance. On May 28 it appeared as an enormous mass of tangled streamers reaching a height of 2′.7, as though rising in two columns in −37° and −41°, the principal mass of the prominence lying parallel to the limb. Spectroheliograms taken by Pettit with the Rumford spectroheliograph using the H_3 line of Ca II showed the prominence in the form of a great arch extending from −42° to +6°, and also revealed the presence of a spot at the limb in latitude +7°. At 2^h57^m G.M.T. the arch, of twisted structure and probably in vortical motion, began to detach itself at its base; in Plate 78 it can be seen receding from the limb and rapidly disintegrating. The spiral or vortical structure remained visible while the arch was breaking up and moving ever further from the Sun; it finally reached a maximum height of 17′, equivalent to about 500,000 miles, at $7^h 57^m$.

Another 1919 prominence, that of July 15, was of similar form but more rapid development. It first appeared on July 1 as two plumes in latitudes −11° and +18°; a spot was situated at −14°. The first photograph taken on July 15, at $3^h 8^m$ (Plate 79), showed the prominence connecting the two eruptive centres and already fully developed with a height of 6′. Successive exposures showed it to be in rapid vortical motion. It finally reached a maximum altitude of 16′ only $1^h 26^m$ after the first exposure had been made.

Similar to this prominence was the one photographed at the Arcetri solar tower on 1938 December 24 and 25. As first observed on December 24 its form was that of a great arch, irregular in appearance, situated at the south-west limb between latitudes $-14°$ and $-73°$; its breadth was therefore 375,000 miles. Its appearance did not undergo any very striking changes during the first day, but towards 11^h U.T. on the 25th the arch broke, and, whilst a quiescent and intense plume remained at the lower latitude, a relatively thin and inconspicuous jet was ejected in high latitudes; this disintegrated into a number of individual clouds, the highest of which attained an altitude of 600,000 miles.

During the last 11-year cycle, on 1946 June 4, the largest eruptive prominence ever to be observed was photographed. It was discovered on Mt Wilson spectroheliograms of May 23 in latitude $55°$ south, oriented almost head-on in the direction of the observer; by June 1 the whole prominence was seen as an immense arch, with its western end situated at a centre of attraction in latitude $43°$ south, the eastern end at another in latitude $53°$ south. It resembled a thin tongue 6000 miles thick and 300,000 miles long, elevated some 70,000 miles above the chromosphere. On June 2 the great arch, whose centre was then almost over the central meridian, extended for $90°$ in longitude at latitude $48°$ south. At $15^h 37^m$ U.T. on June 4 the greater part of the prominence was already projected beyond the disc, its extent being almost equal to one solar radius. A little later the arch broke up, and by $17^h 56^m$ its fragments had attained the greatest altitude observed—1,060,000 miles, or 1·22 solar diameters. The velocity of recession of the different parts of the prominence increased continuously from 16^h to 18^h, undergoing a sudden leap from 85 to 194 miles per second at distances from the Sun at which the gravitational field varied from about 0·4 to 0·08 times its value at the Sun's surface.

The continued observation of the filaments and prominences has permitted certain facts to be deduced concerning the circumstances of their birth, development and motions. At the time of their first appearance the equatorial ends of the filaments are situated in the same latitudes as the spots, where they often arise in disturbed regions associated with young spot groups. The frequent association of the two phenomena—filaments, and centres of photospheric activity—suggests that they may be causally related, or, perhaps, that they spring from a common cause buried beneath the surface of the Sun's atmosphere. In their first stage of development the filaments are small and twisted, and are subject to violent internal motions. Often it can be observed that matter is ejected from their upper regions in long curved trajectories apparently sucked into centres of attraction situated within or close to nearby spots (Pettit's class iii). Little by little the filaments become more stable and move away from the equator, assuming a

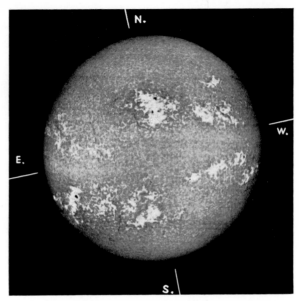

PLATE 56. Spectroheliogram taken with the infrared line of ionised calcium at 8542Å (Meudon, 1937 August 6).

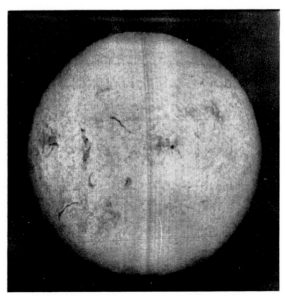

PLATE 57. Spectroheliogram taken with the infrared line of helium at 10830Å (1938 September 17). Exposure, 2 hours.

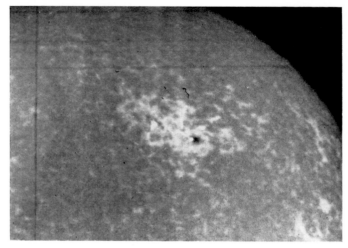

PLATE 58. K_3 flare at the edge of the umbra of a spot
(Arcetri, 1938 April 15).

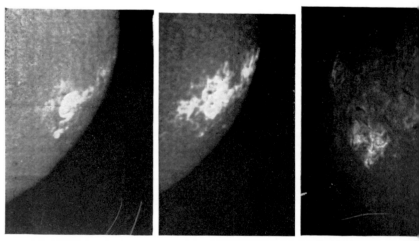

[PLATE 59. Left: $H\alpha$ flare. Right: $K_{2,3}$ flare. (Arcetri,   PLATE 60.   Flare ob
1949 August 5).   served with the D_3 lir
                                                     of helium (Meudor
                                                     1946 July 25^d 16^h 58
                                                     U.T.). *Cf.* Plate 62.

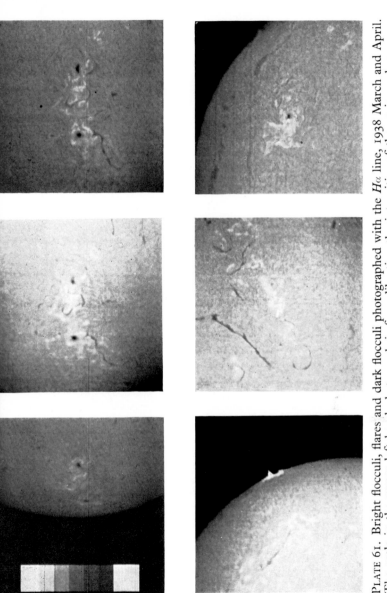

PLATE 61. Bright flocculi, flares and dark flocculi photographed with the $H\alpha$ line, 1938 March and April. The scale in the upper left-hand photograph is for calibrating the intensities of the various phenomena (Arcetri).

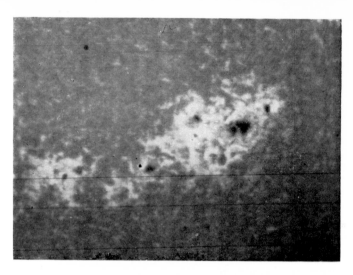

PLATE 62. Giant flare photographed with the $H\alpha_{2,3}$ line (Meudon, 1946 July 25^d 17^h 32^m U.T.).

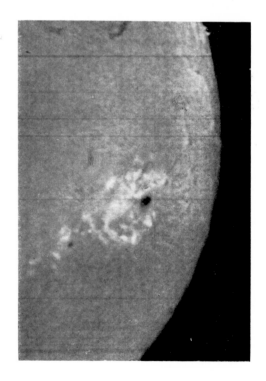

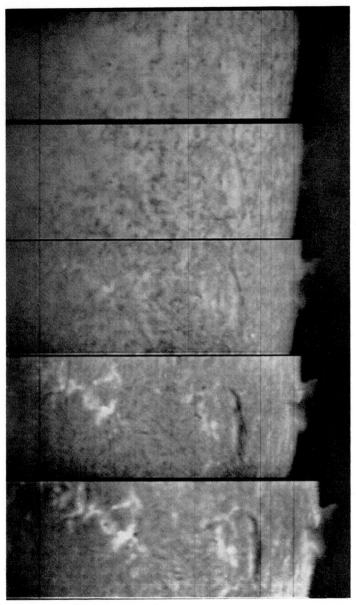

PLATE 63. *H*α spectrograms obtained by giving the second slit successive displacements (from top to bottom of the Plate) of 0·33Å from the wings towards the centre of the line (*H*α₃). (Mt Wilson).

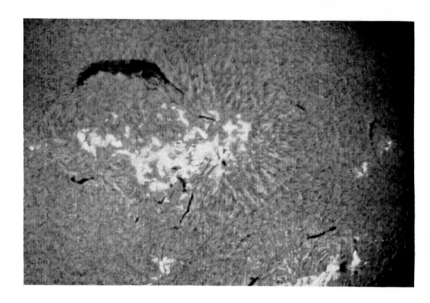

PLATE 64. $H\alpha_3$ spectroheliograms (Meudon). Upper: 1928 July 20^d 7^h 18^m U.T. Lower: 1928 July 21^d 7^h 30^m U.T. Note the total disappearance of the large filament to the left of the upper photograph.

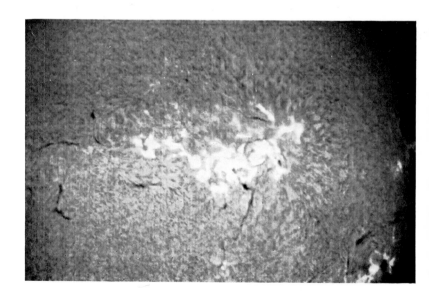

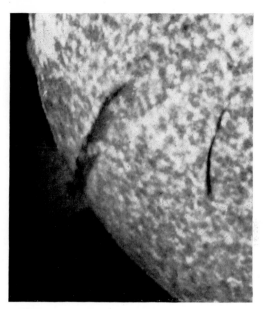

PLATE 65. Notable prominence-filament photographed with the K_3 line at the eastern limb of the Sun (Meudon, 1929 August 27^d 7^h 46^m U.T.).

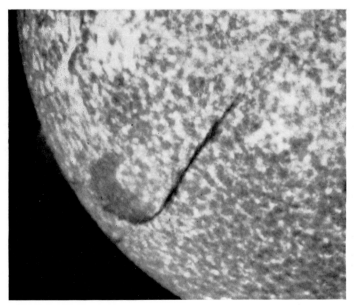

PLATE 66. The same object as that in Plate 65 (Meudon, 1929 August 29^d 8^h 2^m U.T.).

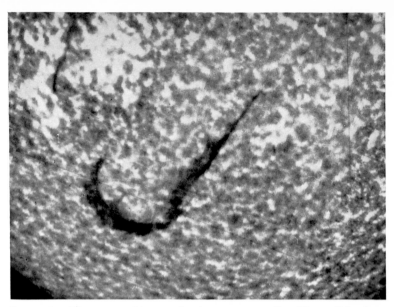

PLATE 67. The same object as in the two preceding Plates (Meudon, 1929 August 31^d 8^h 9^m U.T.).

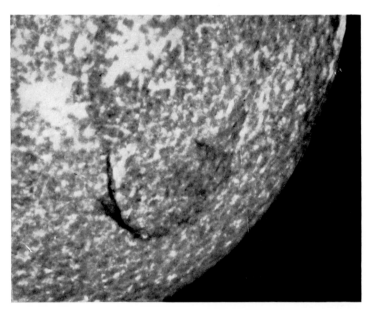

PLATE 68. The same object as in the three preceding Plates, now seen near the west limb. Note the changed intensity of the filament. (Meudon, 1929 September 3^d 15^h 30^m U.T.).

characteristic orientation parallel to the solar meridians; these become distorted by the polar retardation which increases steadily towards high latitudes. The filaments usually attain their maximum development at their fourth crossing of the visible hemisphere, that is to say, in a period of about three months. By this time they are conspicuously curved, since the parts nearer the poles have become oriented along, or nearly along, the parallels of latitude. It is this characteristic orientation that explains the great variety of forms assumed by the quiescent prominences. An equatorial filament, for example, often oriented more or less parallel to the meridian, is seen sideways-on when it reaches the limb. Its typical form in this case is that of a row of trees whose foliage is joined to the chromosphere by solid trunks forming a series of low arches between the one and the other. On the other hand a filament in high latitudes, being oriented more or less east and west, will be seen end-on at the limb, rather in the form of a pyramid or of a single tree. During the fifth rotation the filaments often break up, their equatorial extremity being lost first.

Many of the large filaments are subject to violent interruptions of their normal development. A dense filament will frequently vanish, sometimes to reappear with its original shape and density after a lapse of many days. Sometimes it is involved in a real explosion: the greater part or the whole of the filament is disturbed by violent internal motions, and it is lifted above the chromosphere in the space of a few hours. During the filament's ascent it does not experience a steady acceleration, but rather a series of sudden surges forward, until finally it leaves the Sun altogether. In the majority of cases the explosion marks the end of the filament, though this is not invariably so, and sometimes they reappear with their original shape and size. The stability of the latter, combined with the movement towards the pole and the deformations of the long filaments, lead one to suppose that the incandescent gases of all large prominences owe their origin to some persistent disturbance located at sub-photospheric levels. According to this hypothesis the prominences of the upper chromosphere may be regarded as the visible consequence of disturbances at a lower level which give them life and motion.

The intensity of these phenomena—both as filaments and as prominences—has been determined by various investigators using visual as well as photographic methods. Measures of the Arcetri spectroheliograms made by Colacevich and Viaro suggest that their intensity may vary from 0·01 to 0·20 times that of the continuous spectrum, assuming a value of 0·20 for the intensity of the $H\alpha$ line. Within these limits 0·10 times the intensity of the continuous spectrum is a preferential value. The intensity naturally depends upon the perspective angle under which the phenomenon is viewed. The filaments are often transparent to the light from the underlying chromosphere, as is seen when such a filament over-laps the solar disc as a prominence, when the Sun's limb can be clearly seen through it. Prominences are not, however, seen as filaments on the disc at minima of the solar cycle.

Prominences of classes (i) and (ii) have been extensively studied by a variety of instruments and methods, including ciné cameras. Since the gases are in rapid motion their spectral lines suffer Doppler displacements, from which their radial velocities can be calculated; at the limb their velocities can be determined in the plane perpendicular to the line of sight. Many filaments of short duration move towards the interior of the Sun, presenting the mysterious phenomenon of matter which for a time becomes visible in the form of moving gases which were previously in-visible, as though they had encountered some agent capable of exciting their atoms so as to emit radiation of visible wavelengths: an event reminiscent of terrestrial aurorae, when from time to time the sky is lit up by glowing cloud-like formations. The observed Doppler displacements are in no way suspect, for in the filaments we see real movements of the gases themselves and not simply the passage through a stationary medium of a radiation capable of producing excitation in it. The motion of the gases in the rings and arches that are found above and near to sunspots is usually upward in one part of the arch and downward in another. The examination of suitably accelerated ciné films shows that the motions of the incandescent gases are for the most part directed downward in the direction of the chromosphere where they resemble a rain of fire; this is particularly true of class (iii) pro-minences. Of opposite behaviour to these downward-directed showers are the brilliant 'surges' of chromospheric material, which reach heights of about 30,000 miles, but are of short dura-tion. These surges are probably connected with the flares, of which something has already been said, and it is possible that they are only different aspects of the same phenomenon seen at the solar limb. According to H. W. Newton and M. Ellison, determinations of the radial velocities of these surges reveal an initial period to rapid upward acceleration reaching about 125 miles per second in the first few minutes, simultaneously with the maximum intensity of the flare, which is situated at a lower chromospheric level and has no radial velocity. The upward velocity steadily decreases until the gases come to a halt at the summit of their trajectory, after which they fall back towards the chromosphere again. One may therefore assume that the luminous material carried aloft in the surges is either too dense, or its atoms receive too weak an impulse from the radiations emitted by the flare, to exceed the escape velocity of 383 miles per second which would carry it outside the Sun's gravitational field.

Much experimental and theoretical work has been undertaken in an endeavour to understand the laws governing the equilibria and motions of the prominences. It has been suggested that these result from a complex combination of forces, among which gravity and radiation pressure probably predominate—the latter being proportional to the intensity of the incident light and to the cross-section of the ray intercepted by the body receiving it. Electrostatic and electromagnetic fields may also play an important role in the neighbourhood of spots. According to Pannekoek and Doorn a prominence of normal dimensions has a hydrogen content of 2×10^{13} atoms per c.c.; its total mass is therefore equal to that of a cube of water whose side measures about 10 miles. The large prominences, such as those already described, would have masses several times greater than this. Masses of this order would fall into collapse in a very few minutes in the absence of an upward-directed force sufficiently strong to counter-balance gravity, which is 28 times stronger on the Sun than on the Earth. It is possible to admit that an equilibrium between gravity and radiation pressure exists in the quiescent prominences, which may remain for many days without notable change. If this is so, an explanation must be sought of the fact that after weeks of relative inactivity a prominence will become explosive and after rising for several hours will leave the Sun altogether. Milne supposes that when a prominence begins to rise, through the agency of some small disturbance in the chromosphere, its absorption lines will suffer a Doppler displacement towards the violet, shifting along the continuous spectrum with a corresponding increase of radiation pressure. Instability is thus introduced, as a result of which the prominence will continue to ascend with ever increasing velocity. Pettit and others have studied these explosions in prominences and have found that their various parts move with a constant velocity which is from time to time subject to sudden increases; the intervals between these leaps forward tend to become steadily shorter as the prominence's altitude increases.

An example of these motions, from among the many that have been observed, is that of the prominence observed at Mt Wilson and Zurich on 1938 March 20. This prominence was among the highest that have been encountered; as can be seen from Figure 36 the velocity of ascent during the first hours was very small, but later increased with altitude for several hours; it can be seen that where the curve steepens the velocity does not increase regularly, but in a series of jumps; moreover, the prominence exhibited changes of direction as well as of velocity. Waldmeier believes that the cause of both types of impulse is to be sought in the physical conditions of the condensations which form within the prominence—such as changes in the electrical and magnetic fields. It would be expected that if these derive from the Sun's surface the various condensations in the prominence would be simultaneously affected by a given impulse. This, however, is not borne out by observation: each condensation appears to move independently of the others.

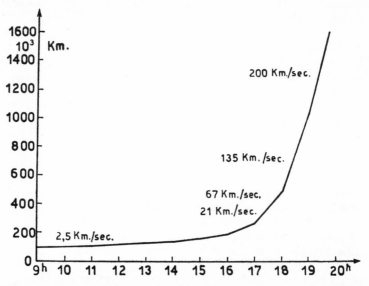

Fig. 36. Ascent of the prominence of 1938 *March* 20 (*Mt Wilson and Zurich*).

It is likely that the problem of the dynamics of the explosions affecting the prominences will only be solved when the electrical conditions obtaining in the chromosphere and inner corona are better understood; it is also essential to know whether the matter distributed through these regions is able to accumulate local electrostatic characteristics similar to those that can be generated by the passage of short-wave radiation, such as X-radiation, which is perhaps emitted by the solar storm centres. We shall see later that the conditions in the corona are such as would allow the emission of ionising radiation of this sort, which requires the existence of great differences of potential between regions adjacent to the chromosphere.

Further series of ciné films of these various phenomena, together with the recent discovery of the emission of high frequency radio-waves by centres of photospheric activity, will probably lead to a better understanding of their many-sided characteristics. Photographs of the prominences taken with an objective prism show that they have the same form in all spectral lines, whence their chemical composition must be the same throughout. But characteristic differences are found when the prominences are examined or photographed in different lines, such as the K, $H\alpha$ or D_3. In the K line the prominences are more compact, in the $H\alpha$ line less so, though showing more detail, while the D_3 line shows only the skeleton of the prominence. Since the auto-absorption of the three lines diminishes in the order $K - H\alpha - D_3$, it is possible to explain such characteristics by supposing that in K light we see only the outermost layers, and in $H\alpha$ the inner layers, while in D_3 the prominence appears almost transparent.

Continuous and systematic investigations have been carried out with the spectroheliograph, the prominences observed with the $H\alpha$ line being compared with those observed with the H and K lines of ionised calcium, extensive series of which exist. A comparison of these photographs, taken at the Mt Wilson and Yerkes Observatories, with visual observations made at Catania, leads to the conclusion that the calcium prominences reach greater altitudes than those of hydrogen. The curve of the areas for the years under consideration (1906–8) is also in general lower for hydrogen than for calcium.

Simultaneous prominence photographs taken with different instruments using these monochromatic radiations, show that in general they are more extensive in calcium light than in hydrogen; the former are also accompanied by numerous filamentous appendages, which in the latter are less intense or are completely lacking (Plate 84). This may, of course, be an effect of photographic contrast or of the instrument's sensitivity to the two radiations, the more so since the two images are identical apart from the size of the prominences and the difference of the appendages; it is therefore concluded that the two elements are completely mingled throughout the prominence.

Furthermore, no separation of the elements is observed in prominences travelling at high velocities, so that in general all the atoms must be moving at the same speed. At the end of the Balmer series at 3647Å the continuous spectrum is seen to be very intense, and according to theory this intensity should fall off exponentially, as is shown by observation. In the spectrum of the prominences we find a marked departure from thermal equilibrium, such as has already been adumbrated in the case of the photosphere, and still more in that of the chromosphere. For excitations of low energy—less than 4 eV—the departures are indeed small, but they increase very rapidly with increase of the level of excitation. Thus the excitation energy of the He I lines is about 20 eV, while the He II line at 4686Å requires 72·5 eV.

17. PERIODICITY AND MIGRATIONS OF THE PROMINENCES AND FILAMENTS

A statistical study of visual and photographic material is being made with international collaboration in order to reveal something of the areas, forms and distribution of the prominences—and also of the spots, faculae, flocculi and filaments—during the various solar cycles. The visual observations date from 1869 when they were initiated immediately following the Janssen-Lockyer discovery by Respighi at the Campidoglio Observatory; they were continued by Fr Secchi at the Observatory of the Collegio Romano at Rome, by the Palermo Observatory, and by many others.

The daily profile of the whole solar limb (i.e. its spectroscopic image) in the light of the $H\alpha$ line was published in the *Memorie della Società degli Spettroscopisti Italiani* from 1869 to 1911 in the form of diagrams from which the position angles and therefore the latitudes of the prominences can be derived, as well as the areas they occupy. The publication of these spectroscopic images of the Sun's limb was continued from 1922 to 1934 by the Arcetri Observatory under the auspices of the International Astronomical Union; since the latter year the diagrams have still been compiled, though not published. These visual observations are supplemented by numerous spectroheliographic observations made with the bright disc of the photosphere suitably masked by a black diaphragm: From this material statistics of the distribution and areas of the prominences are compiled annually. The areas are expressed in terms of a conventional unit known as the 'prominence unit', which is equal to an area whose base is an arc of the Sun's limb 1° long and whose height is 1″ of arc.

The changing behaviour of the prominences in relation to the cycle of solar activity has been investigated by Riccò, Lockyer and others. More recently G. Bocchino—using spectroscopic images of the Sun's limb, from 1880–1931—has calculated the mean diurnal areas of the hydrogen prominences for every 5° of

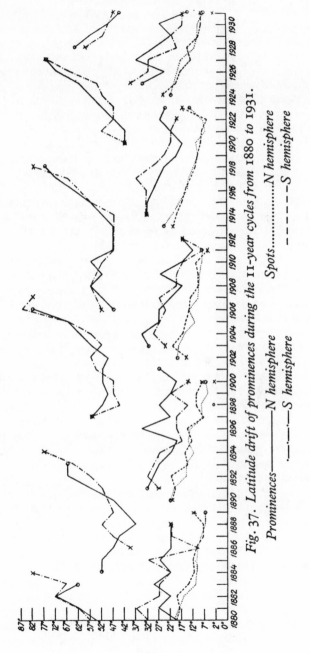

Fig. 37. Latitude drift of prominences during the 11-year cycles from 1880 to 1931.

Prominences——N hemisphere   Spots............N hemisphere
——·——S hemisphere   ─ ─ ─ ─S hemisphere

latitude. The investigation has been extended to 1937 by V. Barocas.

The results so obtained show that the prominences may be divided into two categories, those in low latitudes and those in high. Although this division is not clearly defined at certain epochs, it is nevertheless possible to envisage two distinct zones: one stretching from the equator to $\pm 40°$, and the other from $\pm 40°$ to the poles. From the diagrams it can be seen that the development of the low latitude prominences runs parallel with that of the spots. This is not the case with the prominences in higher latitudes, which are observed to reach maximum north and south latitudes about three years after the spots and the low latitude prominences, i.e. at about the time of maximum spot activity. Moreover it appears that the low latitude prominences take part in a latitude shift similar to that of the spots, though limited to the zone contained by the $\pm 28°$ and $\pm 18°$ parallels (the spots, it will be remembered, are confined between ± 23 and $\pm 7°$).

A comparison of the mean areas of the prominences and the relative spot numbers shows that they vary approximately in step with one another. More precisely, the high latitude prominences appear to attain their maximum area two years before spot maximum, and their minimum about five years before; the low latitude prominences have a secondary maximum two years before spot maximum, though their principal maximum and minimum coincide with those of the spots.

It is of interest to compare these results with those obtained by an examination of the filaments, which, as has already been explained, are none other than prominences seen in projection on the disc. Systematic spectroheliographic observations have not in the past been so extensive as the visual observations of the prominences; nevertheless the *Cartes synoptiques de la chromosphère solaire et catalogue des filaments de la couche supérieure*, have been published since 1919 by Meudon Observatory (based upon spectroheliograms taken there and supplemented by others from Kodaïkanal and Mt Wilson) and by means of these L. and M. d'Azambuja had already been able to confirm, extend and modify the results obtained in the case of the prominences. A preliminary study by G. Godoli of spectroheliograms obtained at Arcetri between 1932 and 1948, while confirming these results, also reveals the extent to which the maximum area of the filaments, unlike that of the prominences, follows that of the spots. This is explicable if account is taken of the form of the filaments, which become prominences at the limb, and of the effects of perspective when observed from the Earth at various solar longitudes and

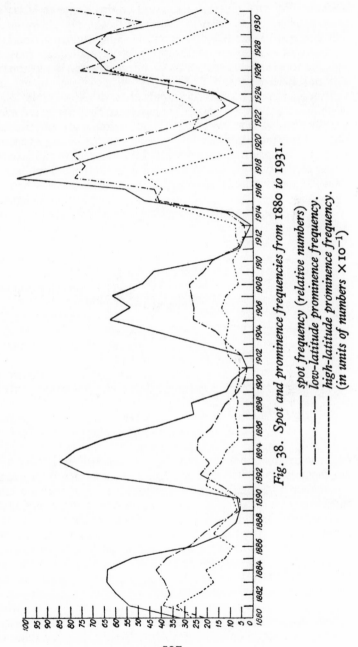

Fig. 38. Spot and prominence frequencies from 1880 to 1931.

——— spot frequency (relative numbers)
—·—·— low-latitude prominence frequency.
- - - - high-latitude prominence frequency.
(in units of numbers × 10⁻¹)

latitudes. For the general orientation of the filaments is, as has been indicated, predominantly parallel to the meridians in low latitudes and perpendicular to them in high latitudes. This leads to discrepant estimates of the areas concerned when it is not possible to establish the true form of the filament or prominence with any exactitude.

Another important fact has emerged from this statistical work on the filament-prominences. We have seen that the prominences may be divided into two groups, high latitude and low latitude, and that they have progressive motions in latitude. But as early as 1913 A. A. Buss had expressed a doubt as to the similarity of origin of the two groups. And M. d'Azambuja has been able to show from an examination of the Meudon diagrams that the polar

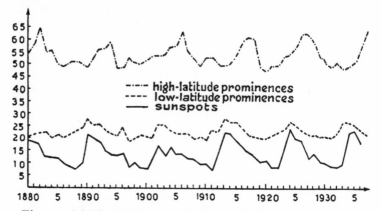

Fig. 39. Distribution in north and south latitude of prominences and spots from 1880 to 1935.

filament-prominences are simply the original equatorial ones which have been displaced towards high latitudes by a general circulatory movement towards the poles, and that they gradually orient themselves along the solar parallels in consequence of the variations of the Sun's rotation—which, as we have seen, is more rapid at the equator than at the poles. The combined Meudon and Arcetri results throw much new light on the development of the phenomenon. Ignoring the division of the prominences into two latitude groups (as is illustrated in Figures 37, 39), one may conclude that at the beginning of an 11-year cycle—i.e. around the minimum of general solar activity—disturbances of the photosphere begin to manifest themselves over a fairly wide latitude zone at about 40°; these are represented below the 40° parallels by pores and small spots of the new cycle, and above them as filament-prominences. As the cycle advances from minimum to maximum the zone of disturbance moves towards lower latitudes, with the production of spots and filament-prominences nearer and nearer to the equator. According to Righini and Godoli the rate of migration of the flocculi towards the poles may be put at about 2° per rotation. D'Azambuja's investigations indicate that the rate of the filament-prominences' polar migration depends on their latitude at the phase of the cycle.

The appearance of the new cycle may occur from three to six years before the maximum, according to the intensity that it will attain (see p. 77); hence the equatorial disturbed zone may survive for from eight to five years after the maximum, continuing to approach the equator more or less slowly, whilst sooner or later another disturbed zone will begin to develop at a mean latitude of 40°, thus opening the new cycle. Figure 40 may be taken as representing the phenomenon of solar activity: it shows the probable mean trend of the disturbance as it is manifested by the spots and the filament-prominences throughout the cycle.

According to Alfvén's 'magneto-hydrodynamic wave' hypothesis (see p. 253), the initial cause in spot-formation lies in a convection phenomenon located in the Sun's central region, which gives rise to spots through the agency of a magneto-hydrodynamic transmission to the solar surface. Assuming that the Sun's magnetic field is of dipole type (p. 188) and that a magneto-hydrodynamic disturbance arises suddenly near the centre of the dipole, then this will produce waves which will be transmitted along the lines of force of the field and will reach the solar surface after an interval which will be a function of latitude. According to Alfvén it is possible that not only the spots but also the high-latitude prominences originate from the same train of magneto-hydrodynamic waves. When these reach the Sun's surface they cause electro-magnetic disturbances which for some reason manifest themselves as spots in low latitudes and as prominences in high.

18. SPECTROSCOPIC DETERMINATION OF THE SUN'S ROTATION PERIOD

When the motions of the gases in the Sun's atmosphere occur along the line of sight they are betrayed in the spectrum by the Doppler effect. These motions may be either irregular or regular. The former typically characterise disturbed regions of the Sun, such as the surroundings of sunspots, and eruptions and prominences; the latter are due to the Sun's axial rotation, and are maximal at the equatorial limbs and zero at the poles.

Distortions and displacements of the spectral lines from their

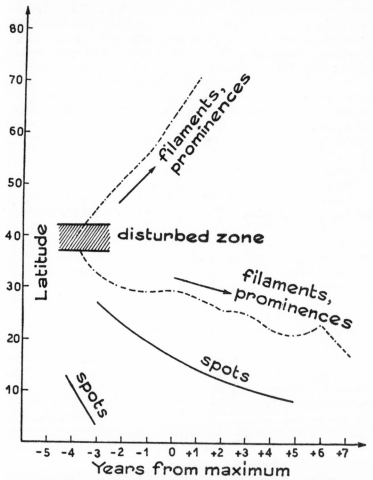

Fig. 40. Theory of the latitude drift of solar phenomena throughout the 11-year cycle (G. Abetti).

normal positions in the spectrum were noted by such early investigators as Secchi, Young and Lockyer; they applied particularly to the hydrogen lines and to the prominences. Secchi's book on the Sun contains interesting drawings of the *H*α line as observed with the spectroscope slit set perpendicularly to the limb in very disturbed regions of the chromosphere.

Hale analysed the filaments by means of his line-shifter, noting and measuring the rapid downward motions of the hydrogen towards the surface. Similar measures can be made with Deslandres' *spectro-enregistreur*, with which velocities up to about 250 miles per second have been measured in the prominences.

The other class of regular displacements which are observed when the spectrum of the limbs is compared with that of the centre of the disc leads to the determination of the Sun's rotation period in the latitude to which the slit is adjusted, and at the level to which the line under observation belongs. This method of measuring the solar rotation is very much more accurate than the others that have so far been described, and has the further advantage that it can be extended to cover the high latitudes where no spots, faculae or flocculi occur.

Since 1871, when Vogel showed that the method was practicable, several series of spectroscopic measurements, both visual and photographic, have been carried out. Among the former should be mentioned those made by Dunér of Upsala from 1880–90 and 1901–3, using the atmospheric lines for reference. He observed points on the limb from the equator to $\pm 75°$ heliographic latitude, and came to the conclusion that Faye's formula, which is similar to those of Spörer and Maunder (p. 85), most satisfactorily represents the spectroscopic observations up to the high latitudes which he investigated.

From 1903 to 1906 Halm at Edinburgh, using like Dunér the differential method, was engaged on a series of observations with a heliometer, whose divided object glass enabled him to switch rapidly from one limb to the other, with a consequent increase of accuracy. His observations indicated the existence of marked systematic variations for the years considered, which led him to suspect that the Sun's rotation period was variable. Variations certainly occur, according to the levels investigated with the different spectral lines, and as a consequence of disturbances in this or that region of the Sun, but changes dependent upon the solar cycle are more difficult to substantiate, especially if we have to compare series of observations made with different instruments and in different localities. As we shall see, the results that have been obtained up to the present time do not justify any conclusions to be drawn.

After these early visual observations photography completely superseded the human eye. It carried the double advantage that a great number of lines can be measured on the plate, and that the investigation can be extended to a wider region of the spectrum. Among the early photographic determinations should be mentioned the classical series undertaken by W. S. Adams in 1906 and 1908 with the horizontal and vertical telescopes at Mt Wilson, where systematic observations are still being carried on.

For his earlier measures (1906–7) Adams used the horizontal Snow telescope in conjunction with an 18-foot spectrograph employing a Rowland grating. Two small totally-reflecting prisms were mounted on the spectrograph slit, their distance apart being equal to the diameter of the Sun's image; a second pair of prisms immediately above the slit received the light from these and reflected it through the slit into the interior of the spectrograph. In this way he was able to make direct comparisons of the spectra of the two opposite limbs side by side, and since the prism mounting could be rotated the two outer prisms could be adjusted to any required latitude of the solar limb.

When the dispersion curve of the prisms or grating has been determined, the shifts of the lines measured in millimetres by a spectrocomparator are converted to angstroms; these, multiplied by the velocity of light in kms per second and divided by the wavelength of the line in question, give the desired velocity in kms per second.

For these linear velocities to yield the true velocities corresponding to the Sun's sidereal rotation period in different latitudes, certain corrections must be applied; these are quickly derived with the help of the special data for physical observations of the Sun which the *Nautical Almanac* and the *American Ephemeris* quote for each day of the current year, and of new tables published at Arcetri by F. Zagar which supersede the older tables of Dunér. With these ephemerides and tables the latitude corresponding to the position angle of the slit is calculated, followed by the two corrections required to convert the measured velocity at this latitude to the true rotational velocity.

The first correction takes in account the fact that the measured velocity includes the component of the Earth's orbital velocity along the line of sight. To obtain the sidereal velocity from the synodic velocity it is necessary to increase the observed velocity by a quantity which can be found in the tables for the date of observation.

The second correction is necessitated by the fact that it is not the actual velocity of the observed point that is measured, but only its line of sight component, i.e. that which is vertical to the plane of the apparent disc. Only when the poles of the Sun are situated on its limb is the total velocity of the observed point measured, for in this case all the points on the limb are moving perpendicularly to its plane. This correction is also found, as a function of the Earth's heliocentric latitude, in Zagar's tables. Strictly speaking another correction—of the same sort as that necessitated by the Earth's orbital motion—should be applied, depending on the line of sight component of the observer's diurnal motion. But this correction is usually neglected since it could never amount to more than 0·002 km per second, and even those observations made with the most powerful instruments under optimum conditions do not yield mean velocities accurate to more than 0·001 km per second.

So far it has been assumed that the measures are made at the limb itself, but if they are made at points inside the limb—as is usually the case, so as to avoid the trembling of the limb due to terrestrial atmospheric turbulence, and also diffused light—the measured velocity will be smaller than the limb value; to convert it to the latter it must be multiplied by the secant of the angle included between the central meridian and the meridian passing through the point of observation.

The diurnal angular velocity ξ for a given latitude is usually calculated from the linear velocity v, as we have already seen is done in the case of the spots (p. 84). ξ is obtained by multiplying v by 360° and by the number of seconds in 1 mean solar day, and dividing the product by that of the Sun's circumference expressed in kms and the cosine of the latitude.

For his 1908 investigations Adams used the 60-foot solar tower at Mt. Wilson (59 feet focal length), together with an auto-collimating spectrograph of 30 feet focal length, which gave a plate-scale in the third-order spectra of 1 mm/0·56Å. He measured the velocity v in latitudes 0°, 15°, 30°, 45°, 60° and 75°, for a score of reversing-layer lines between 4200Å and 4300Å; these belong to the G group and to the head of the first cyanogen band, and their intensities lie between 1 and 4 on Rowland's scale. In addition, he gave special attention to the velocities derived by the blue calcium line at 4227Å and the $H\alpha$ line.

The results of this important series of measures by Adams may be summarised as follows. The two series of 1906–7 and 1908 agree well with one another and with the earlier observations of Dunér. Both series revealed that the lines of different elements give different values of the rotational velocity, and, moreover, that the largest deviations shown by those lines which yield systematically high or low values of the velocity occur also between mid and high latitudes.

The lines yielding the greatest deviations from the mean values of the angular velocity are listed in the following table, together with the deviations themselves (divided into two groups—low and high latitude) and the assumed chromospheric altitudes reached by the lines, as deduced from the chromospheric arcs (p. 207) during total eclipses.

λ (Rowland revised)	Element	Height above photosphere (miles)	Latitude	
			0°–20°	60°–80°
4196·547	La II	300	−0°·1	−0°·3
4197·102 ⎱ 4215·978 ⎰	CN	300	−0·1	−0·3
4257·663	Mn	250	+0·1	+0·3
4226·742	Ca	3000	+0·4	+1·6
6562·816	Hα	6800	+0·6	+2·8

The most natural explanation of these deviations is the supposition that they are an altitude effect: that elements situated at relatively low levels in the solar atmosphere yield correspondingly low values for the angular rotational velocity. In other words, the outer atmospheric layers rotate more rapidly than those nearer the photosphere. But whilst this phenomenon, in general outline, appears to be well established for large differences of level, for small ones (and therefore within the reversing layer itself) it seems to be more complex than a simple altitude effect, and it will probably be necessary to take into account the relation between the velocities and the energy levels of the atoms producing the lines, treating them as multiplets and thus endeavouring to isolate a possible effect due to the different intensities of the lines; these intensities in turn depend on the altitude of the layer above the photosphere.

Adams' Hα results were deduced from a series of observations in various latitudes, either on the limb or 3 mm inside it, to ascertain what effect the reduction of the wings of the line might have on the derived velocity. Comparison of the figures so obtained shows that the points nearer the limb not only yield higher absolute values, but also a smaller variation of velocity with change of latitude. An effect of this sort would be expected in view of the fact that the effective absorption level in the case of an element like hydrogen would probably be higher at the limb than inside it. Similarly, determinations made with the calcium line at 4227Å showed that neutral calcium vapour, like hydrogen, moves more rapidly and with less variations than the reversing layer as the latitude is increased, while the K_3 velocity of ionised calcium is still greater.

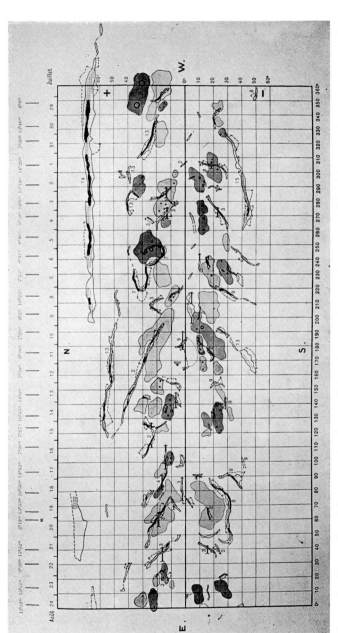

PLATE 69. Example of the synoptic charts of the chromosphere and spots published by Meudon Observatory for each solar rotation (1937, rotation No. 1122).

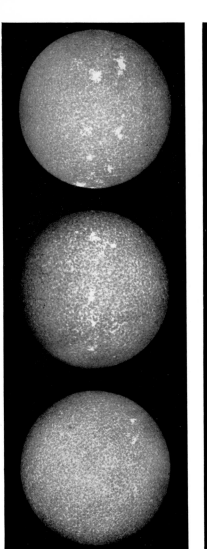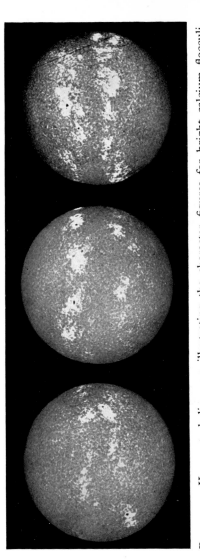

PLATE 70. K_2 spectroheliograms illustrating the character figures for bright calcium flocculi. Upper, left to right: 0, 1, 2. Lower, left to right: 3, 4, 5 (Mt Wilson).

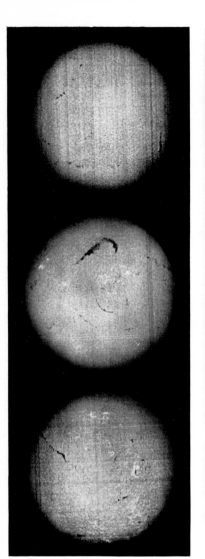
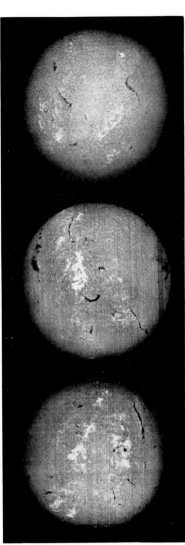

PLATE 71. $H\alpha$ spectroheliograms illustrating the character figures for bright hydrogen flocculi. Upper, left to right: 0, 1, 2. Lower, left to right: 3, 4, 5 (Mt Wilson).

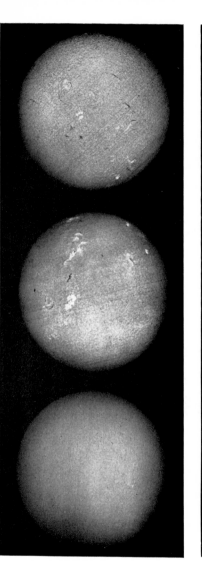

PLATE 72. *Hα* spectroheliograms illustrating the character figures for hydrogen filaments. Upper, left to right: 0, 1, 2. Lower, left to right: 3, 4, 5 (Mt Wilson).

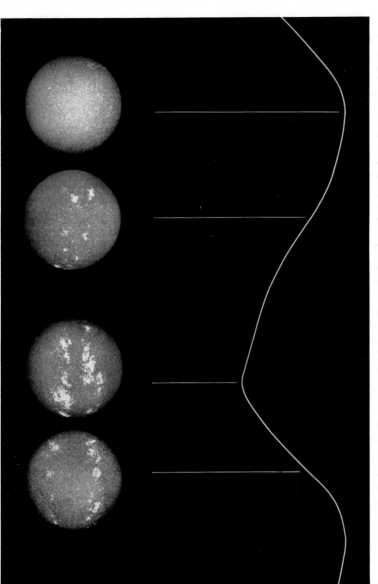

PLATE 73. Typical spectroheliograms of calcium flocculi showing their variations in area and latitude at different stages of the 11-year cycle, indicated by the curve below (Mt Wilson).

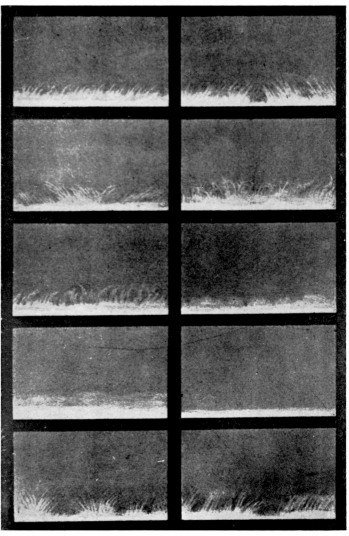

PLATE 74. Drawings by Fr A. Secchi of the chromosphere (*Le Soleil*, Vol. II, Pl. A).

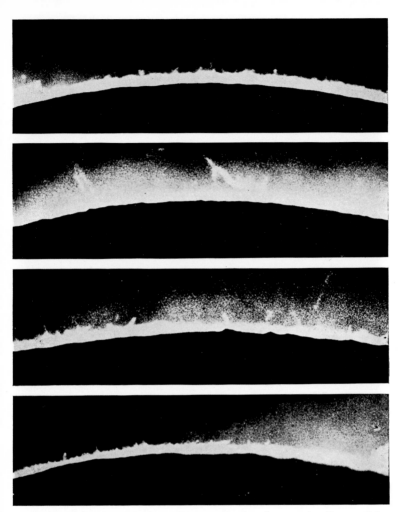

PLATE 75. The chromosphere photographed at four total eclipses of the Sun—1898, 1900, 1905, 1918 (Mt Hamilton). Note the mountains on the black limb of the Moon.

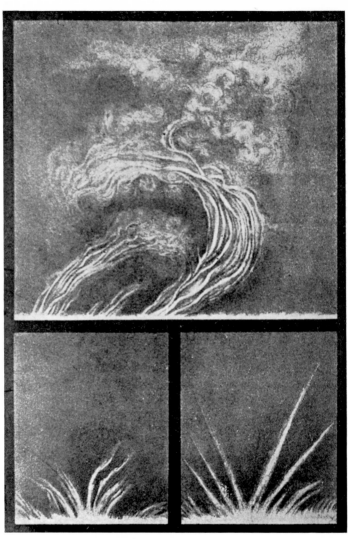

PLATE 76. Drawings by Fr A. Secchi of prominences
(*Le Soleil*, Vol. II, Pl. C).

But the results given by the motions of the calcium flocculi (p. 116), and those obtained at Arcetri by means of the Doppler effect in the $H\alpha_2$ and $H\alpha_3$ components with the slit tangential to the limb, are not in agreement with the foregoing; for in both cases a law is obtained for the rotation which agrees better with that of the spots and the reversing layer than with those obtained by Adams with the $H\alpha$ line and by St John with the K_3.

The following table summarises the results obtained by different methods, both direct and spectroscopic:

ϕ	Spots	Faculae	Calcium flocculi	Reversing layer	4227Å (Mt Wilson)	$H\alpha_2$ (Arcetri)	$H\alpha_3$ (Arcetri)	$H\alpha$ (Mt Wilson)	K_3 (Mt Wilson)
0°	14°.4	—	14°.5	14°.2	15°.1	13°.9	14°.7	15°.2	—
15	14·2	14·3	14·3	14·1	14·8	—	—	14·9	15·5
30	13·7	13·8	13·9	13·5	14·3	11·9	13·6	14·5	—
45	—	12·8	13·2	12·6	13·6	—	—	14·0	14·4
60	—	—	—	11·5	12·5	9·1	10·9	13·5	—
75	—	—	—	—	13·3	—	—	14·2	—

In this Table the values for the sunspots, faculae and flocculi are those already given on pp. 85, 89, 117 and 118; those for the reversing layer are the means of the best measures from 1906 to 1929, the rotational velocity being assumed constant during this period; those for the $H\alpha_2$ and $H\alpha_3$ components are obtained from measures made with the Arcetri solar tower in 1928, those for $H\alpha$ at the limb, and those for the 4227Å line and the K_3 component by Adams and St John as described above.

It should be noted that both the 4227Å and the $H\alpha$ lines show a sudden increase of angular velocity between latitudes 60° and 75°. It must be remembered, however, that at high latitudes the angular velocity is extremely sensitive to small differences of linear velocity; thus, for example, a difference of 0·011 miles per second reduces the value of from 14° to 13°.5. Hence too much importance must not be attached to this increase, which may result from errors of observation and measurement. All the same, Adams having found a similar tendency with different lines of the reversing layer, it is possible that there is some real agency tending to increase the angular velocity of the upper atmospheric levels in the neighbourhood of the Sun's poles.

The values tabulated above are plotted graphically in Figure 41. Here the laws of rotation as derived from the different phenomena can be clearly seen. The reversing layer and the $H\alpha_2$ emission component give the lowest velocities and the greatest equatorial acceleration. These are followed, in order of increasing velocity, by the spots, faculae and flocculi, until at the highest levels, represented by the K_3 component, the velocity is greatest, and almost

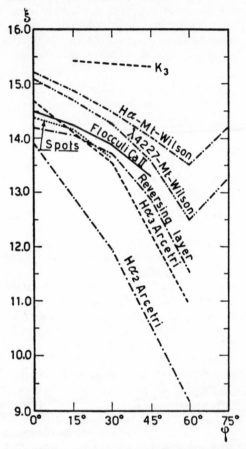

Fig. 41. Comparison of the angular velocities of different solar phenomena. Abscissae: latitude. Ordinates: angular velocity.

constant. The hypothesis relating velocities with atmospheric levels appears incapable of explaining how this trend, which is contradictory as regards the supposed level of the spots, can be assimilated with that of the reversing layer and of hydrogen as determined by measurements of the various $H\alpha$ components.

A theory has been proposed by Wilsing, which assumes the existence on the Sun of layers rotating at constant angular velocities, within which may be contained layers whose angular velocity is a function of latitude; or, again, it may be supposed that the various absorption and emission lines observed at the limb are affected to a greater or smaller extent by the low levels in which they originate. Further observations will certainly be required in order to clarify this trend.

In addition to these spectroscopic determinations of the Sun's rotation, many others have been undertaken, and the differences between the mean values obtained at different times and by different observers raise a suspicion that the rotation period may be variable, possibly with the 11-year cycle.

Newall, discussing the observations made between 1901 and 1913, found that Faye's formula

$$v = (a - b \sin^2 \phi) \cos \phi$$

satisfactorily represents the dependence of velocity on latitude as derived by Dunér, Halm, Adams, Plaskett, de Lury and Schlesinger, but that both a and b may vary during the course of the 11-year cycle, and furthermore that at a given time b may be different in different parts of the same hemisphere. At spot minimum itself the gases at the Sun's surface in latitude 50° lag behind those in the contiguous zones by a maximum amount which is represented by $b=0.4$ or 0.5 miles per second. At the same time the velocity of the equatorial gases is minimal ($a \simeq 1.20$ miles per second), but begins to increase again as the equatorial spots die out. The critical relative velocity between contiguous zones is attained in latitudes rather higher than 40° with the appearance of spots in these regions. At spot maximum a attains its maximum value of about 1.28 miles per second.

But since Newall's investigation covered only a single cycle and his material has been obtained by different methods and with different instruments, it is impossible to arrive at any certain conclusion regarding the variability of the Sun's rotation period.

In order to have a homogeneous series of observations made with a single instrument and employing the same method, observations similar to those already undertaken by Adams were initiated in 1914 with the Mt Wilson solar tower, and have been continued regularly. Similar measures, always made by the same observer and with the same instrument, were started at Edinburgh in the same year. The results obtained at these two observatories, reduced to biennial averages, are not in very good agreement, nor is it possible by combining the two series to draw any definite conclusions as to possible periodic variations, as can be seen from the following table. Since the error in each of these values should not exceed 0·006 miles per second it must be concluded that some systematic error is responsible for the discrepancies between the two sets.

Year	Linear velocity at the equator					
	Mt Wilson				Edinburgh	
	E and W limbs with prisms		E and W limbs without prisms		E and W limbs without prisms	
	km/sec	miles/sec	km/sec	miles/sec	km/sec	miles/sec
1915	1·94	1·21			1·92	1·19
1917	1·93	1·20			1·96	1·22
1919	1·92	1·19			—	—
1920	—	—			2·00	1·24
1921	1·91	1·19			1·98	1·23
1923	1·90	1·18			2·03	1·26
1924	1·90	1·18			1·99	1·24
1925	—	—			1·95	1·21
1927	—	—			1·98	1·23
1929	1·91	1·19			1·98	1·23
1930	1·95	1·21			—	—
1931	—	—			1·97	1·22
1932	1·99	1·24			—	—
1933	1·98	1·23	2·05	1·27	—	—
1934	1·97	1·22	2·05	1·27	—	—

It should be borne in mind that the Mt Wilson measures were made with a powerful instrument—the 150-foot solar tower and the 75-foot spectrograph. Other observations have been made simultaneously with the 150-foot tower, the 60-foot tower and the Snow telescope for purposes of comparison, and it has been found that within the established limits of accuracy the three instruments give concordant values. This should ensure homogeneity and render possible the direct comparison of these more recent measures with those made by Adams from 1906 to 1908, to which reference has already been made. The observations of the 1914–32 period, when compared with the earlier Mt Wilson results, which yield a mean velocity of 1·28 miles per second at the equator, suggest the existence of a variation which cannot be attributed to observational errors.

On the hypothesis that the solar rotation derived from the spots is a measure of the rotation of the photosphere, the linear velocity of the reversing layer in 1906 was 0·037 miles per second greater than that of the photosphere, and in 1918, 0·06 miles per second less, reaching a long minimum in 1925 when the period became about two days longer than in 1906. From 1928 the Mt Wilson observations show a fairly steady increase of the velocity, though up to 1932 it remained lower than that of the photosphere. St John believes that these variations may be explained in terms of long-period drifts in the reversing layer, alternately eastward and westward, which increase or diminish the period of the Sun's rotation.

The suspicion that the observed systematic discrepancies might be caused by diffused light launched the Mt Wilson workers on a programme in 1932 whose aim was to determine its effect on the measured velocities. Indeed, the apparatus used at Mt Wilson for the simultaneous photography of the east and west limbs (p. 142) by means of totally-reflecting prisms might introduce diffracted light from each of the two superimposed spectra, resulting in a diminution of the Doppler shifts. To test this, photographs of the two limbs were taken separately—as is the procedure at Arcetri and Edinburgh, for example. Twenty photographs taken in this way yielded a mean velocity of 1·250 miles per second, while the photographs taken using the prisms gave 1·234 miles per second. The difference of 0·016 miles per second indicates that the values of the rotation obtained at Mt Wilson with the prismatic set-up should always be increased by about 1·5% as a correction for the effect of diffracted light. Furthermore, in 1933 determinations of the rotation were initiated with the slit adjusted 2′.3 inside the limb to reduce also the effect of diffused light within the optical system. The values derived from these direct photographs are systematically higher than those obtained with the prisms, as can be seen from the above table. From this, Nicholson and Richardson conclude that the Mt Wilson values of the solar rotation should be increased by about 4%.

Determinations made at the Arcetri solar tower, taking the two limbs separately and measuring the lines of neutral and ionised atoms and CN bands, have given for the linear equatorial velocity:

1·224±0·006 miles per second (Arcetri, 1933·6)

Other determinations, using the lines of neutral and ionised metals in three different wavelength ranges, gave:

1·236±0·001 miles per second (Arcetri, 1942·5)

Separating the results obtained from neutral and ionised atoms should confirm the Mt Wilson results, i.e. ionised atoms yield slightly lower velocities than those of neutral atoms.

Five sodium lines of various intensities observed by M. Cimino have together given the value

1·236 miles per second (Arcetri, 1943·7)

Determinations in different latitudes, using these lines, have yielded the following values for the diurnal angular velocity:

ϕ	ξ
0°	14°04
15	13·78
30	13·05
45	12·35
60	12·16

It appears from theoretical considerations that a secular (i.e. progressive) variation is extremely improbable, since the loss of mass dependent on the loss of luminosity would be much too small to be observable in so short a period of time. It is more likely that there may be a periodic variation, synchronised with the spot-frequency cycle, or, as we shall see, with that of spot polarities. In the former case the period would be about 11 years, but neither spectroscopic observations nor those of long-lived spots (which over the last thirty years give a constant value of 1·25 miles per second at the equator) show a periodicity of this sort.

In fact H. W. Newton, using the Greenwich spot observations, has derived the following laws of rotation for the five 11-year periods from 1878 to 1933:

$$
\begin{aligned}
\text{I. } & 1878\text{--}88 & \xi &= 14°35 - 2°5 \sin^2 \phi \\
\text{II. } & 1889\text{--}99 & \xi &= 14·39 - 3·0 \sin^2 \phi \\
\text{III. } & 1900\text{--}13 & \xi &= 14·39 - 2·8 \sin^2 \phi \\
\text{IV. } & 1914\text{--}23 & \xi &= 14·39 - 2·6 \sin^2 \phi \\
\text{V. } & 1924\text{--}33 & \xi &= 14·37 - 3·0 \sin^2 \phi
\end{aligned}
$$

The aim of future observations will be ever greater precision, together with the elimination of systematic errors. In the meantime the following conclusions may be noted:

(a) The Fraunhofer lines give widely divergent values of the rotational velocity, owing to their diverse intensities and energy levels, and also according to the region of the spectrum in which they occur, as well as to other causes such as the superposition of different lines.

(b) Different instrumental conditions and observers may give values which are discordant within the limits of observational error, indicating the presence of systematic errors—among which the size of the Sun's image and the point on the limb which is observed are particularly troublesome.

(c) Discordant values may be obtained by the same observer using the same instrument, probably owing to atmospheric conditions—transparency of the sky, diffused light, and steady definition of the Sun's limb.

If, bearing these considerations in mind, it is also found that when the mean values of different observers and instruments are combined (as has become possible in recent years) increasingly concordant results are obtained, in which it is difficult to detect any significant variation, then it would seem reasonable to conclude, at any rate for the time being, that the variability of the Sun's rotation period is problematical; it may also be concluded that future comparisons of observational data, taking the above-mentioned circumstances into account, should aim at the greatest possible observational accuracy and at the same time maximum freedom from systematic errors.

19. *RADIAL MOVEMENTS IN SUNSPOTS, AND SOLAR ATMOSPHERIC CIRCULATION

The vortical structure of the hydrogen flocculi which is often encountered in the neighbourhood of spots—and which led Hale to the discovery of their magnetic fields—would suggest that metallic vapours as well as hydrogen are drawn into the vortices centred on the axes of spots. But the fact that these vapours and hydrogen are situated at very different levels in the Sun's atmosphere suggests that both the general circulation and also the small-scale circulation centred on the spots may differ very considerably. Evershed, indeed, when investigating possible Doppler shifts in spot spectra at Kodaïkanal Observatory in India, discovered certain distortions of the Fraunhofer lines when the slit overlay the umbra and penumbra, which varied according to the orientation of the spectrograph slit relative to the centre of the disc. Such line deformations are now known as the 'Evershed effect', and are interpreted as indicating a movement of the metallic vapours radially outward from the spot in a plane parallel to the Sun's surface.

The effect can be observed in the majority of spots when the slit is placed across both umbra and penumbra in the direction of the solar radius through the centre of the spot ('radial slit'). If the spot is further than about 10° from the centre it will be observed

that the weak and moderately intense Fraunhofer lines are inclined
to their normal positions in such a way that at one edge of the spot
they are shifted towards the violet and at the other edge towards
the red. The shifts are of opposite sign on opposite sides of the
central meridian and in the majority of cases are towards the violet
at the preceding (i.e. western) edge of the spot and towards the red
at the following edge when the spot lies to the east of the central
meridian; when it is to the west of the central meridian the directions of the shifts are reversed. It makes no difference whether the
spot lies in the north or south hemisphere (Figure 42).

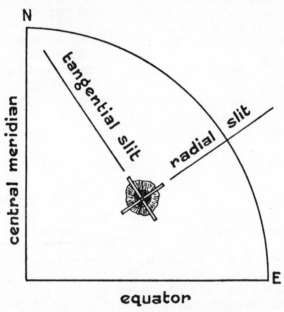

*Fig. 42. Orientations of the spectrograph for studying the motions of
the gases in sunspots.*

If the slit is adjusted to other position angles or is set at right-
angles to the radial direction ('tangential slit') the shifts are
generally smaller and sometimes nonexistent.

The simplest explanation of the observed effects is, as already
said, to attribute to the metallic vapours overlying the umbra and
penumbra a rapid motion radially outward from the centre of the
spot towards its periphery in a plane approximately horizontal and
parallel to the Sun's surface; this would account for the total sup-
pression of the distortions of the lines as the spot nears and passes

the central meridian. The fact that the displacements are always minimal when the slit is tangential indicates that the component of the vortical motion is always smaller than that of the radial motion.

Evershed deduced from the inclinations of the spot lines that the motion accelerates from the umbra towards the exterior of the spot, reaching a maximum value of rather more than 1 mile per second at the outer edge of the penumbra.

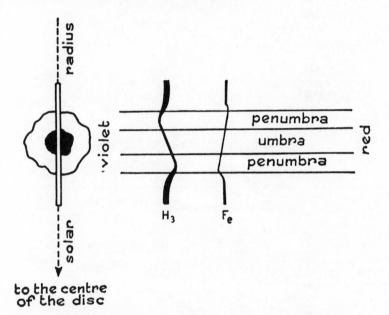

Fig. 43. Typical deformation of the lines of the chromosphere and reversing layer when the slit is oriented radially.

The above account applies to the metallic lines of moderate intensity, but the H_3 and K_3 lines of the upper chromosphere over the penumbra show distortions which are analogous but in the opposite direction (i.e. towards the violet at the edge of the spot which faces the limb). This shows that the calcium vapour in the upper atmosphere has a motion analogous to that of the metallic vapours but in the opposite sense, i.e. towards the centres of spots.

This investigation of Evershed's was followed up by St John in 1910 and 1911, using the Mt Wilson 60-foot solar tower. He determined the shifts of a considerable number of absorption lines so as to allow the various lines to be discussed statistically according to their level, from the highest strata of the chromosphere (*H*, *K* and *H*α lines), through lower levels represented by the more intense magnesium, aluminiun and iron lines, to the weakest lines at the

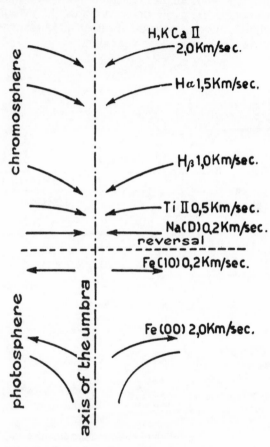

Fig. 44. Distribution of radial velocities in sunspots according to altitude (St John).

lowest levels. Whereas Evershed had determined the displacements of the lines by reference to the spectrum of the photosphere immediately outside the zone disturbed by the spot, St John measured them by comparing the two opposite edges of the penumbra photographically, juxtaposing them by means of a suitable screen so as to obtain the double shift.

St John's observations substantially confirmed Evershed's hypothesis, and in addition showed that since the shifts are proportional to wavelength the phenomenon is a true Doppler effect caused by the flow of reversing layer material from the interior and centre of the spots, and the simultaneous flow of chromospheric material towards the centre and the interior of the spots.

The outward velocities increase in proportion to the distance below a mean level where the velocity is zero, and the inward velocities increase in proportion as the altitude above the mean level increases; this level may be termed the velocity reversal level.

St John summarised his results in the form of a diagram showing the direction of motion and the velocities of the gases at various altitudes above the spots, and for lines of various intensities.

The lines giving a mean radial velocity of recession from the spot centre of 0·6 miles per second are the weakest, with an intensity of about 0 on Rowland's scale; those found at the velocity reversal level have intensities of from 10 to 20; and those giving velocities of approach are among the most intense in the solar spectrum.

St John suggests that the low-intensity lines are produced in the lower levels of the solar atmosphere, whence the direction and velocity of the flux may be considered as a function of depth. According to this hypothesis the effective level of a line may be defined as that part of the total thickness of a given gas which is primarily responsible for the production of the line. For example, the absorption shown by a Fraunhofer line of intensity 4 on Rowland's scale derives from a greater depth than that producing a line of intensity 10.

Light from the photosphere and from the lower and hotter levels of the vapours under consideration is in both cases absorbed selectively and is unable to reach the surface, so that the light emitted with these respective wavelengths derive from more or less clearly defined gaseous envelopes whose radius is greater for an intensity 10 line and relatively smaller for one of intensity 4.

The idea of these effective levels was conceived—as we have already seen (p. 107)—in order to explain the spectroheliograms obtained with different parts of the same line, and has been fully confirmed by these radial motions and by determinations of the altitudes of the gases, such as can be undertaken at total eclipses.

The following table compares the altitudes given by S. A. Mitchell and the motions derived by St John from the lines of the iron spectrum, and also gives the mean ionisation potentials of the different groups of lines measured:

Line intensities (Rowland) .	0–2	3–5	6–8	9–12	15–40
Chromospheric altitude in miles (Mitchell) . .	200	270	370	580	900
Evershed effect in miles per second (St John) . .	1·1	0·7	0·5	0·1	0·06
Ionisation potential in volts .	3·30	2·86	2·20	1·66	0·87

Above 1000 or 1200 miles the lines of ionised elements are visible in the solar atmosphere—of sodium, magnesium, hydrogen and calcium; for these lines, as has been said, the opposite effect to that at the lower levels is encountered.

St John, in his discussion of these radial displacements, notes that they are also larger in the red than in the violet for lines of the same intensity. This may be attributed to the fact that our observational methods penetrate to greater depths in red light owing to the diffusion of the violet, so that the effective levels are deeper with the longer wavelengths.

In conclusion, these investigations of St John, together with results obtained during total eclipses, allow it to be said that visible quantities of the vapours of the different elements extend to different altitudes in the Sun's atmosphere; that the lines of a given element originate at increasing depths as their intensities weaken; that enhanced lines reveal a higher level than ordinary lines of the same intensity; and that it is possible to see to greater depths of the Sun at the red end of the spectrum than at the violet. The resultant distribution shows that the H_3 and K_3 lines of ionised calcium belong to the greatest altitudes, followed by the $H\alpha$ line of hydrogen, and that in general the heavy and rare elements are found in observable quantities only in the lowest regions of the solar atmosphere.

As may be inferred from the observations described above, the phenomenon of the prevailing radial motions of the glass, combined with their tangential motion, is certainly extremely complex, and further systematic observations are required of spots of different sizes and activity, in a variety of heliographic positions, and during different cycles, as well as the examination of different types of spectral line.

At the spot maximum of 1926–32 a series of observations of this type were carried out with the Arcetri solar tower. Departing from the methods hitherto used, the Arcetri determinations involved the measurement of the maximum shifts of the spot lines (Figure 43) by comparison with the same undisturbed line photographed at the centre of the disc; observations at the centre of the disc were of course avoided when any local disturbance was present. The measured shifts, corrected for the effect of the Sun's rotation, may therefore be taken to refer to the normal conditions on the Sun, whereas the regions immediately adjacent to the spots are almost always disturbed. During the period mentioned some 30 spots were observed with both positions of the slit, radial and tangential, and were followed for as long as the Sun's rotation allowed. Furthermore, the appearance of the hydrogen vortices round these spots was studied by means of simultaneous, or nearly simultaneous, spectroheliograms.

The Arcetri results lead to conclusions somewhat different from those of previous investigators, the most important of which is that a constant and regular Evershed effect cannot be ascribed to all spots. In fact the velocities of the outward-flowing metallic vapours are extremely variable, ranging from very low values near zero to a maximum of about 4 miles per second for the radial components. The tangential components are noticeably smaller than the radial, though they are almost always measurable; the maximum value recorded in this series of observations was about 2 miles per second.

The whole series of measures of line shifts in spots made at Arcetri yielded a mean velocity of 0·9 miles per second for the radial components of the motion, and about 0·6 miles per second for the tangential. It is, however, hardly permissible to speak of mean values since the motions of the gases are extremely irregular, and vary from one spot to another. This seems to agree with theoretical considerations regarding the generation of sunspots.

According to V. Bjerknes the cooler photospheric masses constituting the sunspots receive continuous radiation from below, and the suction action centred in their nuclei continues to discharge cooled material quickly enough to keep them sufficiently cool despite the radiation from the interior. Now this process, by analogy with the phenomena of eruptions and prominences, will be of variable activity and regularity, as is demonstrated by the wide range of motions measured in each.

Furthermore these observations show that the maximum velocities are not attained at the outer edge of the penumbra, as Evershed thought, but at the edge of the umbra, i.e. the maximum deviation of the line from its normal position occurs at the border between the umbra and penumbra (Figure 43).

If the radial and tangential components are combined, these observations show that the projection of the motion on the plane containing the spot must be a logarithmic spiral, which is responsible for the direction of rotation of the vortices at the level observed with the spectroscope. The absolute values of the tangential components are always smaller than those of the radial, whence the existence of a rotary motion and also the direction of the vortex can be deduced. The rotation of the vortex is found to be anticyclonic (i.e. right-handed) for metallic vapours in the northern hemisphere. Comparing this rotation with that deduced from spectroheliograms showing high-level hydrogen, it is found that the two directions are opposed, that of the hydrogen being cyclonic.

The direction of rotation of the vapours of metals in spots—right-handed in the northern hemisphere, left-handed in the southern—is what would be expected to result from the combination of the radial motion and that of the Sun's rotation. In the chromosphere, on the other hand, the gases are moving towards and into the spot, whence the filaments should be curved in the opposite direction to that of the low-level gases, as occurs in terrestrial cyclones; this also is confirmed by observation. The vortical structure of the chromospheric hydrogen surrounding the spots shows the predicted cyclonic motion in 82% of cases. Hence the vortical motions observed in and near sunspots are of a purely hydrodynamic character, and appear to owe nothing to the magnetic fields. It should also be noted that the currents detected by means of the Evershed effect are located within the penumbra, whereas the curved filaments are wholly exterior to the penumbra, usually near its outer edge.

In addition to the irregularity and variability of the absolute motions of the metallic vapours, the Arcetri observations also indicate irregularities of the Evershed effect itself, since the sign of the radial components at the edges of the umbra is not always that required by Evershed; the opposite case is also to be encountered, when the outer edge of the spot (i.e. that facing the Sun's limb) gives negative components indicating approach, and the inner edge positive ones; or, again, both components may be of the same sign.

These abnormal cases are usually found when the nucleus of the spot is not single and regular but double, or in general more or less complex. When the Evershed effect is regular the two components may have the same absolute value, showing that the velocity of the outward flow of the vapours is the same at each edge, and parallel to the Sun's surface; alternatively, the component at the outer edge may have a larger absolute value than that at the inner, in which case one may hypothecate a motion no longer parallel to the Sun's surface but inclined to it. The mean angle of this inclination can be calculated, and has been found to vary from 0° up to a maximum of 30°.

It sometimes happens that the absolute value of the component at the outer edge is smaller than that at the inner, in which case the hypothesis of an inclined motion is not longer applicable—unless the axis of the vortex is strongly inclined to the solar surface, and this the investigation of the Zeeman effect shows to be improbable.

It must therefore be concluded from these observations that just as the absolute value of the velocities is variable, so the characteristics of the motion are irregular and variable, perhaps only achieving the regularity claimed for them by the Evershed effect when the spot evolves a single and regular nucleus, without upheavals or rapid transformations.

On account of the altered complexion of the Evershed effect that the Arcetri observations have achieved, M. Nicolet, in his monograph on the Sun, has termed it the 'Evershed-Abetti effect'.

20. DISPLACEMENTS OF THE ABSORPTION LINES AT THE CENTRE AND LIMB OF THE SUN'S DISC

The earliest determinations of the wavelengths of the Sun's Fraunhofer lines, and their comparison with the corresponding lines obtained in the laboratory, revealed discrepancies which were only partly explicable in terms of a Doppler effect dependent on the Sun's rotation. Other disturbing factors were clearly in operation. It was suggested that there was a pressure effect due to the different levels of the solar atmosphere producing the Fraunhofer lines; from direct comparisons with the lines of the arc spectrum—line shifts due to the Sun's rotation having first been allowed for—Jewell, Mohler, Humphreys, Fabry and Buisson obtained values ranging from 5 to 7 atmospheres in the reversing layer, assuming that pressure was the only other cause of the shifts.

Later work, and the discovery of the 'pole effect' in the lines of the arc, showed these results to be very far wide of the mark. Evershed, Perot and Salet examined groups of lines with very different pressure coefficients, so that it was enough to know the differences of the wavelengths and was unnecessary to determine their absolute values. This method has the added advantage of freeing the results from the assumption that pressure alone is responsible for the displacements.

In this manner values of less than 1 atmosphere were derived, varying over a few tenths of an atmosphere. But since the elimination of the pole effect caused a marked reduction of the differences between the pressure coefficients of the various types of line, it was necessary to accumulate a greater mass of observational material in order to establish with accuracy the small shifts due to pressure. This was carried out at Mt Wilson by St John and Babcock.

These observers used as the basis of their measures the international system of solar wavelengths, determined by grating spectrographs and interferometers, and pressure coefficients also determined at Mt Wilson in order to reduce these wavelengths to their values *in vacuo*. Furthermore, to reduce to a minimum the effect on the wavelengths of differences of level in the solar atmosphere, they confined their attention to lines which, being of approximately equal mean intensity, appertained to approximately the same level.

Groups of lines in the same spectral region were examined so as to render the Doppler and relativity effects negligible, and at the same time it was demonstrated that anomalous refraction could not materially affect the results. From the eleven groups of lines with different pressure coefficients thus chosen, the differences Sun *minus* vacuum were derived, and hence the value of the pressure at the level where these particular lines were produced. These values, as given by the different groups of lines, are notably discordant; the mean pressure—that of an atmospheric level some hundreds of miles above the photosphere—is $0 \cdot 13 \pm 0 \cdot 06$ atmospheres, showing that the pressure in the reversing layer amounts to only a small fraction of an atmosphere. This explains the remarkable definition of solar lines which in the laboratory become wide and ill-defined even at moderate pressures. This low value of the pressure in the reversing layer agrees with the calculated pressures of the different atmospheric levels by indirect and theoretical methods.

From the theory of ionisation (p. 223) Saha has calculated that calcium will be completely ionised at a pressure of 10^{-4} atmospheres (see p. 224). This should occur at the upper limit of neutral calcium which, from the presence of the 4227Å line, may be put at about 3000 miles.

St John has calculated from the increased intensity of the enhanced lines that the pressure at medium levels is of the order of 10^{-1} to 10^{-2} atmospheres, while Russell has found that to explain the increased intensity of the Fraunhofer lines of the metals and

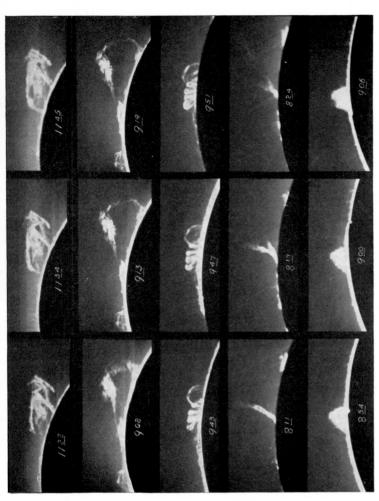

PLATE 77. Classification of prominences proposed by Pettit (Mt Wilson). From top to bottom: types 1, 2, 3, 4, 5.

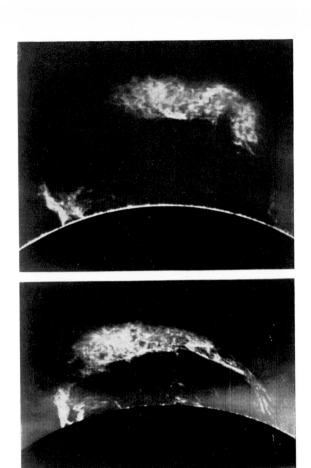

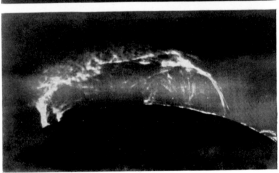

PLATE 78. Eruptive prominence of 1919 May 29, photographed with the H_2 line of ionised calcium (Pettit). From bottom to top: 1^h 41^m, 2^h 57^m, 5^h 33^m U.T.

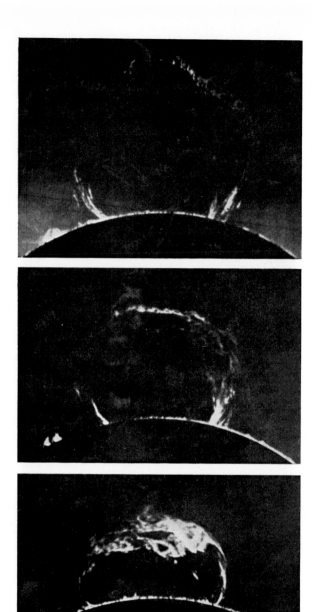

PLATE 79. Eruptive prominence of 1919 July 15
(Pettit). From bottom to top: $3^h 8^m$, $3^h 52^m$, 4^h
7^m U.T.

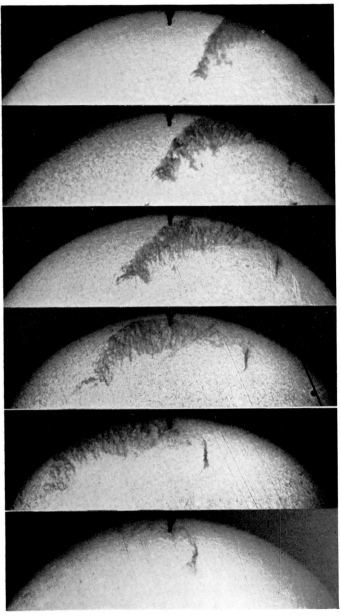

PLATE 80. Eruptive prominence-filament photographed by Pettit at Mt Wilson with the $H\alpha$ line. From top to bottom: 1946 May 30^{d}71, May 31^{d}64, June 1^{d}64, June 2^{d}61, June 3^{d}62, June 4^{d}66 U.T.

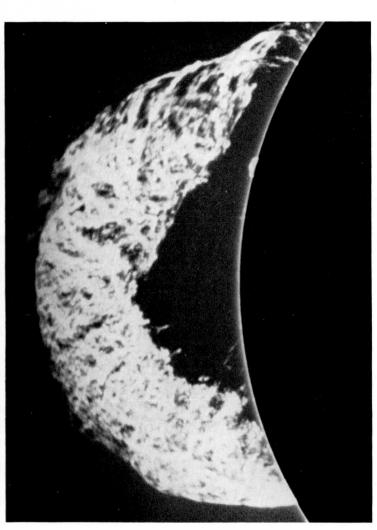

PLATE 81. Eruptive prominence (the same as in Plate 80) photographed by W. Roberts at Climax in $H\alpha$ light with a polarising filter, 1946 June $4\overset{d}{.}69$ U.T.

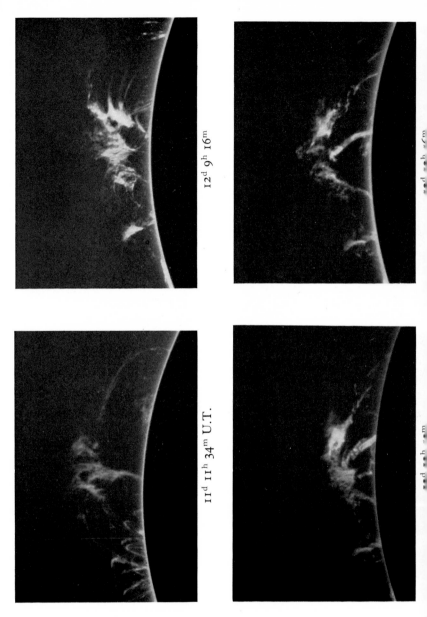

PLATES 82-3. Instantaneous ciné photographs of the eruptive prominence of J

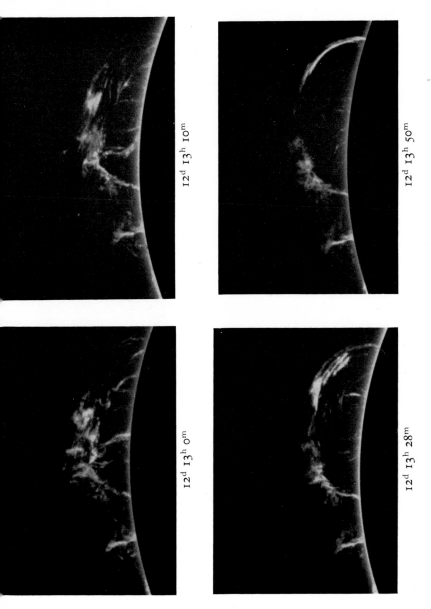

taken directly with a red filter isolating the $H\alpha$ line by B. Lyot at the Pic du Midi.

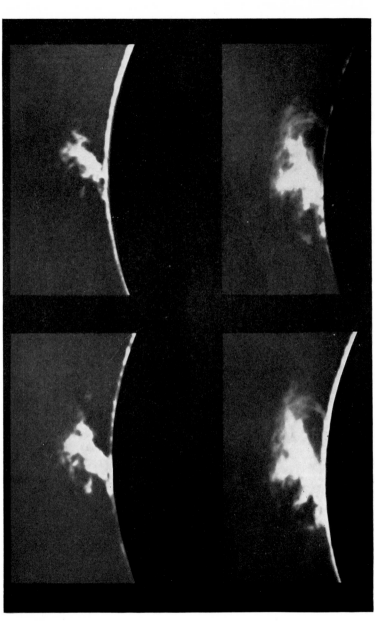

PLATE 84. Comparison between spectroheliograms taken with the $H\alpha$ line (upper) and the K line (lower), 1926 March 10 (Mt Wilson).

alkaline earths with decreasing temperature from the 6000° of the photosphere to the 4000° of the spots, a percentage ionisation must be assumed such as would arise under pressures exceeding 10^{-2} atmospheres in the absorbing region.

Moreover a discussion by Russell and Stewart of the various methods whereby the pressure at the Sun's surface may be evaluated—e.g. the definition of those lines that are sensitive to pressure, the general opacity of the external regions, the absence of solar light in the flash spectrum, the width of the Fraunhofer lines, the rotational equilibrium in the outer regions, radiation pressure, and the chemical equilibria existing in the solar atmosphere—indicates that the total pressure of the photospheric gases cannot exceed 10^{-1} atmospheres and that the mean pressure of the reversing layer is not greater than 10^{-4} atmospheres.

On the assumption that the vapour of Ca II is in equilibrium under the opposed forces of gravitation and radiation pressure, R. H. Fowler and E. A. Milne deduced a mean pressure of the order of 10^{-13} atmospheres for the stratum of this vapour lying between a level 5500 miles above the photosphere and its upper limit of, as we have seen, some 10,000 miles.

On the basis of these results St John and Babcock have constructed an interesting diagram of the probable stratification of the elements, together with the pressures and the dominating currents in the Sun's atmosphere.

Figure 45 shows the elements found at various levels; their heights are given in miles, the directions of the radial motions of the vortices over the spots and the convective motions on the disc are indicated by arrows, and the respective velocities are expressed in miles per second. In the case of the H and K lines of Ca II the tangential component of the vortical motion (indicated by a circle) is the velocity derived from direct measurement; in the case of $H\alpha$ it is based on the lines of flow visible on spectroheliograms. At the highest observable level above the visible surface the ionised calcium flows into the spots at about 1·2 miles per second. As the altitude decreases hydrogen, ionised titanium, and the vapours of neutral calcium and sodium also flow into the spots, with decreasing velocities. At the highest level reached by iron and aluminium the mean velocity is nil; at lower levels the direction of the flux is reversed, as has already been explained, and the velocity towards the exterior increases as the altitude diminishes.

The convective motions refer to undisturbed regions of the disc and are obtained by the spectrographic integration of wide areas of the surface, involving the direct comparison of lines belonging to different levels but to the same region of the spectrum. The progressive increase of the differences may reasonably be explained as resulting from ascending and descending currents above the Sun's surface.

The pressure at each level (determined in the manner already described) and the mean angular and linear velocities from 0° to 45°, as determined by means of the various spectral lines (p. 145), are also shown. It is evident that high velocities and great altitudes go together, and hence in the upper levels there must be a dominant and continuous westward drift, whose velocity decreases with decreasing altitude above the photosphere. The diagram also shows the heights obtained from the emission lines of different elements in the flash spectrum during total eclipse. Although this diagram will doubtless be considerably modified and augmented by future observations, it may nevertheless be said that its agreement with theoretical considerations is close enough to provide a general picture of the constitution of the Sun's atmosphere. It is possible to trace, in the distribution of the elements and in the chromospheric circulation which is suggested by the observations described above, some sort of analogy with the equivalent terrestrial phenomena.

It is known that the percentage composition of the terrestrial atmosphere does not vary to any material extent throughout the first 10 miles above the Earth's surface, on account of the mixing agency of storms and convection currents. Above this level the density of the heavier gases decreases more rapidly than that of the lighter, with the result that with increasing altitude the percentage of the latter increases although their absolute density decreases; at a height of about 60 miles hydrogen constitutes practically the whole of the atmosphere, with traces of helium and some other gases.

The conditions in those regions of the solar atmosphere which are accessible to spectroscopic study appear to be very similar to those in the terrestrial atmosphere, the lighter elements gaining a percentage superiority over the heavier at high altitudes. The lowest two miles of the Earth's atmosphere are a region of continuous disturbance, with strong convection currents and irregular temperature gradients. In the stratum between 2 and 5 miles above the Earth's surface conditions are more stable and their variations more uniform, although it may be the seat of vertical convection currents during storms. Finally, the outermost and relatively calm region is one of uniform or inverted temperature gradients, which mingles only to a limited extent with the underlying strata.

The lowest level of the solar atmosphere—i.e. the region comprising the lower strata of the reversing layer, and in particular the

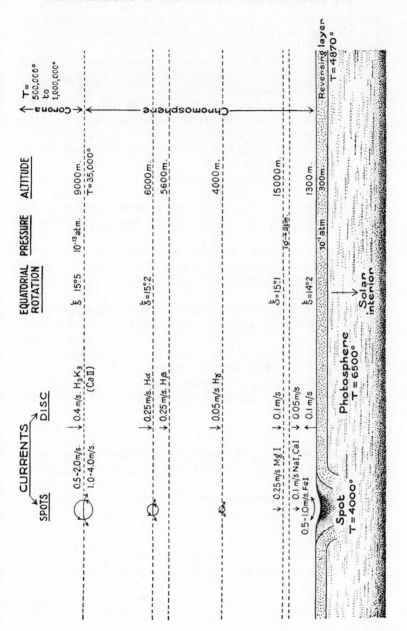

Fig. 45. Diagram of the solar atmosphere.

163

underlying gases—is marked by very considerable disturbances. It is here that the highest regions of the spot vortices are generally located, as well as the outpourings of material from the Sun's interior. The reversing layer overlying this region of continual turmoil is relatively calm, though to a greater or less extent involved in the upheavals below.

The chromosphere seems to be altogether distinct from this region, the frontier between the two layers apparently occurring at the level of zero tangential velocity—i.e. at the level of velocity reversal in the case of the radial flow of gases with respect to the axes of the solar vortices.

In the case of terrestrial cyclones little is known from direct observation of the movements of the atmosphere above the storm centre, whereas in the case of solar storms the viewpoint is external to them and hence the motions of the highest levels can be observed.

Although the general circulation in the two atmospheres must necessarily be very different, it nevertheless seems that cyclonic storms—whatever their primary causes may be—probably obey the same hydrodynamic laws, and that observations of two bodies as dissimilar as the Sun and the Earth are able to complement one another in explaining the various phenomena.

Turning now to the shifts of the Fraunhofer lines of the photosphere, as exhibited by the direct comparison of their wavelengths with those of the same elements obtained in the laboratory, it should be added that the wavelengths at the limb do not even coincide with those of the same lines measured at the centre of the disc.

Halm, who in 1907 discovered and measured these relative shifts between the centre and the limb, found them to be of the order of 0·01Å towards the red. He then attributed them to an effective pressure in the reversing layer which was greater at the limb than at the disc centre; the lower levels are indeed subject to a greater pressure, the light-path from the limb regions being longer than that from the centre of the disc. From a similar comparison of the spectra of the limb and of the disc centre Buisson and Fabry came to the conclusion that the shifts are due to the widening of the lines at their red edge, while their violet edge remains in the normal position. Later researches by Adams, extended to cover a great number of lines from the red to the violet, confirm the foregoing results, as can be seen from the table on p. 165 giving the shifts for groups of different wavelengths and intensities.

Limb-centre Displacements in Ångstrom Units (Adams)

Region	Intensity			
	I	2–3	4–6	Most intense lines
4300Å	+0·004	+0·005	+0·006	
4800Å	+0·005	+0·006	+0·008	very small;
5300Å	+0·006	+0·007	+0·009	virtually nil
5800Å	+0·007	+0·008	+0·009	
7300Å	+0·009	+0·009	+0·010	

The more recent determinations of the Sun's atmospheric pressure, already referred to, do not allow us to accept Halm's explanation of the limb effect, and other causes must be sought— among the possibilities being the gravitational field, the Doppler effect, and convection currents in the solar atmosphere.

It follows from the theory of relativity that the wavelength of a given radiation is increased (i.e. shifted towards the red) in proportion to the gravitational potential at the surface of the heavenly body emitting it. Such a shift—which was not only predicted by Einstein but constituted an experimental test of his theory—would be similar to a Doppler effect at the Sun's surface indicating a velocity of 0·394 miles per second. This corresponds to a red shift of $\Delta\lambda=0\cdot008$Å for a radiation of wavelength 4000Å. The shift would be proportion to wavelength and therefore indistinguishable from a true Doppler effect caused by some such agency as convective motions. But we have seen that the latter are dependent on the intensities of the lines, whilst the Einstein effect would not be; hence it should be possible to distinguish between them by comparing the wavelengths measured *in vacuo* with those measured at the centre and limb of the Sun's disc.

From determinations of a large number of lines made with the powerful instrumental resources of Mt Wilson, St John came to the conclusion that the shifts of the Fraunhofer lines are very largely due to a combination of an Einstein effect and a Doppler effect caused by convective motions; this may justly be described as the 'St John effect'. In fact the shifts at the centre of the disc of spectral lines originating at a mean altitude above the photosphere of about 300 miles agree with those predicted by general relativity. Below this level (where 99% of the solar lines originate) there must be ascending currents which increase in intensity at increasing depths in the photosphere. The iron lines belonging to the lowest level give an upward velocity of approximately 0·1 miles per second.

The St John effect vanishes at the limb since the motion of the gases is there perpendicular to the line of sight, and the difference $\lambda_{limb}-\lambda_{vacuo}$ corresponds almost exactly to the Einstein effect. In the case of high, medium and low level iron lines the residual $\lambda_{limb}-\lambda_{vacuo}$ differs by $+0·0015\text{Å}$ from the effect predicted theoretically by Einstein.

This difference must be a residual limb effect due perhaps to anomalous dispersion or differential diffusion, because other possible effects, such as the Zeeman effect (due to the Sun's general magnetic field) are much too weak, and the Stark effect has not as yet been observed on the Sun. As to anomalous dispersion, the low pressure of the reversing layer makes it unlikely that its effect on wavelength could be detected at the limb. According to the Rayleigh-Schuster theory, on the other hand, molecular diffusion could account for this residual shift at the limb. The coefficient of diffusion in fact varies as the square of the refracting power, and since the resultant refraction is slightly greater at the red edge of a line than at the violet, this would give rise to a differential effect tending to broaden the line at its red edge.

The relatively short light-path in the low density levels at the centre of the disc is sufficient to explain the absence of any differential broadening in this region, whereas the much longer light-path through the lower layers at the limb would produce conditions favouring the appearance of such an effect.

The conclusion to be drawn from what has so far been said, which represents the present stage of the investigation, is that three main causes are responsible for the differences between solar and terrestrial wavelengths, and that it is possible to distinguish between their effects. They are : (a) the influence of the Sun's gravitational field on the motions of its atoms, which was predicted by the theory of general relativity (Einstein effect), (b) convection currents in the observable strata of the solar atmosphere (St John effect), which would seem to be corroborated by the discovery of an analogous effect in stellar atmospheres, more pronounced in high temperature stars than in cooler ones, (c) differential diffusion, whose maximum effect is felt in the longer paths traversed by the light from the limb (limb effect).

The Einstein effect shows itself over all parts of the solar disc. The St John effect—downward at high levels and upward at very low levels—is maximal at the centre of the disc and decreases to zero at the limb. The limb effect, if objective, should probably be attributed to the causes already mentioned, and must be a function of the intensity of the lines and hence of the level that is observed with the spectroscope.

The explanation of these effects is neither clearly understood nor final, as is shown by the results of investigations carried out by Burns and Meggers, who measured a large number of fundamental solar wavelengths and compared them with those obtained with a vacuum arc. These confirmed the increase of the red shifts with increasing intensity of the lines concerned and showed that an asymmetrical absorption line is shifted indefinitely with increasing absorption; hence, in order to explain these red shifts, it is only necessary to assume that all the solar lines are slightly asymmetrical, and that this asymmetry increases slightly with wavelength. The height above the photosphere at which the lines of the flash spectrum can be observed is determined in the first place by the intensity of the line, and the altitude thus directly determined is therefore always a function of this intensity.

The red shifts may therefore be regarded as a function of intensity rather than of altitude. According to these observers, before the existence of the gravitation shift can be established it will be necessary to determine the value of another and slightly larger displacement which manifests itself as a shift proportional to line intensity. At present only its differential effect can be measured—an increase of the shift of the intense lines as compared with the weaker.

The researches (1948) of M. G. Adam at Oxford may be mentioned as indicating the still unresolved state of the problem of these displacements. She measured with an interferometer the wavelengths of the solar absorption lines at the centre and limb of the Sun's disc. The wavelengths were determined for fourteen selected lines of Fe, Mn, Ni and Ca near the telluric oxygen band at about 6300Å. The lines of the nearby band were used for reference, and were linked in turn with the fundamental wavelength of neon; in this way the absolute wavelengths of the solar lines were determined along the whole diameter of a large image of the Sun. The wavelengths at the centre were displaced by $+0.005$Å as compared with those of an arc *in vacuo*; moving towards the limb, only a small variation in the value of the displacements was noted until about 0.9 of the radius of the solar image had been passed, i.e. at 0.1 of a radius inside the limb. A rapid increase was then encountered, which reached $+0.013$Å at 0.98 solar radii. After correcting the wavelengths for the differences between the physical conditions of the Sun and the vacuum arc, the residual displacements should ultimately prove the existence of the Einstein effect combined with the St John effect. According to Adam, if it is admitted that the solar lines are subject to displacements due to the gravitational field, then one cannot concede the existence of radial currents, which would neutralise these displacements over about 80% or 90% of the solar disc, leaving the Einstein effect in the region of the limb only. If, on the other hand, one assumes that the solar lines are not affected by a gravitational displacement we should have to appeal to some other effect which would be capable of displacing the lines towards the red by approximately the amount predicted by Einstein, but only in the vicinity of the Sun's limb.

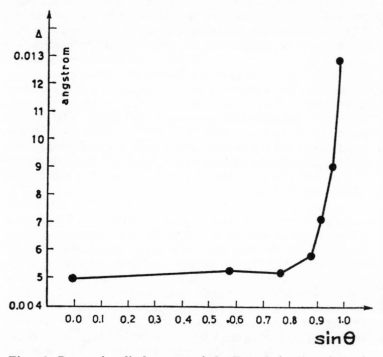

Fig. 46. Progressive displacement of the Fraunhofer lines from the centre of the disc to the limb (M. G. Adam).

It can be seen that the problem requires deeper investigation, both from the experimental and theoretical standpoints. In order to arrive at a definitive conclusion it will be necessary to determine the absolute wavelengths at the centre of the disc as functions of wavelength, of line intensity, and of the state of excitation and ionisation of the atoms concerned.

21. *THE MAGNETIC FIELDS AND MAGNETIC CLASSIFICATION OF SUNSPOTS; THE POLARITY LAW OF THE SPOTS

We have seen that the existence of vortical motions in the gases of the Sun's surface overlying the spots have been established by spectroheliograms taken in the light of the $H\alpha$ line. The appearance of the simpler vortices revolving round the spots usually indicates a rotation whose direction is analogous with that found on Earth, namely anticlockwise in the north hemisphere and clockwise in the south.

The direction of the vortices formed in the terrestrial atmosphere is obviously determined by the increasing linear velocity of the air from the poles to the equator in consequence of the Earth's rotation. The laws governing the solar cyclones must be more complex, as can be seen from the fact that their direction does not exhibit the same uniformity, examples of vortices rotating in opposite directions being found over adjacent spots in the same hemisphere.

Filaments are sometimes attracted by the nuclei of spots, vanishing into them with velocities that may reach 60 miles per second. This, however, is not a general rule, and in following such developments the spectrohelioscope is more useful than the spectroheliograph.

Hale has found that when a filament is swallowed up by a nearby spot in this way it terminates as a dark and usually roughly circular head which, when the slit is set in the position giving maximum intensity, is sometimes seen to be accompanied by a short tail. Very often this head lies exactly over the outer edge of the penumbra, which can be clearly seen when the second slit is adjusted to a position beyond the wings of the $H\alpha$ line. This head, the advance of maximum intensity, and the considerable downward velocity, are the essential characteristics of such phenomena.

The presence of a vortical movement in regions occupied by spots is nearly always betrayed by the general distribution of the hydrogen flocculi. It was this distribution that in 1908 suggested to Hale that a sunspot might be the centre of a vortex in which electrified particles, produced by ionisation in the solar atmosphere, are made to revolve at high velocities. If it is assumed that there is a preponderance of either positive or negative ions in the revolving gases, a magnetic field must be induced, the orientation of which will be determined by the position of the axis of the vortex.

It has in fact been established by means of the Evershed effect that the motions of the vapours of metals are predominantly radial

169

rather than vortical; this, however, may be an effect of the level at which the spectroscopic observations are made, where the influx and efflux of the gases in the direction of the vortical axis cannot be

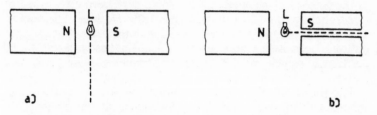

Fig. 47. *Observation of the Zeeman effect.* (*a*), *perpendicularly to the lines of force of the magnetic field;* (*b*), *parallel to the lines of force.*

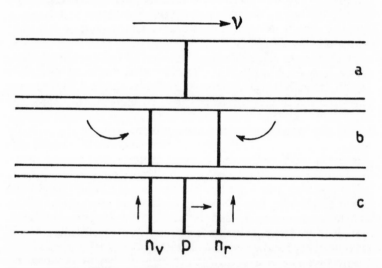

Fig. 48. *The Zeeman effect.* (*a*), *spectral line observed with no magnetic field present;* (*b*), *violet and red n components observed parallel to the field's lines of force;* (*c*), *n and p components (triplet) observed perpendicularly to the lines of force.*

detected. Nevertheless, Hale himself was able soon afterwards to confirm by means of a suitable technique, that the spots are centres of sufficiently strong magnetic fields to be revealed by the Zeeman effect.

It is known that when a normal Zeeman triplet is observed along the lines of force of a magnetic field (Figure 47 *b*) the central component p is not seen, and the two lateral components n are circularly polarised in opposite directions. If a quarter-wave mica plate and a nicol prism are mounted in front of the spectroscope slit the rotation of the latter through 90° will eliminate either of the n components as required.

Having suppressed one component with a certain position of the nicol prism, it can be made to reappear by reversing the magnetic field, when the other is thereupon suppressed. This provides us with a simple method of determining the polarity of a magnetic field, which can be employed so long as the angle between the line of sight and the lines of force does not exceed about 60° or 70°. If this condition is not fulfilled, the p component for the triplet is also visible and the elliptically polarised light of the n components can only be partially suppressed.

Consider a spot situated at the centre of the disc, and suppose that it is the seat of a vortex whose axis coincides with the line of sight. In this case, if the vortex gives rise to a powerful magnetic field the spectral lines originating in the gases overlying the spot will be split into doublets whose components are circularly polarised in opposite directions.

This doubling of the lines was noted as long ago as 1870 by Young, and was later investigated by W. M. Mitchell; at that time, however, it was attributed to a reversal of the lines, such as is seen to occur in the most intense lines as a result of increasing thickness and density of the gases. With the greater dispersion obtainable with the spectrographs of the solar towers, Hale succeeded in separating the components and demonstrated that it is not a case of double reversal but the Zeeman effect; for he was able to prove by means of the nicol prism and quarter-wave mica plate that the two components are circularly polarised and that the polarity is reversed when the direction of the vortex is reversed, as is the case in opposite hemispheres of the Sun.

If the normal Zeeman triplet is observed perpendicularly to the lines of force (Figure 48 c) the p component is plane polarised, with the plane of vibration parallel to the field, while the vibrations of the n components are contained in a plane perpendicular to the field. Hence when a spot is carried to the limb by the Sun's rotation it should be found that the lines usually separate into elliptically polarised lateral components; and when, finally, the axis of the vortex is perpendicular to the line of sight the normal triplet of the transverse Zeeman effect should be observed.

Laboratory experiments have shown that under the Zeeman effect different lines split in different ways: whilst some exhibit the normal triplet others divide into quadruplets or into doublets each of whose components consists of a very fine double line. In the magnetic fields of the sunspots (which are much weaker than those obtainable in the laboratory) the closely adjacent lines forming a doublet cannot be individually distinguished; furthermore it is necessary to know the inclination of the vortex axis to the Sun's surface in order to make an exact comparison with the conditions of laboratory experiments.

The separation of the components of doublets and triplets caused by a magnetic field, varies considerably with different lines. Some are unaffected by the field, others are widened, and others again are completely separated. It is therefore important to compare the widening and splitting of the lines in spot spectra with the corresponding phenomena obtained with an artificial magnetic field. The following table shows that in almost all cases the results of solar observation agree with those obtained in the laboratory.

Iron Doublets

λ	$\Delta\lambda_{spark}$	$\dfrac{\Delta\lambda_{spark}}{5\cdot1}$	$\Delta\lambda_{spot}$	δ	$\dfrac{\Delta\lambda_{spark}}{\Delta\lambda_{spot}}$
6213·14	0·703	0·138	0·136	−0·002	5·2
6301·72	0·737	0·144	0·138	−0·006	5·3
6302·71	1·230	0·241	0·252	+0·011	4·9
6337·05	0·895	0·175	0·172	−0·003	5·2

The second column tabulates the distance between the outer components of the lines observed in a laboratory magnetic field of 15,000 gauss. These values, divided by 5·1 in the third column, are comparable with those in the fourth column. In column 5 are tabulated the differences between the figures in the preceding two columns. It may therefore be concluded that the intensity of the magnetic field of this particular spot is about 2900 gauss. The most intense fields observed in sunspots attain a value approaching 5000 gauss.

Some lines, such as the D lines of sodium and the b lines of magnesium (which are known to originate in a much higher level than the majority of the other metallic lines), show a very small separation of the components. These lines are, however, quite sensitive to magnetic field, and it must therefore be concluded that the field in spots diminishes rapidly towards the outer layers of the solar atmosphere.

The line of sight to a spot near the centre of the Sun's disc is parallel (or nearly so) to its magnetic field; hence in the simplest case the lines are split into two components by the Zeeman effect, and their difference of wavelength is given by the law

$$\Delta\lambda = 4\cdot7 \times 10^{-5}\lambda^2 H$$

where λ is expressed in cms and H, the intensity of the field, in gauss. Thus for a spot whose field is 3000 gauss the separation of the two Zeeman components in the red region of the spectrum amounts to 0·1Å.

It was owing to the necessity of increasing the size of the solar image (so that the structural details of more or less complicated spots can be well separated) and at the same time of obtaining wide dispersion (for the distinct separation of the components of the lines under the influences of often weak magnetic fields) that Hale was led to construct the 150-foot focal length tower telescope and 75-foot focal length spectrograph at Mt Wilson. The former gives a solar image 17 inches in diameter, and the latter a linear dispersion in the second order spectrum of 1Å=0·12 ins (3 mm).

Since 1917 daily observations, both visual and photographic, have been made with these instruments of the polarity and intensity of the magnetic fields of the visible spots. The polariser used for this work consists of a nicol built up on sections to cover the full length of the spectrograph slit (5 inches). A composite quarter-wave plate is mounted over the nicol; this is made up of a number of adjacent mica plates, each 2 mm wide, whose principal sections are normal to one another and inclined at 45° to the slit.

If one of these mica plates suppresses the red component of a magnetic doublet, let us say, then the next will suppress the violet component, and so on; thus the nicol will transmit the violet component, for example, with even-numbered plates and the red with the odd-numbered. If the Fraunhofer lines are split by a magnetic field they will thus be given a serrated appearance by this polariser, and the height of the teeth (i.e. the amount of the separation of the lines) will be determined by the intensity of the field; adjacent mica strips will transmit the red and violet n components alternately.

If the sign of a current producing a magnetic field is reversed, the n components will be seen to change places, thus providing a simple method of determining the polarity of a magnetic field even if it is complex, variable, and confined to a relatively small area of the Sun.

In order to study the phenomena of plane polarisation the compound quarter-wave mica plate is replaced by either a compound half-wave plate or, for special work, circular half- or quarter-wave plates which can be rotated to various position angles.

Visual observations of the magnetic fields of sunspots are carried out at Mt Wilson in the following manner. It is first noted which of the two components, red or violet, is transmitted by a given strip of the quarter-wave filter, whence the polarity of the field is established; the intensity is then measured with a micrometer consisting of a small plane parallel plate, suitable inclination of which brings different sections of adjacent spectral lines (displaced, as has been explained, by the magnetic field) into coincidence. The micrometer having been calibrated by measuring lines whose separation for a given field strength has been determined in the laboratory, the angle through which the plate is turned is converted to gauss. The well-defined triplet at 6173Å is usually observed, its n components still being individually distinguishable at field strengths of 1000 gauss.

Since the line of sight does not usually coincide with the direction of the lines of force the circular vibrations enter the analyser as elliptically polarised light which possesses a proportion of the linear vibrations of the median component. It is therefore necessary to determine the action of the quarter-wave analyser and the nicol prism on this medley of plane and elliptically polarised light, and to deduce the relative intensities of the components.

Seares has shown that, if γ is the angle between the line of sight and the lines of force, and if the sum of the intensities of the n_v (violet), n_r (red) and p (central) components is taken as being equal to unity, so that

$$n_v + p + n_r = 1$$

then their relative intensities in each mica plate of which the composite quarter-wave analyser is composed are given by

$$n_v = \tfrac{1}{4}\,(1 - \cos \gamma)^2$$
$$p = \tfrac{1}{2}\sin^2 \gamma$$
$$n_r = \tfrac{1}{4}\,(1 + \cos \gamma)^2$$

The variation of the intensity of the three components with varying values of γ is shown in Figure 49.

It is of interest to compare the results obtained in the laboratory using emission lines and varying angle with those observed in the Fraunhofer lines of spots. The intensity trend for a normal triplet obtained in the laboratory naturally follows the expressions quoted above when different values of γ are applied. On the Sun, if a spot is near the centre of the disc and is observed with a nicol prism and a composite quarter-wave analyser, γ must be approximately equal to zero unless the axis of the vortex is strongly inclined to the solar surface; hence, corresponding to the various strips, the components n_v and n_r of the iron triplet at 6302·7Å are seen alternately (Plate 94), and the p component faintly, according to the inclination of the vortex axis to the line of sight. If the spot is near the limb the observation is made with a nicol prism and a half-wave composite analyser, as already explained.

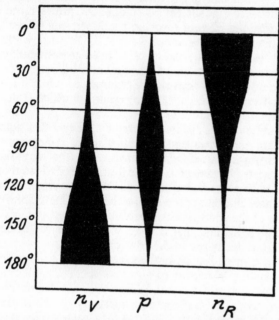

Fig. 49. *Relative intensities of the three components of a normal Zeeman triplet, for inclinations of the line of sight to the lines of force ranging from* 0° *to* 180°; *as observed with a Nicol prism and a quarter-wave mica plate.*

Plate 95 also shows the iron triplet at 6302·7Å observed in this manner. The p or n components can be clearly seen in alternate strips. If, in the case of a spot near the limb, it is assumed that the lines of force at the centre of the spot are perpendicular to the solar surface and that towards the borders of the umbra and over the penumbra they become increasingly inclined, as shown in Plate 96, it can be ascertained whether the polarisation phenomena vary according to theory as the setting of the slit relative to the spot is changed progressively from position 1 to position 7. When the spot is regular, opposite polarities are encountered at its opposite edges, in accordance with the assumed inclination of the lines of force at the particular points examined. In fact, when the spot is observed with the slit in positions 2 or 3, for example, the lines of force are directed away from the observer and n_r appears more intense than n_v. Between 3 and 4 the n components become equally intense, indicating that the line of sight is approximately perpendicular to the lines of force (Plate 95). In succeeding positions of the slit the n_v component grows more intense, showing that the lines of force on the inner side of the spot are directed towards the observer.

In this way the real polarity of a spot—corresponding to that derived from observations of the umbra when the spot is near the centre of the disc—can also be determined when it is near the limb by observing that part of the penumbra which is nearest the disc centre.

These observations are complicated by the fact that polarities of the spots are not always regular, particularly in the case of complex groups. Nevertheless, observations made in this way—and also, for limb spots, by means of a nicol and the half-wave analyser mounted with a graduated circle allowing the angle between its principal axis and that of the nicol to be read—have shown that at the centre of the spot the angle between the lines of force and the solar radius is nil, and that it increases to about $70°$ at 0.9 of the distance from the centre to the edge of the spot.

Plates 97 and 98 reproduce two sections, a few angstroms long, of a map of the spectrum of sunspots made by Ellerman with the 150-foot solar tower at Mt Wilson and a polariser consisting of a nicol prism and a composite quarter-wave mica plate. The spots were observed during the 1912–23 solar cycle, and always when near the central meridian; the chart shows to what extent the magnetic field affects all the Fraunhofer lines that are visible between 3900Å and 6600Å.

A large number of lines which are not influenced by the field belong to the bands which we have seen (p. 99) to be present in spot spectra. The map also shows which lines are split into normal triplets and which have a more complex structure. The most intense lines seem in general to be less affected by the field, so that some of them are not completely separated. This demonstrates that the intensity of the magnetic field diminishes as the height above the spot increases; and, in fact, the Zeeman effect is not exhibited by such high level lines as the D lines of sodium or the b lines of magnesium.

PLATE 85. Eruptive prominence photographed during the total eclipse of 1918 June 8 (Yerkes Observatory). The white disc represents the Earth on the same scale.

PLATE 86. Eruptive prominence photographed with the K_3 line at Meudon, 1929 November 7^d 12^h 40^m U.T.

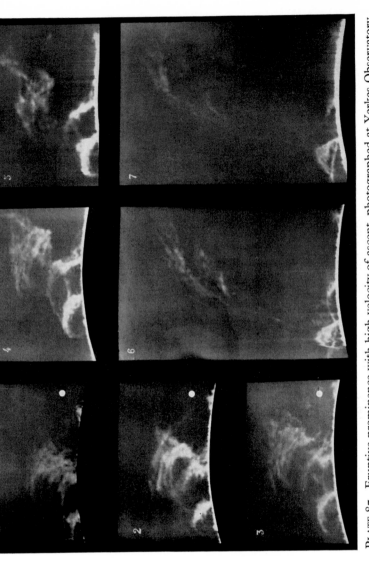

PLATE 87. Eruptive prominence with high velocity of ascent, photographed at Yerkes Observatory, 1920 October 8:

1. $15^h 32^m$ U.T., 75,000 miles   2. $17^h 43^m$ U.T., 85,000 miles   3. $18^h 24^m$ U.T., 95,000 miles

PLATE 88. Eruptive prominence, 1931 August 6$^\text{d}$ 17$^\text{h}$ 35$^\text{m}$ U.T. (Pettit).

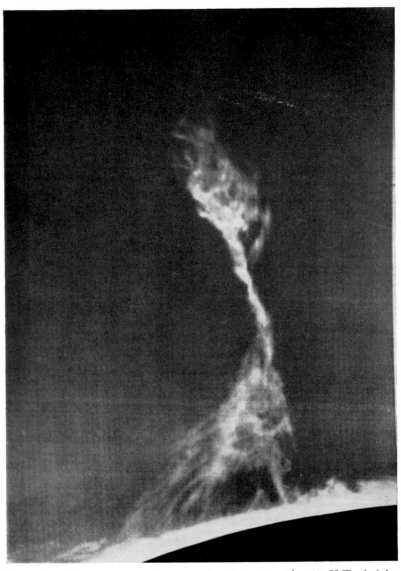

PLATE 89. The same prominence as in Plate 88: 18^h 16^m U.T., height 280,000 miles (Pettit).

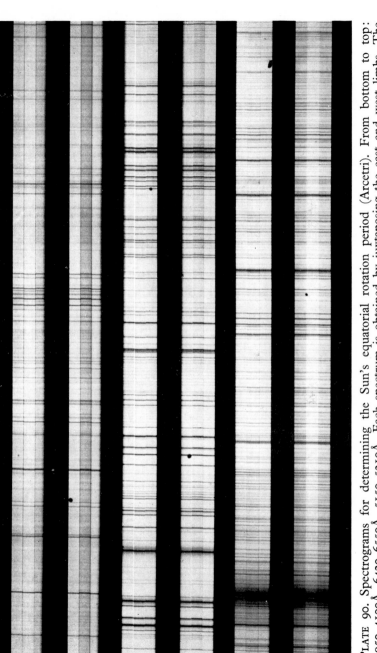

PLATE 90. Spectrograms for determining the Sun's equatorial rotation period (Arcetri). From bottom to top: 3950–4100Å, 6420–6550Å, 5150–5310Å. Each spectrum is obtained by juxtaposing the east and west limbs. The Doppler effect in the solar lines can be seen.

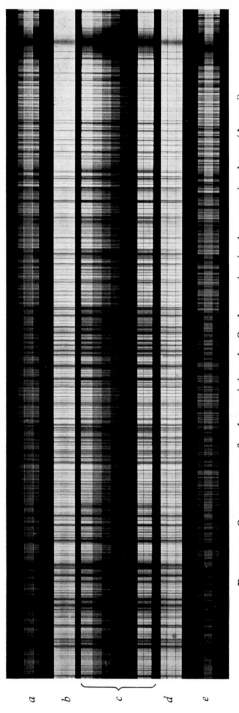

PLATE 91. Spectrograms for determining the Sun's rotation in the reversing layer (Arcetri). *a*, *b*, *e*, spectra of the equatorial limb and of the centre of the disc; *d*, spectra of the east and west limbs; *c*, spectra obtained with a graduated filter for the photometric calibration of the plate.

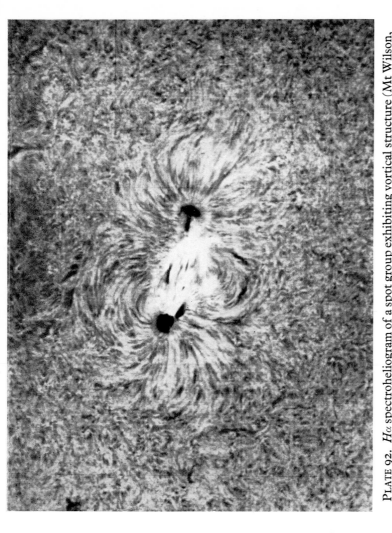

PLATE 92. *Hα* spectroheliogram of a spot group exhibiting vortical structure (Mt Wilson, 1924 August 30).

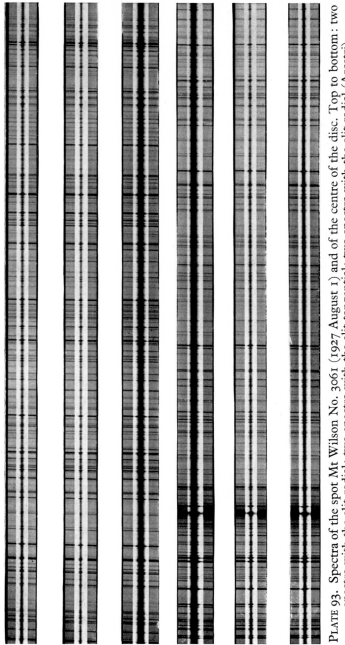

PLATE 93. Spectra of the spot Mt Wilson No. 3061 (1927 August 1) and of the centre of the disc. Top to bottom: two spectra with the slit radial; two spectra with the slit tangential; two spectra with the slit radial (Arcetri).

Nicholson has investigated the relation between the area of a spot and the strength of its magnetic field. The latter is maximal at the centre of the umbra and diminishes steadily to zero near the outer edge of the penumbra. The curves shown in Figure 50 are based on about a thousand observations of the leaders of bipolar groups and of single spots, made at Mt Wilson between 1917 and 1920. The central curve represents the mean intensity of the field at the centre of spots of different sizes, and the upper and lower curves the mean deviations of individual spots from their mean values. For the spots examined the areas of the umbrae relative

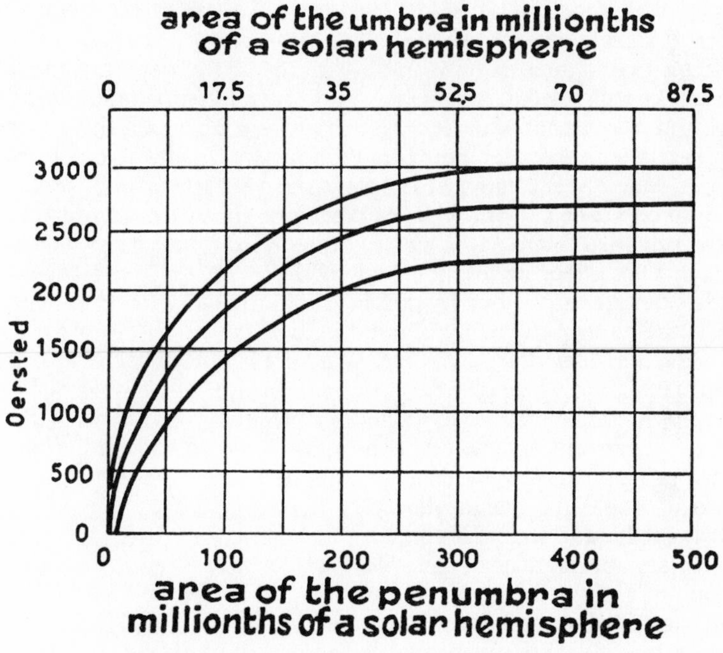

Fig. 50. *Correlation between the areas and magnetic fields of spots*
(*S. B. Nicholson*).

to those of the penumbrae were as 0·175:1, and did not vary materially with the size of the spot. The same curve represents the relation between the central intensities and the areas of the umbrae when the area scale is adjusted by a factor of 0·175. The considerable deviations of individual spots from the mean are due partly to errors of measurement, although other factors—such as differences of age and temperature of the spots—are also contributory. A relatively dark spot—and therefore one that is cooler than the normal—usually showed a higher field intensity than the mean value for its area.

According to determinations made by W. Grotrian, H. v. Klüber and their collaborators at Potsdam Observatory, a discussion of the Mt Wilson material and of observations made at the Einstein tower show that the magnetic field also varies with time by from 20 to 30 gauss per hour, and perhaps also exhibits irregular variations of short duration.

When the characteristics of spot groups were under discussion (p. 82) it was pointed out that these frequently consist of a pair of spots which may be several degrees apart. The western or p member of such a group is often the first to be formed, but sooner or later a second nucleus comparable with the first in size (though not infrequently smaller, or divided into several components) forms behind the leader. Sometimes the two members of the group appear simultaneously, at others the following member is formed first. Many small spots accompany the two larger ones, either scattered around them or distributed over the space between the two principal nuclei. It is also to be noted that the axes of these groups are more or less inclined to the equator. The magnetic characteristic of the bipolar groups is that the two principal members are almost invariably of opposite polarity.

The tendency towards bipolar structure is fairly general among sunspots, for even single spots often show traces of asymmetry due to the presence of faculae or flocculi preceding or following the spot. Spectroheliograms often show that a single spot or a group of small spots having the same polarity is situated at the preceding end of a mass of calcium flocculi whose longitudinal axis is but little inclined to the solar equator.

These appearances of the spots and flocculi, taken in conjunction with observations of the magnetic field, have led to the development of the following 'magnetic classification' at Mt Wilson. It consists of three classes and is based principally on the determination of the magnetic polarity and the distribution of the flocculi accompanying the spots.

(I) *Unipolar spots*

Single spots, or groups of small spots having the same polarity. In this class the flocculi may be distributed in one of three ways: (α) unipolar spots with flocculi fairly symmetrically distributed on the preceding and following sides of the centre of the group (Plate 99); (α_p) the centre of the group precedes that of the surrounding flocculi (Plate 100); (α_f) the centre of the group follows that of the surrounding flocculi (Plate 101).

(II) *Bipolar spots*

The simplest and most charactetistic type of bipolar group consists of two spots of opposite polarity. The line joining the pair of spots is generally slightly inclined to the equator. Each member of the group may be accompanied or replaced by numerous small spots, but in the great majority of cases the leading and following members are of opposite polarity. This leads to a fourfold subdivision of the class: (β) bipolar groups both of whose members, whether composed of one or more spots, are of approximately equal area (Plate 102); (β_p) the leader is the principal member of the group (Plate 103); (β_f) the trailer is principal member (Plate 104); (β_γ) the trailer and leader are accompanied by small components of opposite polarities (Plate 105).

(III) *Multipolar spots*

(γ). Groups of this type, which account for hardly 1% of the total number of spots observed, consist of irregularly arranged spots of opposite polarities which cannot be classified as bipolar spots (Plate 106).

Regular observations are made at Mt Wilson on the basis of this classification, using the iron line at 6137.553Å; it is noted which of the n components—n_r on the red side or n_v on the violet—is transmitted by a given element of the composite quarter-wave mica plate used in conjunction with a nicol prism. The distance between the two components gives the approximate field strength at the point observed in the spot, and this is expressed in units of 100 gauss.

Figure 51 shows how these magnetic observations of sunspots are executed at Mt Wilson. In Figure 52 the northern spot (Mt Wilson no. 1556) was on 1919 September 13 in latitude 2° north and longitude 15° east of the central meridian. The nucleus transmitted the n_r component, and the field intensity was 3400 gauss. The other small spots or pores on the following side showed opposite polarities and an intensity of 500 gauss. The southern spot (no. 1555) was situated at 2° south and 12° east, transmitted the n_v component, and had a field strength of 2900 gauss. The small spots preceding it were of opposite polarity and had field intensities of from 500 to 700 gauss.

The following percentages of the different classes and sub-classes were obtained from the magnetic classification of 2174 groups which were observed in the manner described between 1912 and 1924:

Class	α	α_p	α_f	β	β_p	β_f	β_γ	γ	un-classified
Percentage occurrence	14	20	4	21	29	8	3	1	7

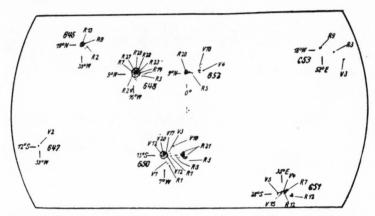

Fig. 51. Observations of spot polarity (Mt Wilson, 1917 May 14).

As a clue to the law of sunspot polarity it may therefore be taken that the bipolar class is the dominant type. This is also confirmed by direct observation in so far as it is very often found that in cases where there is a single and well-developed spot it is preceded or followed by small spots or flocculi.

The regular observation of polarities at Mt Wilson revealed that at the change-over to a new solar cycle the polarities of the spots in the two hemispheres were also reversed. Specifically, before the 1913 minimum the polarity of northern hemisphere leaders of bipolar groups was S or negative—i.e. corresponding to the polarity of the terrestrial north magnetic pole—whilst that of the trailers was N or positive. In the southern hemisphere the polarities were the reverse, N for the leaders and S for the trailers.

As has already been explained, the last spots of a cycle appear in low latitudes while the first ones of the new cycle appear in high latitudes; as the cycle progresses, the latter move steadily down

180

to lower latitudes. The spots of the new cycle which began to appear in small numbers in 1912 in high latitudes exhibited opposite polarities to those in low latitudes belonging to the previous cycle. As the new cycle progressed, from 1913 to 1923, it became evident as the spots increased in number that the new polarity was a general characteristic of the spots observed, the exceptions amounting to only 4%.

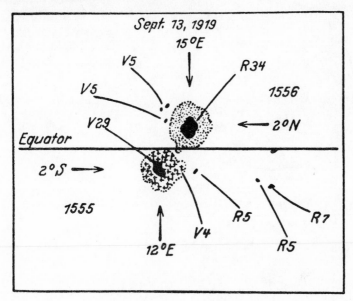

Fig. 52. Spots of opposite polarity in the two solar hemispheres (Mt Wilson, 1919 September 13).

The mean latitude of the spots gradually decreased, as in every cycle, and towards its end (1922–23) they had reached equatorial regions. Simultaneously, in June 1922, the first spots heralding the new cycle (1923–34) appeared in about latitude 30°. These were followed by other spots of different classes, but predominantly bipolar groups, the great majority of which exhibited reversed polarity—i.e. that of the first cycle to be observed (1901–13) after Hale's discovery of the magnetic fields.

The phenomenon of polarity reversal was repeated in the new cycle which began in 1933–34: on 1933 October 10 a small spot in latitude +26° was observed at Mt Wilson to have the opposite polarity to that of the other spots in the northern hemisphere, and on October 28 a small bipolar group was observed in latitude −32°

whose polarity was the reverse of that shown by other southern hemisphere spots; at the same time a group in latitude $+9°5$ showed the polarity proper to the previous cycle in the north hemisphere. Thus the polarity reversal at the beginning of each new cycle has now been confirmed for four cycles, and the important

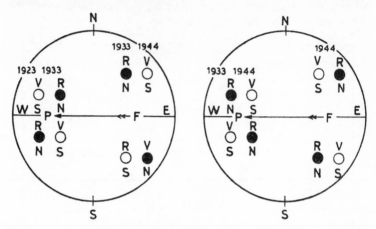

Fig. 53. *Reversal of magnetic polarity in spots belonging to successive cycles (Hale).*

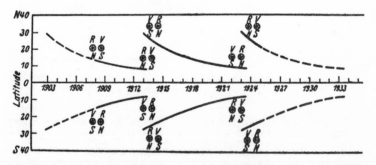

Fig. 54. *The law of polarity reversal in spots of different cycles (Hale).*

law discovered by Hale may be stated as follows: 'The sunspots in high latitudes, which mark the beginning of a new $11 \cdot 1$-year cycle, following a period of minimum activity, are of opposite polarity in the northern and southern hemispheres. As the cycle progresses the mean latitude of the spots in each hemisphere decreases slowly but the polarity remains the same. The high-latitude spots of the next $11 \cdot 1$-year cycle, which begin to develop rather more than a year before the disappearance of the low-latitude spots of the preceding cycle, are of opposite polarity to the low-latitude spots of the preceding cycle.'

It may therefore be concluded that, whilst the interval of about 11·1 years represents the period of variation of the frequency (or total area) of the spots, prominences and flocculi, the complete sunspot period corresponding to the interval between successive appearances in high latitudes of spots having the same magnetic polarity must be taken as double this period. The cycle of about 22 years may be termed the magnetic period of the spots to distinguish it from the half-period of the other manifestations of solar activity. An analysis by Turner of Wolf's relative spot numbers has suggested that these (or the areas of the spots—see p. 75) may perhaps also follow this double period.

Plate 107 shows the bipolar group (Mt Wilson no. 8129) which crossed the Sun's disc between 1946 July 19 and August 2. At maximum development its area measured 3685 millionths of the visible solar hemisphere. The intense flare that developed on the morning of July 25 was followed by a great magnetic storm and by aurorae on Earth.

In Plate 108 is shown the 1947 group (Mt Wilson no. 8392), of complex polarity, whose magnetic field attained a maximum intensity of 3800 gauss.

22. *RELATIONS BETWEEN THE HYDROGEN VORTICES AND THE SPOTS; BIRTH AND LIFE HISTORY OF SPOT GROUPS

The extensive disturbed zones which the spectroheliograph reveals in the hydrogen atmosphere around sunspots (whose vortical appearance led Hale to his discovery of the magnetic fields) may be due to actual hydrodynamic vortices resembling gigantic cyclones, or to electromagnetic phenomena in which the moving particles of the solar atmosphere are compelled to follow the lines of force of the spots' magnetic fields.

Statistical investigations of the Mt Wilson spectroheliograms show that no relationship exists between the polarity and the direction of the vortices overlying different spots; furthermore, there is no reversal of the direction of the hydrogen vortices corresponding to the reversal of the magnetic polarity at successive spot minima. These results thus do not favour the electromagnetic theory. In addition, it has been established by means of the same spectroheliograms that 81% of the northern vortices and 84% of the southern revolve in the same direction as terrestrial cyclones. This fact, in conjunction with that of the circulatory movements of the solar atmosphere above the spots (p. 161), suggests that the phenomenon of the vortices is electrodynamic rather than electromagnetic, and that the direction of the rotary motion is generally determined, not by the direction of the vortices overlying the spots, but by an eastward or westward deviation of north-going or south-going atmospheric currents towards centres of attraction over the spots—this drift resulting from the Sun's rotation.

When the Evershed-Abetti effect was under discussion it was seen that both the radial and tangential components of the motion of metallic vapours in the sunspots can be determined, and that from these components the actual motion of the vapours from the spot centre towards the exterior can also be derived; this motion in general follows the law of a logarithmic spiral. From these calculations, or simply from the determination of the tangential components, the direction of the rotation of the vortices at the spectroscopic level of these vapours has been established.

It has been shown that the absolute values of the tangential components are always smaller than those of the radial, and in the Arcetri series of observations they show a well-defined rotary movement (its percentage value being 50) which betrays the direction of the vortex. In other cases the components at the two edges of the penumbra have the same sign; hence, even if its direction may sometimes be guessed, when the absolute values are unequal, it is illegitimate to speak of a true vortex—one should rather visualise a deviation of the vapours in a given direction. And this is plausible enough in view of the proper motions in longitude that have been established for the spots.

If the directions of the vortices as deduced from these measurements are compared with those shown in spectroheliograms taken in hydrogen light, and the polarities of the spot nuclei determined at Mt Wilson, it is found that the sign of the vast majority of vortices at the level of the reversing layer metal vapours is opposite to that of the vapours at the higher hydrogen level. Thus whilst, as we have already seen, the hydrogen vortices are characteristically anticlockwise in the north hemisphere, those of the metallic vapours are clockwise; both are reversed in the southern hemisphere.

The spots examined are in nearly every case the leaders of bipolar groups (β_p in the Mt Wilson classification), and it must therefore be concluded that during the 1922–33 cycle the vortex of the p member of each bipolar group—which in the north hemisphere was of S or negative polarity—rotated in a clockwise direction, and that the rotation exhibited by hydrogen at the level of the $H\alpha$ flocculi was anticlockwise.

The problem of the dominant electric charge in spot vortices and of the direction of rotation of the vortices themselves was on several occasions discussed by Hale; on one such occasion he wrote: 'We are not yet able to determine with certainty the sign of the electric charge dominating in the vortices of sunspots. If it is always the same, the vortices of the leading and following components forming the bipolar groups must rotate in opposite directions. Moreover, the polarities of opposite sign of corresponding spots (leading or following) in the same hemisphere in successive cycles, must also indicate opposite directions of the vortices. A series of observations of the Evershed effect at low levels in bipolar spots is necessary for solving this problem and thus determining the sign of the prevailing charge. This, however, on the hypothesis that the Evershed effect at low levels actually does represent the vortex of the spots, which is still uncertain.'

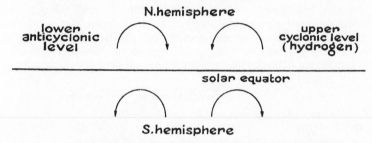

Fig. 55. Directions of the vortices at different levels in spots.

In this connexion Bjerknes also has written, 'We do not know what agreement exists between the direction of rotation and the sign of the magnetic field; a reliable determination of this agreement would be of fundamental importance to the theory of sunspots and perhaps also to magnetism.'

In the Arcetri series of observations it was impossible to make determinations of the following members of bipolar groups since these rarely possess sufficiently large nuclei to allow their spectra to be photographed. Thus it is not possible to say whether the direction of the vortex overlying the trailer is opposite to that over the leader, nor, naturally, can any conclusion be reached regarding the associated change of direction from one cycle to the next.

We may nevertheless agree with Bjerknes that owing to the Sun's rotation the outflow of gases will assume a spiral character, and that in this we may see an explanation of the spiral structure often exhibited by the upper levels. Since this is dependent on the Sun's rotation and not on the underlying photospheric vortex there is no reason why the direction of these spiral structures should change when the magnetic polarity switches over at the beginning of a new spot cycle.

It must similarly be concluded that the rotary or cyclonic motions of the metallic vapours are closely related to those of the overlying hydrogen vortices—at any rate in the leaders of bipolar groups (β_p)—and that owing to their hydrodynamic nature they will exhibit the same phenomena as terrestrial anticyclones which are likewise formed by two contrary vortex systems with radial and vortical motions, one superimposed on the other.

This hypothesis may find confirmation in the fact that the rotational motions of the metallic vapours are rather small and indefinite, often showing a tendency to veer in one particular direction. This agrees well with Milne's calculations, based on the hydrodynamic hypothesis, which show that the effect of the gaseous efflux will predominate over that of the rotation, since the cyclonic motion due to the Sun's rotation is negligible compared with the velocity of the efflux: 'The point is', writes Milne, 'that outflow is a necessary part of spot-structure, cyclonic rotation an accidental one.'

It must rest with future experimental and theoretical research to explain how the hydrodynamic phenomenon is related to the electromagnetic effects seated in the spots, to the sign of the predominant charge, and to the change-over of polarity.

This set of phenomena exhibited by the spots throws some light on the birth and life-history of spot groups, whose development usually follows a definite plan, although exceptions are occasionally observed among small and short-lived groups.

At the time of its first appearance on the photosphere a typical group consists of two small spots of opposite polarity, situated at approximately the same distance from the solar equator and separated from one another by 3° or 4° of longitude. The initial development is relatively rapid, the group attaining its maximum area in about a week. During this stage spots develop within the group itself, usually near the principal components but also in the space between them. As soon as the area of the group begins to increase the principal components move apart from each other until they are separated by 10° or more in longitude. The western spot is generally rather larger than the eastern, as well as being more symmetrical and less subject to rapid changes.

Maximum activity lasts only a few days, after which a phase of slower decline sets in. The first to disappear is the eastern or following component, which has all along shown itself to be the least stable member of the group; its disappearance usually takes the form of subdivision into smaller spots which gradually decrease in size. After another week or so nothing remains of the group but the western (preceding) component. This may survive for many weeks, or even months, gradually shrinking but seldom splitting up into smaller spots as did the following component of the group.

The first indication of the formation of a new group—particularly noticeable in calcium spectroheliograms—is the appearance of bright flocculi in the Sun's upper atmosphere over the whole area that is to be occupied by the group; these usually appear a day or two before the spots themselves. The flocculi survive the disappearance of the following components, so that even if no previous observations have been made, a spot can be identified as the preceding component of a group from its position relative to the overlying calcium flocculi. As soon as this remaining spot begins to shrink, the flocculi, and particularly those following the spot, do likewise, so that in the final stage they are symmetrically distributed around the underlying spot.

As has already been noted (see Figure 45), it is possible to distinguish at least five different levels in the solar atmosphere. The lowest is that of the vortex which produces the magnetic field. Above this, in the photosphere, lies the spot which can be seen or photographed directly. Between this and the hydrogen level of the $H\alpha$ spectroheliograms lies the region that can be photographed with the other intense lines of the solar spectrum; the parts of the H and K lines denoted by H_2 and K_2, which are relatively bright in the vicinity of spot groups, reveal the upper levels of this region. Still higher lie the region photographed with the $H\alpha$ line and that corresponding to the central H_3 and K_3 components, which is the highest chromospheric level of all.

We have already seen that bright masses of hydrogen, ejected from the spot, are observed in these highest levels, especially with the spectrohelioscope, while dark clouds of cooler hydrogen are formed above them and are sucked into the vortex. These filaments are the ones that are frequently observed in the form of spirals curving in towards the spots.

In the earliest stages of a spot group, and particularly when numerous spots are present, these vortices are sometimes rather confused, but when the group reaches its final stage (i.e. when a single spot remains) they are very conspicuous and altogether symmetrical.

23. *THE SUN'S GENERAL MAGNETIC FIELD

The Zeeman effect (which on occasions extends far beyond the limits of the penumbra) and the configuration of the hydrogen flocculi both suggest that magnetic fields of wide extent may exist on the Sun in regions far removed from visible spots. Moreover the general shape of the corona (pp. 210–211) suggests that the whole Sun may be regarded as a magnet: indeed, the coronal rays, especially those in the vicinity of the poles, are reminiscent of the lines of force round a magnetised sphere. Again, as Deslandres pointed out, the form and velocity of prominences receding from the Sun appear to be subject to its magnetic field.

Following up these hints, Hale was led to search for direct evidence of a general solar magnetic field analogous with that of the Earth. Since such a field would in any case be of inconsiderable intensity compared with that of the spots, it was first necessary to discover where the largest Zeeman effect would be manifested in the lines of the reversing layer, and then to develop the appropriate technique for observing it.

It was in fact to be expected that the effect would not show itself as an actual splitting of the spectral lines, as in the case of the spots, but merely as a broadening; the first requirement was therefore wide dispersion, such as that provided by the 75-foot spectrograph of the large Mt Wilson solar tower, which in the third order spectra has a linear scale of 0·2 ins per angstrom.

If such a widening existed, a polariser of the type already described (p. 173)—i.e. one consisting of a series of quarter-wave mica strips, each 2 mm wide, plus a nicol prism—should show the line displaced alternately to right and left when passing from one strip to the next, according as to whether a given strip transmits one or the other component. Since extremely small displacements would in any case be involved (of the order of 0·001Å, or 0·005 mm on the plate) they had to be measured with a micrometer of the type consisting of a plate with plane parallel faces (p. 174).

The basic assumption that was made—both in choosing the most profitable manner of making the observations and also for setting up the formulae to express the characteristics of the field—was that the magnetic field of the Sun is similar to that of the Earth. The measurements made on a few lines in a region situated on the meridian showed that, in accordance with this hypothesis, the displacements are maximal and of opposite sign in latitudes 45° north and south.

The characteristics of the field which had to be determined are: i, the inclination of the magnetic axis to the axis of rotation; λ, the longitude of one of the magnetic poles, measured from the central meridian in the direction of the Sun's rotation; and the maximum intensity of the field.

These initial measures having established the existence of a general solar magnetic field, the Mt Wilson astronomers selected some thirty lines, of intensities ranging from 0 to 5 on Rowland's scale, which were known from laboratory investigations to yield particularly wide separations of their components under the influence of a magnetic field. The displacements measured with these lines along the Sun's central meridian from the north to the south pole were represented by a curve which, as had been anticipated, showed a positive maximum at 45° north latitude and a negative maximum at 45° south latitude.

From such curves, determined at different times and for different positions of the Sun's rotational axis, simple formulae of spherical trigonometry yielded the inclination i, the period of rotation of the magnetic axis about the axis of rotation P, and the intensity of the field at the magnetic pole H_p.

From observations made at Mt Wilson between 1912 and 1914—an epoch of minimum solar activity being chosen so that advantage could be taken of relatively tranquil photospheric conditions—Seares deduced the following figures:

$$i = 6°.0 \pm 0°.4$$
$$P = 31^d52 \pm 0^d28$$

The intensity of the field varies from 10 to 55 gauss according to the lines used, and appears to decrease rapidly with increasing altitude; thus whilst an intensity of 55 gauss would be given by lines attaining a level of 150 miles above the photosphere, one of 10 gauss corresponds to lines reaching an altitude of about 250 miles. Further observations are required to clear up this point, however, for we have already seen (p. 155) that high-level lines are usually the more intense, and the measurement of the small Zeeman displacements is correspondingly more difficult in their case. In any event it can now be accepted that only lines originating in a not very deep stratum are influenced by the magnetic field in a manner that can be detected and measured by these methods.

Since that time observations have been continued at Mt Wilson with the aim of discovering possible variations in the constants of the magnetic field and of establishing whether such variations may be related to the different phases of solar activity. Meanwhile it can be stated that the sign of the general field is the same now as it was at the outset of this programme of measurements, even though the magnetic polarity of the spots has changed sign at the beginning of each new cycle.

The considerable technical difficulties which are encountered in the measurement of the Sun's general magnetic field, and the problem of its variation with the intensity of the lines employed, have suggested the necessity of repeating the determinations from time to time and possibly also of employing other methods of investigation. These have acquired still greater importance since the discovery and determination of intense general magnetic fields in stars possessing considerable rotational velocities.

In 1940 H. D. Babcock at Mt Wilson began a series of measures using the Fe lines at 5250Å, 5329Å, 6173Å and 6302Å in solar latitudes ±45°, where the field effect is maximal; in conjunction with the spectrograph he used a Lummer plate and a new type of polariser. By this method it is possible to determine smaller values of the field intensity than those measurable by the classical method of Hale. From the measures made in 1940, 1941, 1943, 1946 and 1947 it appears that the existence of a general field may be accepted, its polar intensity varying from 5 to 60 gauss. In this way Hale's results were confirmed, but in addition it appeared that the field varies as a function of time. G. Thiessen, of Hamburg Observatory, undertook similar determinations in 1945, but by a combination of interference and photoelectric methods. With a grating spectrograph and a Fabry-Perot interferometer he eliminated almost the entire spectrum with the exception of a small region about 0·04Å wide; this was made to fall on a multiplying photocell. This narrow spectral region is situated at the edge of the line that is to be measured, in such a way that its small periodic displacements—produced by the rotation of a quarter-wave mica plate in conjunction with a polaroid filter, or by means of oscillations set up by small pressures within the interferometer—are revealed at their maximum intensity. The corresponding oscillations in the electric current produced by the photocell are raised above the thermal-agitation noise by means of resonance oscillations in a galvanometer enclosed in a vacuum. This photoelectric method is capable of revealing the existence of a magnetic field whose intensity is 1 gauss.

With this equipment, used in conjunction with a 23½-inch refractor, and employing the Cr I line (5248Å) at solar latitudes ±45° on the central meridian, positive effects in the same direction were obtained, indicating the presence of a magnetic field of $H_p = 1·5$ gauss, with a probable error of 0·5 gauss. The direction of this field, relative to the solar rotation, is opposite to that of the Earth's. These 1947–48 determinations, indicating the existence on the Sun of a weak and barely measurable magnetic field, were in marked contrast to the values obtained by Hale and to those of Thiessen by his visual method in 1945, which gave

$$H_p = 53 \pm 12 \text{ gauss}$$

In this case, also, it appeared that the field was variable, but confirmation of this must await future determinations by different methods.

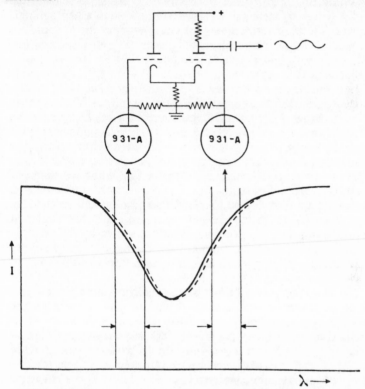

Fig. 56. *Profiles of a solar line, having a half-width of about* 0·1Å, *are shown for the two states of opposite polarisation. The slight shift in position occurs at a frequency of 120 cycles per second, in response to the alternating analyzer. For 5250·216Å the shift is 0·0008Å in a field of 10 gauss. The two slits transmit light to two photomultipliers that are connected to a different amplifier.*

Horace and Harold Babcock have recently devised and constructed a new apparatus at the Hale solar laboratory in Pasadena, by whose means the magnetic fields at the Sun's surface can be observed. This consists of (a) a large plane grating which concentrates the light predominantly into the green region of the fifth order spectrum, and provides a dispersion of 0·09Å per mm, (b) a photo-electric receiver with two slits focused symmetrically on the wings of a given line, and two photomultipliers connected to an amplifier, (c) an arrangement for scanning the whole solar disc and recording the intensity and polarity of the magnetic fields at the Sun's surface by means of a cathode-ray tube and a photographic camera. This apparatus allows the observation of the longitudinal Zeeman effect, which consists of the separation of a spectral line into two oppositely polarised components in the presence of a magnetic field (p. 171).

The observations are made by allowing the image of the Sun, 14 ins in diameter, to trail over the spectrograph slit. The magnetic effect is revealed by vertical fluctuations of a bright spot on the screen of the cathode-ray tube. A uniform horizontal movement is imparted to the bright spot in step with the displacement of the solar image. At the same time a fiducial line is traced by a second luminous spot, which coincides with the first when the intensity of the field is nil. The whole disc is surveyed in fifty minutes and the results are recorded by photographing the cathode-ray screen. The measures are made daily, usually with the iron triplet at 5250·2Å; the appearance of the records is shown by the example in Plate 109. In these a deviation from the fiducial lines equal to their distance apart corresponds to a field intensity of about 10 gauss.

The first conclusions drawn by the Babcocks from these interesting observations were that the magnetic fields present on the Sun are very numerous, some fairly intense, with extensive or localised multipolar areas, others so weak as to be only just observable. As was to be expected, spot groups gave the most intense deviations, and magnetic fields were observed extending for distances of several minutes of arc in their vicinity. Persistent fields not associated with visible spots may be identified with regions occupied by bright Ca II flocculi. Fields of this type, with variable intensities of 10 gauss or less, can be followed across the diagram from day to day during the course of the solar rotation. The magnetic field also sometimes persists for several days after the disappearance of the spot. In high solar latitudes up to ±70° (the limit at which useful observations can be made) a persistent magnetic field with an intensity of from 1 to 2 gauss was recorded. Since in these high latitudes the lines of force are probably inclined, the field may in reality be considerably more intense than this. It was noted that the predominant magnetic polarity was opposite at the north and south poles; at the time these observations were made (1952) the Sun's dipolar field was opposite that of the Earth.

It is evident that this new and important method of observation devised by the Babcocks, when continued throughout the course of the 22-year magnetic cycle, will throw light on many of the complex characteristics of the Sun's magnetism.

Chapter IV

METHODS OF STUDYING THE OUTER ENVELOPES OF THE SUN'S ATMOSPHERE DURING ECLIPSES AND IN FULL SUNLIGHT

24. THE CORONAGRAPH AND THE POLARISING FILTER

When the Moon's disc completely covers that of the Sun—i.e. at total solar eclipse—it is possible to see, outside the chromosphere, another envelope of considerable extent, whose brightness distribution is related in a particular manner to the Sun itself. This outer envelope is called the 'corona'.

Since it is clearly of great importance to determine the form and physical characteristics of this outermost envelope of the Sun's atmosphere, attempts have been made to observe it not only during the brief moments provided by eclipses, but also by direct and . indirect methods in full sunlight. Compared with the photosphere, however, the corona is extremely faint: its inner regions are no brighter than the surface of the full Moon, which is 600,000 times fainter than that of the Sun. The intensity of the corona is about equal to that of the sunlit sky at a distance of from 8° to 10° from the Sun; but in the neighbourhood of the limb the preponderance of photospheric light is so great that it is of the utmost difficulty to photograph the corona in sunlight.

Various attempts made by Hale and others in the past—such as taking spectroheliographs up mountains to considerable heights above sea level, so as to avoid the lowest and most dust-laden strata of the Earth's atmosphere—met with no success. Only as recently as 1930 did B. Lyot succeed in photographing the inner corona and the more intense lines of its spectrum in full sunlight.

He was able to achieve this result by constructing an instrument in which the diffusion of light by its optical elements was reduced to a minimum. The 'coronagraph' built by Lyot consisted of a plano-convex lens, 5·1 inches in diameter and of 134 inches focal length, made of special glass and worked with care to avoid scratches, bubbles, etc. This lens is mounted at A (Figure 57) and forms an image of the Sun on the black metal disc B, which is some 15 seconds of arc larger than the solar disc. A field lens C, placed behind the disc, forms an image A' A'' of the lens A on the diaphragm D, at whose centre is mounted a small screen, E. The rim of this diaphragm cuts out light diffracted by the edges of the first lens; the small screen eliminates the light of the solar images formed by reflection at the surfaces of this lens. Behind the diaphragm and screen an objective F, protected from diffused light, yields an achromatic image of the corona at B' B''. These elements are mounted in a drawtube M, adjustment of which allows the solar image to be focused on the screen. All these optical parts are enclosed in a wooden tube G, 16 feet 5 inches long, whose inner surfaces are smeared with thick oil; the tube is closed by a cover H, which is opened only during observation; the lens A, with its

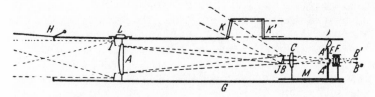

Fig. 57. Diagram of the Lyot coronagraph.

cell, completely closes the tube, thus reducing air currents. The cover H is made of silvered metal; a concave diaphragm I, and a disc J, also silvered, reflect unwanted radiation to the exterior so that the air in the coronagraph shall not be heated, which would interfere with the definition of the images. Light reflected from the diaphragm is returned through the aperture in the cover; that from the silvered disc through the windows K and K'.

For the coronagraph to yield all the results that Lyot hoped, it was essential that it should be used at a high-altitude station; the Pic du Midi, situated in the Pyrenees at an altitude of 9410 feet above sea level, was chosen for this purpose. Under these conditions the coronagraph, with a simple ocular fitted with a red filter, revealed numerous prominences, some only a few seconds of arc in height, and at their base the chromosphere. With the same instrument Lyot later, in July 1931, succeeded in photographing the corona under conditions of exceptional atmospheric transparency. Only the inner corona was visible, but within it several coronal rays were well seen, extending from 4′ to 7′ beyond the limb. This faint image of the corona was projected against a luminous background whose brightness was about 4 millionths that of the Sun.

Lyot was of the opinion that, despite his stringent precautions, diffusion within the coronagraph always accounted for the greater part of this background light, while a small fraction only was due to atmospheric diffusion; hence the instrument is possibly still susceptible of improvement. In any case it is recognised that eclipses provide—and always will provide—a more complete view of the corona than it is possible to obtain outside eclipse, and this is especially true of its outermost regions. The same may be said of the observation of the emission spectra of the chromosphere and the corona.

Lyot, continuing his experiments, combined his coronagraph with a spectrograph, which could easily be converted into a spectroheliograph, and with this he succeeded in photographing the two brighter lines in the green and red regions of the coronal spectrum all round the solar disc. He was also able to measure the intensity of the green line, establishing the fact that near the limb it amounted at some points to 70 millionths of that of 1Å of the Sun's continuous spectrum, and at others to only 3 millionths. In the case of the coronal spectrum also, it is evident that, as we shall see, more can be achieved by observations carried out during a total solar eclipse.

The 'monochromatic polarising interference filter', to which reference was made on p. 58, was constructed and perfected by Lyot in 1938 and permits the simultaneous study of the prominences, chromosphere and corona. If the transmission band is relatively wide (from 5 to 10Å) only the prominences at the solar limb are visible. If the transmission band is reduced to 1Å or even less, by means of successive polaroid elements and quartz plates, and the filter is mounted at the focus of the coronagraph, then observations with, for example, the $H\alpha$ line permit the direct visibility of the entire surface of the Sun's disc, just as does the progressive motion of the slits of the spectroheliograph. Indeed the spectroheliograph is surpassed by the filter since slits are obviated, and there is the additional advantage of visual observation with great clarity of detail. Besides the $H\alpha$ line, the filter allows the isolation of the principal coronal emission line at 5303Å in the green. In 1940 Lyot added to the monochromatic filter a special optical arrangement which permitted him to isolate different radiations and take moving films of them. In this way he was able to expose three films simultaneously—one with the green coronal line at 5303Å, one with the red line at 6374Å, and one with the $H\alpha$ line. This three-colour ciné camera attached to the Pic du Midi coronagraph has already provided important results, which will be briefly described.

196

25. TOTAL ECLIPSES OF THE SUN

Despite the enormous interest of eclipses, from the sight-seeing as well as from the scientific point of view, few extant records and descriptions of this spectacular natural phenomenon date from before the nineteenth century; this is no doubt because of the short duration of total eclipses (never exceeding a few minutes) and also because of the very restricted zones of the Earth's surface from which the eclipses can be observed as total. Owing to the faintness of the corona its full extent can only be seen when the eclipse is actually total; the same is true of the red flames, or prominences, which ring the solar globe. If even a thousandth part of the Sun's disc remains uncovered by the Moon, the beauty of the phenomenon and the appearance of the corona and prominences are completely lost.

Since 1800, and more especially since Fraunhofer's discovery, the observation of eclipses has aroused increasing interest, both on account of the phenomenon itself and also as it was realised how much information it could give regarding the physical constitution of the Sun.

The eclipse of 1851 was made memorable by the fact that it was the first to be recorded photographically—by daguerrotype. But it was at the 1860 eclipse that the first notable photographic results were obtained, by Fr Secchi and Warren de la Rue. Fr Secchi was enabled by the generosity of Pope Pius IX to observe the eclipse from the totality zone at Desierto de las Palmas, near Castellón de la Plana on the eastern coast of Spain. De la Rue went to Ribellosa on the west coast, and both observers obtained good photographs of the eclipse, from which they concluded :

(*a*) the prominences are real objects situated at the Sun's limb, and not optical effects, as some had thought;

(*b*) the corona is likewise a real object, which is more developed at the equator than at the poles, and even more at 45° than at the equator.

Fr Secchi was less fortunate at the eclipse of 1870, visible from Sicily, for which he went to Augusta; other Italian astronomers— Tacchini, Nobile and Lorenzoni—observed from Terranova. Whilst Secchi was barely able to observe the eclipse between the clouds towards the end of totality, Tacchini and his collaborators succeeded in confirming both the objectivity of the corona and the presence of the reversing layer. At the same eclipse, and under more favourable weather conditions, Young was able to observe the whole of the reversed solar spectrum (the flash spectrum—see pp. 101-2) and although he was unable to ascertain whether all the bright lines occupied the same positions in the spectrum as the dark lines, their identity was immediately obvious, both as regards the general arrangement and the relative intensities of the lines.

Young added that this observation confirmed the existence of the continuous spectrum found by Secchi at the limb, and proved the truth of Kirchhoff's hypothesis regarding the constitution of the Sun and the origin of the spectral lines. Only as regards the thickness of the reversing layer did these observations show Kirchhoff to have been at fault: as Secchi had anticipated, its depth is small compared with the overall dimensions of the Sun. These early observations had already given Fr Secchi an inkling of the physical constitution of the corona, which he thought must be composed of substances whose temperature is high enough to render them incandescent. These substances are principally hydrogen, helium, and an unknown element (or rather, as we shall see later, known elements existing under physical conditions very different from those with which we are familiar on the Earth) first noted by Young in 1869, which was given the name 'coronium'.

Secchi was also of the opinion that by means of some special arrangement whereby total eclipses could be artificially simulated it would be possible to see the corona in full sunlight, particularly in view of the fact that Tacchini thought he had detected traces of it under conditions of unusual atmospheric transparency at Palermo. Secchi and Tacchini even went as far as to discuss a project for observing under still more favourable conditions from Mt Etna; the Sicilian skies, as Secchi remarked, 'are of an admirable clarity, compared with which those of Rome are polluted and foggy'. This proposal was taken up again and realised several years later by Hale, who with Riccò climbed to the summit of Etna with the same intention but without success.

At the eclipse of 1868 August 18—visible from the British East Indies, the Malay Peninsula and Siam—Janssen, as already described (p. 123), observed the bright-line spectrum of the prominences and with Lockyer paved the way for their continuous observation outside total eclipse.

A slitless spectroscope was used for the first time, following a suggestion by Young, at the 1871 eclipse. With such an instrument the emission lines appear at the moment of totality as bright rings, from whose extent the height of the various gases above the photosphere can be derived. Lockyer found that hydrogen, which is distributed uniformly round the Sun, reaches to a height of more than about 200,000 miles, and the green ring due to the mysterious coronium, to a height of 300,000 miles.

At the eclipse of 1878, visible in the United States, the corona was observed to be much less brilliant than in 1870 and 1871, as well as having a noticeably different shape: the polar rays resembled the lines of force round a magnetised sphere and the equatorial coronal rays were of enormous extent. Observing from a mountain in Colorado, Langley was able to trace these rays for a distance of 6 solar diameters from one limb and from the other limb for as far as 12 diameters.

The mystery of the constitution of the corona thus became even more baffling, for it was impossible to imagine how the solar atmosphere—subject to the laws of gravity—could extend for the enormous distance of more than ten million miles from the Sun's surface. This eclipse occurred at a minimum of solar activity, and it began to be suspected that the shape of the corona varies with the 11-year cycle.

The eclipse of 1882 May 17, visible with a very short period of totality from Egypt, has become famous for the bright comet that was seen and photographed close to the Sun during the total phase, but was unobservable both before and after the eclipse. The Sun was on this occasion at a maximum of activity and the form of the corona, as in 1871, was again almost rectangular, and altogether lacked the long equatorial rays and the intense, short, curved polar rays.

Janssen continued the observation of the coronal spectrum at the eclipse of 1883 and concluded that at its base its spectrum is a complete reproduction of the Fraunhofer spectrum, whence the coronal light must consist to a considerable extent of reflected sunlight. Since the coronal matter is known to be highly rarefied it follows that these regions must be rich in cosmic matter in a corpuscular state, from which the Sun's light is reflected.

At the eclipses since 1890 ever more powerful instruments were employed for the direct photography of the corona and also of its spectrum, notably by the Lick Observatory astronomers and by Lockyer; by their means the spectrum of the corona was clearly distinguished from that of the chromosphere.

Very numerous photographs of the internal and external corona were obtained with long and short focus cameras at the eclipse of 1900 May 28, visible in the United States and in Europe. Excellent photographs of the flash spectrum and of the corona were also taken with large prismatic cameras and with plane and concave gratings; at the same time Abbot made bolometric measurements of the radiation of the corona at various distances from the solar limb. The eclipses of 1905, 1914 and 1918 were also noteworthy for the large number of photographic observations that were undertaken; these made it clear that the form of the corona varies in step with the solar cycle.

Observations at the eclipses of 1919 and 1922 were mainly directed to testing Einstein's theory of relativity, which predicted a displacement of the positions of stars which happened to be close to the Sun's limb at the moment of totality. Two expeditions were organised by the Greenwich and Cambridge Observatories for the 1919 eclipse: one to northern Brazil and the other to the island of Principe in the Gulf of Guinea (West Africa). Measurement of the photographs obtained provided the first confirmation of Einstein's prediction, which was re-confirmed by much richer observational material obtained during the 1922 eclipse by the Lick Observatory expedition to northern Australia.

Summing-up the conclusions of the latter expedition, Campbell and Trumpler wrote: 'Having guarded our results, by means of the checkfield observations, against any systematic errors due to the photographic process, or to the method of measurement, and having found that abnormal refraction in the Earth's atmosphere must be rejected as a possible explanation, the conclusion seems inevitable that the observed star displacements are due to a bending of the light rays in the space immediately surrounding the sun. As to the amount of the light deflections and the law according to which these diminish with increasing angular distance from the sun's centre, the observations agree within the limits of accidental observing errors with the prediction of Einstein's generalized theory of relativity, and the latter seems at present to furnish the only satisfactory theoretical basis for our results.'

Subsequent eclipses have likewise been observed by numerous expeditions to remote parts of the world, and despite the clouds which on several occasions have prevented any observations whatsoever being made, additional photographs and important results have been obtained; the use of red-sensitive plates has, furthermore, made possible the extension of our knowledge both of the flash spectrum and of the coronal spectrum.

At the 1926 eclipse Stetson of Harvard Observatory and Coblentz of the United States Bureau of Standards, observing in Sumatra, measured the radiation of the corona with the same equipment that had yielded good results at the 1925 eclipse, visible from the United States. They were able to establish the fact that the intensity of the corona in 1926 was 40% greater than in 1925, an increase probably to be associated with the greater number of spots.

Mengarini, Horn d'Arturo and Taffara observed this same eclipse from Oltregiuba and obtained photos of the corona which, when compared with those taken $2\frac{1}{2}$ hours later by the English expedition in Sumatra, showed several changes in the coronal petals surrounding a notable prominence.

Similar observations were made at the eclipse of 1927 June 29, visible from Scandinavia and England, and good photographs of the corona were obtained; it was of the maximal or circular type, the Sun then being exactly at a maximum of its activity.

Numerous expeditions established themselves in the totality zone of the 1932 August 31 eclipse, which crossed Canada and the western states of America. Although the weather was generally rather unfavourable several of the expeditions were able to carry out their programmes.

The eclipse of 1936 June 19 was visible from a totality zone stretching across the whole of the U.S.S.R. from the Black Sea as far as the Japanese island of Hokkaido. Numerous expeditions were sent to the zone from different countries, the Italian expedition (G. Abetti, G. Righini, L. Taffara) setting up its station at Sara in the district of Orenburg, not far from the Ural Mountains. The coronal spectrum was photographed with a double spectro-coronagraph consisting of two telescopes of 4·9 feet focal length combined with two prismatic spectrographs, one for the visible region of the spectrum, the other for the violet; the chromospheric spectrum was photographed with a grating spectrograph; and the corona itself with a multiple long-focus camera fitted with violet and yellow filters.

The ever-increasing ease with which stations in uninhabited regions remote from observatories can be reached, and the employment of new instruments and new techniques, have rendered the observation of total eclipses both easier and more interesting. The expeditions are not organised by astronomers alone, but also receive the support of other bodies with considerable financial means at their disposal—such, for instance, as the National Geographic Society in association with the U.S. Navy.

The eclipse of 1937 June 8 was memorable for the exceptional observational difficulties that it presented, the totality zone lying almost wholly over the Pacific Ocean; the only mainland touched was the west coast of South America, and that shortly before sunset. Since it was impossible to set up the necessary instruments on board ship the choice of an observing site was confined to Canton Island, a tiny member of the Phoenix group lying some 1800 miles south of Honolulu. Since the Moon was relatively near the Earth and at its greatest distance from the Sun, and since, moreover, the totality zone lay close to the equator, this eclipse provided an exceptionally long period of totality—7^m4^s on the central line of the totality zone. Unfortunately this line was in mid-ocean, and there was no other choice than Canton Island, where the duration of totality was 3ᵐ 33ˢ. The island is deserted coral formation rising to about 30 feet above sea level. Astronomers, geophysicists, radio technicians and naval officers were transported from Honolulu to Canton Island with their load of instruments and equipment in a warship of the U.S. Navy. The programme was organised and directed by S. A. Mitchell, veteran of at least ten eclipse expeditions to various parts of the world, and was carried out according to plan under perfect weather conditions.

At these recent eclipses great importance was accorded to observations by radio as a means of investigating the upper levels of the terrestrial atmosphere and the effect upon them of radiations emitted by the Sun under the special conditions of solar eclipse.

Full details regarding future eclipses may be obtained from Oppolzer's *Canon der Finsternisse*. In this monumental work are listed the elements of 8000 solar and 5000 lunar eclipses—all the partial, total and annular eclipses occurring between 1205 B.C. and A.D. 2152. Diagrams showing the track of the Moon's umbra across the Earth's surface are given for every total eclipse visible during these 34 centuries.

Notwithstanding the fact that the possibility of observing the prominences and corona outside eclipse has somewhat detracted from the importance of total eclipses, it is nevertheless obvious that they will always be of extreme value in the study of the Sun's outer envelopes, especially as the invention of still more perfect and rapidly operating instruments allow the maximum advantage to be taken of the brief moments when the solar glare is cut out by the body of the Moon.

26. OBSERVATION OF THE FLASH SPECTRUM AND CHROMO-SPHERE DURING ECLIPSES

The spectrum of the reversing layer—which from the abrupt manner of its appearance during eclipses is termed the flash spectrum—was first observed by Young in 1870. He himself explained it by supposing that the Fraunhofer lines of the ordinary solar spectrum originate in the reversing layer, which the brevity of the phenomenon shows must be an envelope no more than a few hundred miles thick.

The vast majority of the lines of the Fraunhofer spectrum are found reversed in the spectrum of the reversing layer, which, however, is distinct from the chromosphere and should be regarded as its lowest and densest region adjacent to the boundary of the photosphere. The first photograph of the flash spectrum was obtained in 1893, and showed 164 bright chromospheric lines between K and $H\beta$. At the 1905 eclipse Mitchell, using a high-dispersion concave grating without a slit, obtained some very fine spectra, and his subsequent detailed examination of these notably increased our knowledge of the appearance, extent and intensity of the lines of the chromospheric spectrum. During the eclipse of 1925 Curtis and Burns succeeded in photographing the infrared region by means of panchromatic plates and a short focus concave grating, whilst Mitchell at the same eclipse used the grating he had already employed in 1905 to photograph the normal spectrum from 3300Å to 7200Å.

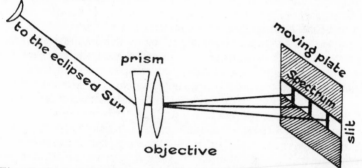

Fig. 58. Layout for the moving plate spectrograph for photographing the flash spectrum (Campbell).

Much valuable information has also been obtained at other eclipses with the aid of slit spectrographs and objective prisms. It is extremely important in the observation of the flash spectrum to make use of exactly the right moment—immediately before second contact, or immediately after the third—so that the spectrum of the chromosphere as near as possible to the photosphere may be seen or photographed. Visually, with a spectroscope, many high-level lines are to be seen reversed several minutes before totality, principally in the vicinity of the cusps of the solar crescent, and it is easy to judge the exact instants at which the spectrum of the reversing layer should be photographed; the number of the resultant crescents or arcs will be greater or smaller according to the number of the emission lines, and their size will depend upon the altitude of the atmospheric level containing the gases producing them.

Another method of photographing the flash spectrum is the so-called moving plate method, originated by Campbell and used by him and by the observers of Lick Observatory. A narrow slit is mounted immediately in front of the photographic plate, parallel to the dispersion of the spectrograph, so that only a narrow section of the central part of the chromospheric arcs can be recorded on the plate; if, now, during the exposure a uniform motion is given to the plate behind the slit, in a direction perpendicular to its length, a continuous record will be obtained of the flash spectrum and its variations at each moment as the eclipse advances.

The first experiments with this method were made by Campbell in India at the eclipse of 1898, using a Rowland plane grating. It was subsequently employed by him at the 1900 and 1905 eclipses, and on the latter occasion he obtained magnificent photographs of the spectrum from 3820Å to 5300Å with an objective prism giving a dispersion of about 6 mm per angstrom at $H\gamma$. In addition to this he obtained photographs of the spectra of the chromosphere and corona as far as 3400Å, using a spectrograph consisting of two 60° prisms mounted in front of the objective, both the lens and the prisms being of ultraviolet-transmitting glass. This method also offers the possibility of investigating the intensity variations of the chromospheric lines with altitude; on the other hand it is difficult to photograph the weaker low-level lines with the moving plate, owing to the shortness of the exposure.

The most noticeable difference between the chromospheric spectrum and that of the photosphere resides in the relative intensities of individual lines—emission in the former case and absorption in the latter. Hitherto these intensities have been expressed, as was done by Rowland, by means of a non-uniform empirical scale; hence it is difficult to compare the values obtained from different plates at different times, and by different observers. Nowadays—with improved photographic techniques, plates appropriately calibrated for each exposure, and the use of microphotometers—more accurate measures of intensity, expressed in terms of a uniform scale, are beginning to be obtained. For the time being the intensities of the chromospheric spectrum are being estimated by Mitchell using an empirical scale analogous to that of Rowland.

The characteristic intensity differences between the lines of the photosphere and those of the chromosphere arise from the fact that the chromospheric light is observed tangentially to the surface of the Sun during eclipse, whence are seen different layers from those producing the Fraunhofer lines when the centre or limb of the solar disc are observed. Suppose, for example, that we are concerned with two different elements, one of low density extending to a great height above the level of the photosphere, while the other is heavier and consequently confined to a lower level; it is then possible to imagine that the absorptions produced by the atoms in the two strata of gas will be equal in the case of rays emerging perpendicularly to the surface of the Sun at the centre of its disc. In such circumstances it is probable that the two gases will produce equally intense lines in the spectrogram. During eclipse, on the other hand, the exposure is progressive and the Moon's disc moves gradually in front of the Sun's, with the result that the exposure is much shorter for the low-level gases than for those at high altitudes. It is thus understandable that although the two gases may produce equally intense lines in the absorption spectrum, this equality will not be maintained in the emission spectrum; the heavy, low-level gas will give rise to narrow arcs in the chromosphere while the other will produce broader and relatively more intense arcs.

Whilst there are other factors which contribute to the intensity differences it is certain that the principal cause of these relative differences between the dark and bright lines is the diversity of altitudes at which the various gases occur. As we have already seen, the H and K lines of Ca II and those of hydrogen are also the most intense lines in the spectrum of the chromosphere, for the very reason that calcium and hydrogen extend to greater heights than any of the other elements.

There are thus considerable differences between the intensities of the lines in the two spectra; indeed the spectra, when compared with one another, would seem to be those of two stars of different type rather than of the same celestial body. It is precisely because of these discrepancies—of which the most notable concern hydrogen and helium—that eclipse observations are so important.

It is well known that absorption lines of helium are not found in the spectrum of the photosphere, whilst in that of the chromosphere helium lines are among the most conspicuous. In the former, moreover, only a few hydrogen lines are to be seen, although in the latter Mitchell has photographed all 34 lines of the Balmer series. On the basis of his own photographs obtained with gratings as well as those of other observers taken at different eclipses, he published an extensive catalogue of chromospheric lines between 3066Å and 8863Å. These are compared with the lines listed in *Rowland's Revision*, and the intensity of each emission is given on a scale analogous to that employed by Rowland; also quoted is the height reached by the atoms producing each spectral line, deduced from the breadth of the chromospheric arcs.

It has been found that the intensities of the photospheric lines approach more closely those of the electric arc, while the lines of the flash spectrum approximate to the intensities of the spark. In terms of Draper's classification of stellar types, the spectrum of the photosphere is altogether similar to those of type G stars, whereas the chromospheric spectrum belongs to the preceding type F (p. 289).

With increasing altitude there is a slight decrease of temperature, accompanied by a very rapid drop of pressure, as compared with the lower levels. Ionisation is consequently more complete the higher the level. The greatest altitude is attained by ionised calcium, at about 10,000 miles above the surface of the photosphere; the spectral changes attendant upon increasing altitude of the source are satisfactorily explained by the theory of ionisation.

An investigation of the chromosphere, similar to that of Mitchell, was undertaken by Menzel; his material was flash spectrograms obtained by the moving plate method on different Lick Observatory eclipse expeditions. Important conclusions were reached regarding the constitution and distribution of the elements, the more important of which are described below.

The density distribution in the chromosphere can be derived from the relation between the intensities and corresponding altitudes of the chromospheric lines, or from the intensities measured at different levels. The two methods give identical results. The density gradient of the metallic elements in the lower chromosphere is roughly what would be expected in an atmosphere of pure hydrogen in gravitational equilibrium. The higher levels of the chromosphere appear to be still more rarefied. Of two photospheric lines whose intensities are about the same, that with the lower excitation potential will be the more intense in the flash spectrum and will be found at the greater altitude.

The mean temperature of the chromosphere is of the order of 1000 degrees lower than that of the reversing layer. The temperature gradients in the chromosphere are not steep—probably much less than the upper limit determined as 0·5 degrees per km. The chromosphere contains a greater number of highly excited atoms than would be expected from Boltzmann's law. This excess, which increases with excitation potential, is very similar to the so-called deviation of stellar atmospheres from thermodynamic equilibrium, discovered by Adams and Russell, except that the effect is greatly intensified in the chromosphere and becomes still greater in the prominences.

Menzel and Mitchell also determined the relative quantities of the different elements in the chromosphere, finding that they are about the same as those derived by Russell for the photosphere (p. 229), except that hydrogen, helium and the rare earths are more abundant in the chromosphere than in the reversing layer.

From measurements of the amplitude of the chromospheric arcs in flash spectrograms obtained at different eclipses the following altitudes of various gases above the mean level of the photosphere have been obtained:

Lines	Altitude (miles)
Ca II (*H* and *K*) .	9000
H (*Hα*) . . .	7500
He (*D₃*) . . .	4600
Fe II, Ti II, Ca II .	1600
Na, Mg . . .	950
Fe, Ti, Cr . .	140

It is clear that these 'altitudes' are to some extent conventional, since they are primarily dependent on line intensities. But since they are the 'effective levels' of the weak lines at lower levels than the more intense lines, it is certainly possible to compare these results with those obtained from the motions of the gases around sunspots. Altitude measures made on plates showing the chromospheric arcs are affected to a marked degree by irregularities of the Moon's limb and by prominences. These results furthermore depend on the sensitivity of the instrument and plate, and are therefore only qualitative. It nevertheless seems reasonable to suppose that lines observed at the greatest altitudes correspond to effective levels superior to those appearing at low altitudes, and also that no well-defined stratification exists in the chromosphere.

The most important lines of the chromosphere (as of the photosphere) are the *H* and *K* lines of Ca II, the Balmer series of hydrogen represented by 40 lines, and lines of He I and He II, Sr II, Ba II, Fe II, Ti II and Cr II. Other characteristics are the continuous spectrum at the end of the Balmer series (3674Å), the CN and C_2 bands, and many lines of the spark spectra of the rare earths. As the solar limb is approached the first to disappear are the absorption lines of hydrogen, ionised metals and rare earths, followed by the molecular bands. The absorption lines of neutral metals are still in evidence 0".5 inside the Sun's limb. The higher level of excitation observed in the chromosphere, due to the low pressure there, corresponds to that in the atmosphere of an F5 giant (p. 291). The observations of the chromosphere made with the interference filter by Lyot at the Pic du Midi and W. O. Roberts at Climax (Colorado) have thrown much new light on its constitution.

It has already been said that, as was noticed by Secchi, the chromosphere does not have the aspect of a homogeneous atmospheric envelope, but appears as a *mélange* of innumerable bright, pointed jets or flames; these, also known as spicules in America, resemble small prominences ejected from the photosphere—usually vertically in the neighbourhood of the poles and obliquely at the equator. They measure several hundred miles in diameter and rise to a height of about 600 miles. They survive on the average for about five minutes, and their development seems to be more rapid in the vicinity of the poles; their behaviour suggests that there is a close connexion between spicules and the photospheric granulation. According to Lyot's observations three regions may be distinguished within the chromosphere: (*a*) a dense stratum with a well-defined upper boundary; its height, which varies from one point to another, ranges between 5″ and 7″—i.e. about half the height of the chromosphere in *Hα* light—though at some points it barely reaches 3″; (*b*) a very indistinct stratum, visible only at certain points of the limb in front of prominences, whose light this layer seems to absorb to an altitude of 1″ or 2″; (*c*) a series of spicules which may be looked upon as small prominences.

Lyot's ciné films, when projected at the normal speed, accelerate the actual solar motions by 400 to 600 times; they confirm that the spicules are short-lived, coming and going either at the same spot or vicinity, while the dense stratum of the chromosphere seems to be in a state of continuous agitation. Some prominences (generally very small ones) may develop a brilliance surpassing that of the chromosphere; when such prominences project from beyond the limb the chromosphere, which is completely opaque to the radiation which they emit, appears dark in front of them.

27. *FORM, BRIGHTNESS AND SPECTRUM OF THE CORONA

Our knowledge of the form, variations and spectrum of the corona is still very incomplete, owing to the short period of its visibility during eclipses; it must be remembered that from the day that helium was discovered in the chromosphere and 'coronium' in the corona, astronomers have had a total of less than one hour at their disposal for its observation. We have already described how past eclipses have been observed with telescopes of diverse types and sizes, usually of long focal length so as to obtain a large image of the eclipsed Sun on the photographic plate. In this way, with exposures of varying lengths, it is possible to record in great detail the form and arrangement of the coronal petals, and their intensities in the inner corona—i.e. the region immediately overlying

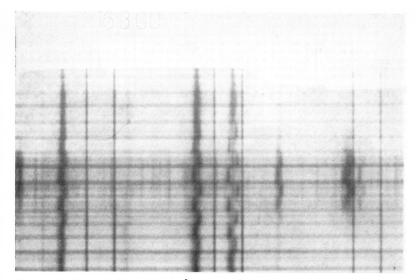

PLATE 94. Iron triplet at 6302·7Å observed in the spectrum of a spot near the centre of the disc with a Nicol prism and a composite quarter-wave mica plate. The triplet exhibits circular polarisation in a plane parallel to the lines of force.

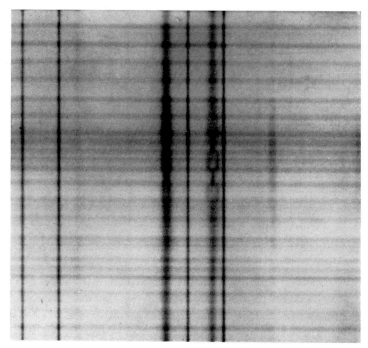

PLATE 95. Iron triplet at 6302·7Å observed in the spectrum of a spot near the Sun's limb with a Nicol prism and a composite quarter-wave mica plate. The triplet exhibits plane polarisation perpendicular to the lines of force.

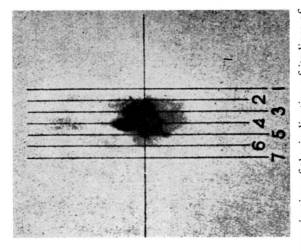

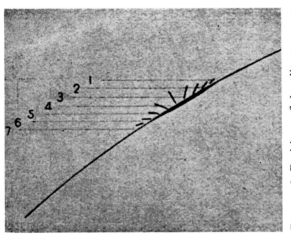

PLATE 96. Positions of the slit over a spot for the examination of the inclination of its lines of force.

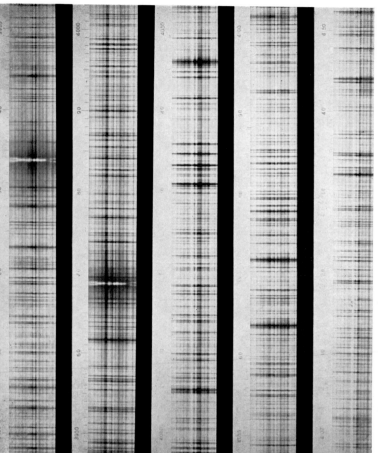

PLATE 97. Spot spectra showing the Zeeman effect; photographed at Mt Wilson with a Nicol prism and a composite quarter-wave mica plate; 3900Å to 4150Å.

PLATE 98. Spot spectra showing the Zeeman effect; photographed at Mt Wilson with a Nicol prism and a composite quarter-wave mica plate; 6150Å to 6400Å.

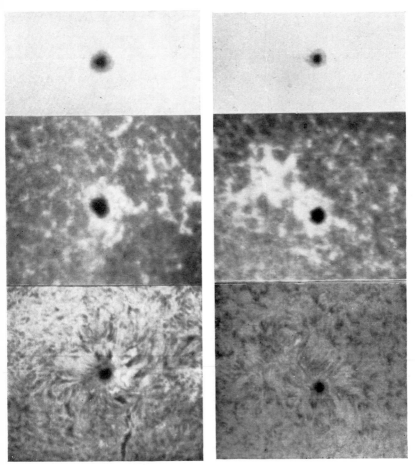

PLATE 99. Unipolar spots (α).   PLATE 100. Unipolar spots (α_p).

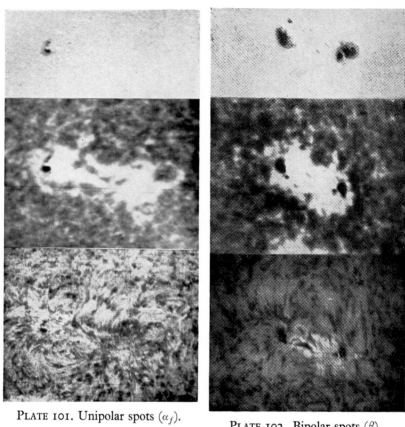

PLATE 101. Unipolar spots (α_f).

PLATE 102. Bipolar spots (β).

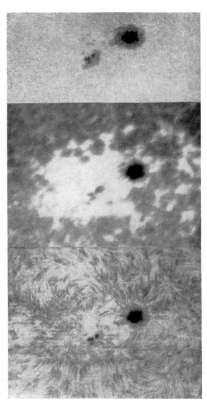

PLATE 103. Bipolar spots (β_p).

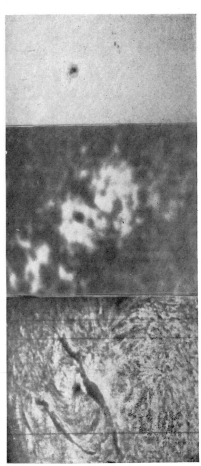

PLATE 104. Bipolar spots (β_f).

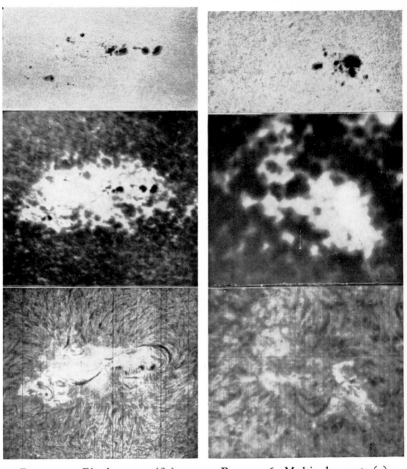

PLATE 105. Bipolar spots ($\beta\gamma$).   PLATE 106. Multipolar spots (γ).

the chromosphere, whose greater intensity clearly distinguishes it from the outer corona, which is much more diffuse and faint, and extends for several solar diameters from the limb.

The inner corona appears as a ring of pale yellow light against which the vivid red prominences are projected; it is probable that the emission lines of its spectrum originate in a zone extending for about 150,000 miles round the Sun. The outer corona is pearly white in colour and is composed of faint filaments or rays which diverge more or less rapidly from one another and are curved in a manner reminiscent of the lines of force round a magnetised sphere. Long, pointed rays or petals, made up of individual filaments, are visible around the Sun's disc to distances of two, three or even more solar diameters.

Photographs taken at stations within the totality zone which are separated by as great a distance as possible in longitude do not generally reveal any notable changes in the corona; this indicates that the coronal material is not in very rapid motion unless such motion occurs along the curved rays, or unless there is some strong and active centre of disturbance at the limb. Observations of the coronal spectrum made during the 1923 eclipse revealed an outward movement from two opposite points on the solar limb, the velocity being about 13 miles per second.

It was soon noticed, as a result of both visual and photographic observations, that the form of the corona is closely related to the phase of the 11-year cycle of solar activity at which the eclipse occurs. At times of maximum spot activity the corona is sensibly circular, and, in Janssen's words, presents the appearance of a gigantic dahlia or aureola, with petals developed in high latitudes (Figure 59). At sunspot minima, on the other hand, it is generally less extensive save at the solar equator, where are situated long petals whose outer parts are gradually lost to view against the diffused light of the sky (Figure 60). Langley, who observed the 1878 eclipse from an altitude of 14,000 feet above sea level, was able to trace the equatorial petals for a distance of 24 solar radii.

In the minimum type of corona there can also be seen in the vicinity of the solar poles relatively short filaments whose curvature reminds one of the lines of force near the pole of a magnet. At times intermediate between spot maxima and minima the corona is likewise of an intermediate type: the longest rays show a preference for the spot zone, giving it a rectangular appearance.

W. J. S. Lockyer, who originated the classification of the various coronal forms into polar, intermediate and equatorial types, came to the following conclusions:

(a) These different coronal forms are clearly dependent on the latitude zone in which the centres of prominence activity are situated.

(b) The corona is of the polar or irregular type when the maximum of prominence frequency occurs near the poles of the Sun; of the equatorial type when there is only a single zone of activity

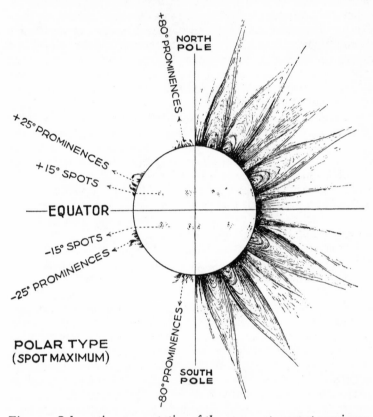

*Fig. 59. Schematic representation of the corona at sunspot maximum.
Polar type.*

in each hemisphere, at about latitude 45°; and of the intermediate type when there are two centres of activity in the mid-latitudes of each hemisphere.

(c) There is apparently no direct connexion between the activity of sunspots and the production of the coronal rays or petals.

On the basis of results obtained at more recent eclipses Mitchell has been able to refine Lockyer's conclusions, showing that the minimum or equatorial type of corona makes its appearance two years before the Sun reaches its minimum as indicated by the spots and prominences. Similarly, the maximum or polar type begins to develop two years before the maximum of spots and prominences. In view of what has already been said regarding the migratory movements of the prominences (p. 136) one must conclude that the general appearance of the corona is strictly related to the distribution of the prominences on the solar globe and follows the vicissitudes of this distribution, shifting with them to different latitudes during the course of the 11-year cycle.

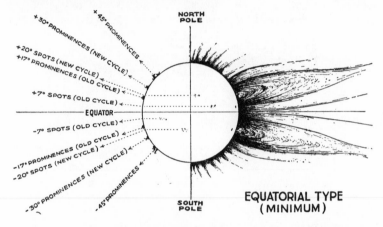

Fig. 60. Schematic representation of the corona at sunspot minimum. Equatorial type.

The green and red monochromatic images of the inner corona, taken by Lyot outside eclipse, show certain differences when compared with calcium and hydrogen spectroheliograms. Ciné films taken with a Lyot filter are a better source of information regarding the internal motions of the corona, whose study during the brief moments of totality must necessarily be very incomplete. These reveal striking variations of brightness within short time intervals, but these are not true movements of coronal material: some parts brighten from time to time, while others fade, without it being possible to follow any well-defined point. The small motions that can be detected by means of stereoscopic images (by combining plates exposed at convenient intervals) do not show any notable changes. More complicated motions may nevertheless occur in the corona—such, for example, as vortices, which would be difficult to recognise in different photographs.

Unlike the prominences, which we have seen to be animated by rapid motions, the corona as observed in the light of the two monochromatic radiations (green and red) is completely at rest. Petals, luminous pencils or clouds will brighten from time to time, like the rays of an aurora borealis, but without sensible motion. If such motions were frequent and of the order of 10 miles per second, as has been suggested by certain observations made during eclipses, they would certainly be visible in the monochromatic images. On the contrary, the ciné films show that the appearance from time to time of clouds and arcs at different distances from the Sun's limb can easily be mistaken for apparent motions. To conclude, it seems that we are concerned rather with variations of relative intensity of

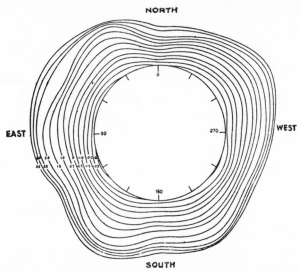

Fig. 61. *Mean isophotes of the corona at the eclipse of* 1936 *June* 19. *(Italian expedition to Sara, U.S.S.R.)*

the different elements of which the corona is composed, and in this respect it differs markedly from the prominences. The coronal rays and clouds, which sometimes make up complicated formations, are born on the spot, along invisible trajectories which probably already existed, and whose origin and mode of formation are still unknown. This phenomenon seems to be quite general, and any theory of the corona must take it into account.

From photographs of the corona taken during total eclipses and measured photometrically, its brightness can be derived; this, on account of the structure of the corona, varies from place to place, but as a first approximation it may be considered to be uniform around the solar disc. At each eclipse the general arrangement of the isophotes can thus be traced, as shown in Figure 61, where the curves representing intensity decrease in geometrical progression with a ratio of 1·58, equivalent to a halving of the magnitude. S. Baumbach, using numerous observations made during eclipse,

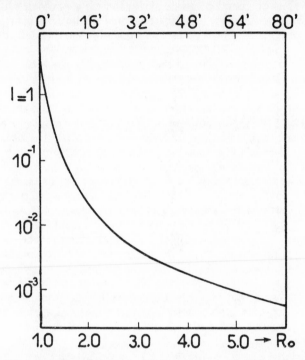

Fig. 62. *Mean brightness of the solar corona (Baumbach).*

has derived the curve reproduced in Figure 62, which shows the mean brightness of the corona as a function of distance from the Sun's centre. The rapid diminution within the region of the inner corona will be noticed, while the variation is less rapid in the outer corona. Wishing to represent this curve by an empirical formula he found that the mean brightness is given by

$$I(R) = \frac{0 \cdot 053}{R^{2 \cdot 5}} + \frac{1 \cdot 42}{R^7} + \frac{2 \cdot 56}{R^{17}}$$

where R is the distance from the Sun's centre expressed in units of the solar radius, and $I(R)$ is the brightness of the corona referred

213

to that of the centre of the Sun's disc, which is taken as equal to 10^6. It is therefore not possible to represent the whole curve with a single exponent.

The overall intensity of the corona has also been measured several times; this may be taken as roughly half the overall intensity of the full Moon. At the eclipse of 1937 June 8, J. Stebbins and A. E. Whitford found by measurements with a photoelectric cell that the ratio was 0·47, or about 10^{-6} that of the Sun. This integrated brightness seems to be constant, and independent of the 11-year cycle.

A continuous spectrum of the inner corona was observed by Rayet in 1868, and the Fraunhofer absorption lines in the spectrum of the outer corona by Janssen in 1871. The boundary between the inner and outer corona lies about 10′ from the Sun's limb. The Fraunhofer lines become visible at a distance of about 4′ from the limb, and their intensity increases with distance. The emission lines of the corona are visible in its spectrum up to 6′ or 7′ from the Sun's limb. On the assumption that the coronal emission can be represented by the spectral curve of a black body corresponding to a temperature T, it is only necessary to determine the relation between the intensities at two wavelengths in order to obtain T, the so-called 'colour temperature'. By using filters and the appropriate photographic emulsions it is possible to make the two wavelengths coincide with the maximum intensity of normal emulsions (about 5550Å). In this way the difference $m_p - m_v = C$ (where m_p, m_v are respectively the photographic and visual magnitudes), known as the colour index, can be derived from the known relation (Pogson's law) between the intensities (I_p, I_v, the intensities at the two wavelengths) and the magnitudes m_p and m_v:

$$m_p - m_v = 2·5 \log \frac{I_v}{I_p}$$

Various observations, not all in mutual agreement, would seem to suggest the occurrence of a 'reddening' effect in the outer corona. If this is confirmed it would appear to indicate the existence in the corona of diffusing particles whose size is of the order of the wavelength of light. The overall colour of the corona corresponds to a colour index of about +0·7.

N. Lockyer first measured the wavelengths of six of the coronal emission lines, including the most intense one, the green line at 5303·7Å. Subsequently, during eclipses, Deslandres obtained photographs of the coronal lines in the violet and ultraviolet, while at the eclipse of 1893, A. Fowler succeeded in photographing nine monochromatic rings (corresponding to nine emission lines) using a prismatic camera. At the eclipse of 1898, when for the first time the coronal spectrum was secured with wide dispersion, 14 lines were recognised, among them being those of unknown origin which were at that time attributed to the hypothetical coronium.

The publications of Lick Observatory contain a list by Campbell and Moore of the wavelengths of the better established coronal lines; these cannot, however, be very exact since considerable discrepancies are to be found between different observers' measures of even the most intense line, that in the green.

Because of the apparent simplicity of the coronal spectrum it was thought that its interpretation in terms of series relationships would be an easy matter, and various hypotheses have indeed been proposed concerning the nature of the element which might be capable of producing it. However it transpired that the problem was more difficult than originally thought, and only in relatively recent years does a solution seem to have been reached.

I. S. Bowen, having studied the so-called 'nebulium' emission lines visible in nebular spectra, made the suggestion that they must be produced by some of the elements H, He, C, N or O, which are known to occur in nebulae. It seemed likely that on account of the very low density an emission might result from the transition of an electron from a metastable state. Such transitions—termed 'forbidden' since they do not occur under normal terrestrial laboratory conditions—may be able to occur in the celestial laboratory where long free mean paths are rendered possible by the low densities. As C I, N I, N II, O I, O II and O III are the only ions capable of existing in metastable states in the nebulae and of producing lines in the visible region of the spectrum, they are identifiable without difficulty.

Eight of the most intense nebular lines have been classified by Bowen as due to transitions from metastable states in the ionised atoms N II, O II and O III. Several of the fainter lines have been identified as belonging to the spectra of highly ionised oxygen and nitrogen.

It may be asked how it is possible for an atom to radiate those lines of its spectrum which are not produced under normal laboratory conditions, while not showing those which are already familiar from terrestrial experiments. Eddington believed that in addition to the long free path made possible by the very low densities of the nebulae there was another requisite, namely, that the exciting radiation should be so weak that there would be little probability of the atom absorbing a quantum during the whole span of its metastable state. He therefore concluded that the spectrum of coronium cannot consist of forbidden lines, because although it is true that the density of the corona may be low enough, the exciting radiation is, on the other hand, extremely intense.

More recent eclipses, from 1918 to 1932, have increased our knowledge of the coronal spectrum and have also extended it to the red region, while it has been possible to measure the wavelengths of its lines with ever increasing precision. At the eclipse of 1930 Mitchell, observing from the small island of Niuafoou in the Pacific Ocean, discovered a new line in the extreme red at 6776Å.

Mitchell has observed that the details of structure visible in the lines 5303Å and 6374Å make it unlikely that these originate from the same atom, or at any rate from the same atom in the same state of ionisation. Now the former is the familiar coronal green line, which occupies the same region of the spectrum as the analogous lines observed in nebular spectra (which, as we have seen, appear to have been identified by Bowen) and also lines of the spectra of aurorae. The latter line (6374Å) is believed, on the strength of measures made by Hopfield, to belong to the spectrum of neutral oxygen; this identification supports Eddington's theoretical views.

More precise measures of the intensities of the spectral lines, and an increasingly complete knowledge of the coronal emission lines, such as Lyot has been able to achieve outside eclipse, have led to a more plausible interpretation of the mysterious coronal spectrum.

In 1933 the German astrophysicist W. Grotrian determined the 'equivalent widths' of eleven coronal emission lines. The value of the equivalent width E—which is defined in terms of the relation between the area of the photometric profile and the intensity of the adjacent continuous spectrum—represents the width in angstroms of an equally intense band of the continuous spectrum producing the energy emitted by the line. Clearly this measure is much more accurate than the estimation of the line's intensity in terms of an arbitrary scale, the method employed since the time of Rowland. Other measures of an analogous nature were later made by Lyot, and of the coronal spectrum at the eclipse of 1936 by G. Righini, who also determined the intensity of the continuous spectrum in absolute units by means of comparison with a standard lamp; he thus obtained not only the equivalent widths but also the absolute energy emitted by the lines.

In order to classify the lines of the emission spectrum it was necessary to find some relationship between the various lines, and for this purpose use is made of the observation of the coronal rings obtained with slitless spectrographs. Near to prominences, which represent regions of increased excitation, the rings exhibit structural characteristics and analogies indicating lines produced by the same atom or the same state of excitation and ionisation. A plausible identification of the coronal spectrum was originally due to Grotrian: noting that forbidden lines of Fe VII were observed in the spectrum of Nova RR Pictoris, and coronal lines in that of RS Ophiuchi, he advanced the hypothesis that these could be

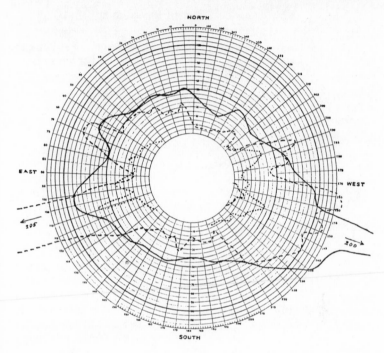

Fig. 63. Brightness of the coronal lines observed by Lyot at the Pic du Midi, 1947 April 12.

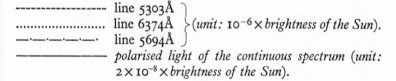

------------------ line 5303Å ⎫
.... line 6374Å ⎬ *(unit:* $10^{-6} \times$ *brightness of the Sun).*
—·—·—·—· line 5694Å ⎭
——————— *polarised light of the continuous spectrum (unit:* $2 \times 10^{-8} \times$ *brightness of the Sun).*

ascribed to forbidden transitions within highly ionised iron atoms, and demonstrated this in the case of Fe X. Later the Swedish physicist V. Edlén succeeded in proving theoretically and experimentally that atoms of iron, nickel and highly ionised calcium are responsible for the majority of the coronal emission lines, of which the most intense are due to iron atoms with 9, 10, 12 and 13 electrons less than the 26 that constitute the neutral atom.

The transitions which give rise to these lines are all 'forbidden' and are due, as can be seen from the Table below, to ions whose potential varies from 230 to 650 eV. It seems that the intensities

The Emission Lines of the Corona

λ	Identi-fication	Ionisa-tion Potential	Excita-tion Potential	Equiva-lent Widths	Intensity (arbi-trary units)	Remarks
Class I						
3900·8	—	—	—	0·4	2·5	
3986·9	Fe XI	261	4·7	0·4	3	⋆
6374·51	Fe X	233	1·9	5·0	40	⋆
7891·94	Fe XI	261	1·6	6·0	30	†
Class II						
3388·1	Fe XIII	325	6·0	11·1	44	
5116·03	Ni XIII	350	2·4	0·8	8	
5302·86	Fe XIV	355	2·3	20·0	198	⋆
6701·83	Ni XV	422	1·8	1·2	9	
7059·62	Fe XV	390	31·7	0·8	5	†
8024·21	Ni XV	422	3·4	0·3	1·5	†
10746·80	Fe XIII	325	1·2	48·0	130	†
10797·95	Fe XIII	325	2·3	30·0	81	†
Class III						
3601·0	Ni XVI	455	3·4	1·1	6	
4086·3	Ca XIII	655	3·0	0·3	2·5	⋆
Class IV						
5445	Ca XV?	814	4·5	0·05	0·5	
5694·42	Ca XV?	814	2·2	0·3	3	†
Unclassified						
3328	Ca XII	589	3·7	0·7	2·5	
3454·1	—	—	—	1·4	7	
3642·9	Ni XIII	350	5·8	0·7	4	
4231·4	Ni XII	318	2·9	0·7	6	⋆
4311	—	—	—	—	—	
4359	A XIV?	682	2·8	—	—	
4412	—	—	—	—	—	
4567	—	—	—	0·3	3	
4586	—	—	—	—	—	
5536	A X	421	2·2	<0·4	<4	

⋆ Observed in RS Ophiuchi
† Observed without eclipse by Lyot

shown in the table are individually and collectively markedly variable with the sunspot period, being in general greater around the maximum of solar activity. All the lines are brightest near the spot zone, and hence during the early part of the 11-year cycle the maximum intensities are to be encountered in high latitudes. The zone of excitation in the corona is, like the spots, later displaced towards the equator as the cycle advances.

Because of the important bearing of the diverse conditions prevailing in the corona and of the variability of the intensity of the lines, and therefore its state of excitation in its different zones, the inner corona is nowadays observed regularly by coronagraph at high altitude observatories. The intensity of the stronger lines, i.e. the green and red, is measured at a fixed distance from the solar limb (about 1') for every 5°. Such intensities are recorded all round the Sun's disc, providing a daily 'profile' showing the regions where the corona is more and less intense in the monochromatic light of the chosen lines (Figure 63).

Figure 64 reproduces the profiles representing the intensity distribution of the line at 5303Å, obtained by Waldmeier at the Arosa Observatory; the first is for a day in 1945, near the minimum of solar activity, and the second for a day in 1947 near the maximum. In the Figure the maximum intensities of the principal zone are indicated by arrows directed inward, those of the secondary polar zone by outward-pointing arrows.

Since these observations were initiated it has been noticed—in 1939, two years after the maximum of sunspot activity—that the principal intensity maxima of this coronal line were confined between the 15° and 20° parallels of heliographic latitude, while the secondary maxima were located at about latitude 60°. As the 11-year cycle progressed the latitude of the primaries decreased, and by 1942–43 (i.e. 1·5 years before spot minimum) jumped to about 40° (beginning of the new cycle), whereafter their latitude progressively diminished again. The secondary polar zone did not at first exhibit any marked latitude variation; in 1940–41, 3·5 years before spot minimum, it was located in about latitude 63°; it seems that it was displaced towards lower latitudes during 1942–43; and immediately after spot minimum reappeared once more at 60°. Thereafter the polar zone was displaced increasingly rapidly towards the poles, and by the second half of 1947, immediately after sunspot maximum, reached the poles and disappeared. This movement of the zone of excitation of the green coronal line is analogous with that already described in the case of the spots and the filament-prominences, and would indicate that in the corona also the origin of the solar disturbances is located in middle

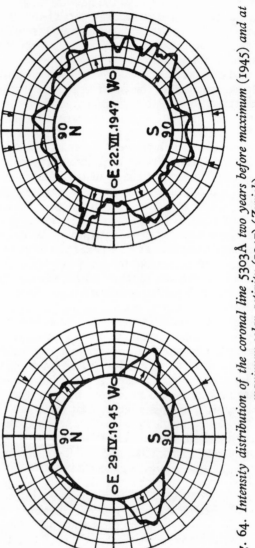

Fig. 64. Intensity distribution of the coronal line 5303Å two years before maximum (1945) and at maximum solar activity (1947) (Zurich).

latitudes and subsequently separates towards the poles and the equator. However, it is necessary to await the accumulation of more observational material, concerning these and other coronal radiations. Such observations should throw some light upon the still very obscure relations between the prominences and the coronal petals, and also on the formation and frequency of the latter throughout the 11-year cycle.

The interpretation of the coronal emission spectrum is difficult. A minimum temperature of 20,000°K is required to account for the spectrum of the chromosphere and prominences where He II is found. The energy required to remove 13 electrons from an iron atom is considerably greater even than this: Menzel has calculated that it would be of the order of one million degrees absolute. The widths of the coronal emission lines are consistent with a Doppler interpretation involving iron atoms in thermal agitation appropriate to such a temperature. Only at about one million degrees could an atmosphere of ionised hydrogen exist in equilibrium between the force of expansion due to the high temperature and the retentive force of gravity.

As has already been remarked (p. 209), the form of the polar rays and the equatorial streamers, particularly during epochs of minimum solar activity, is strongly reminiscent of the pattern made by the lines of force surrounding a magnetised sphere, and from their disposition something may be deduced concerning the orientation, intensity and variations of the Sun's general magnetic field. Measures of photographs of the corona taken at various eclipses supply confirmation of the fact that the Sun's magnetic axis does not coincide with the axis of rotation and that the poles are probably not diametrically opposite one another.

In conclusion, the experimental results that have so far been obtained regarding the nature of the corona may be summarised thus:

(a) The inner corona (within 10' of the Sun's limb) gives a continuous spectrum, and the middle and outer corona a spectrum of absorption lines which may be ascribed to the presence of macroscopic particles in the Sun's vicinity.

(b) The brightness of the spectrum decreases rapidly with increasing distance from the limb.

(c) The emission spectrum is only shown by the inner corona.

(d) The light of the corona is partially polarised; the degree of polarisation increases with distance from the Sun's limb up to a certain limit, and is independent of wavelength.

(e) The energy distribution of the inner coronal spectrum is the same as that of the Sun; the Sun and the corona are thus the same colour.

(f) The form of the corona varies throughout the 11-year cycle, owing to the movement of coronal material towards both high and low latitudes. It seems permissible to conclude from the examination of eclipse photographs that the equatorial type, associated with minima of solar activity, should be regarded as the 'normal' form of the corona, and that when the Sun is disturbed this also is modified and assumes the irregular polar type.

Survey of The Sun's Outer Layers (H. C. Van de Hulst)

Solar Layer	h (miles)	r (unit: $R_\odot$)	T (°K)	Hydrogen
Outer corona . .	900,000	3	1,500,000	
Medium corona .	450,000	2	1,500,000	
Inner corona . .	90,000	1·2	1,500,000	} ionised
	13,000	1·03	1,000,000	
Upper chromosphere (most uncertain)	9,000	1·02	300,000	} ionised
	4,500	1·01	25,000	
Lower chromosphere	2,500	1·006	6,100	
	600	1·0014	5,300	} neutral
	300	1·0007	4,900	
Sun's limb . .	0	1·0000	4,500	
Photosphere . .	−60	0·9999	4,500	
	−130	0·9997	5,000	
	−210	0·9995	6,400	} neutral
	−225	0·9995	7,000	
	−235	0·9995	7,300	

Chapter V

PHYSICAL CONSTITUTION OF THE SUN

28. THEORY OF IONISATION

We have seen (p. 100) that the modifications observed in the spectra of different strata of the Sun's surface depend on the greater or smaller incidence of ionised atoms at each level. Ionisation—the loss by an atom of one or more of its electrons—is an analogous phenomenon to chemical dissociation, where a molecule of a gas splits into two separate gaseous molecules. It is known that such dissociation is facilitated by decreasing the pressure: thus is explained the increased number of ionised atoms and the appearance of the spark spectrum when we pass from the lower to the higher levels of the Sun's atmosphere, where the pressure is necessarily lower.

It is to the Indian physicist Megh Nad Saha that we owe the idea of treating ionisation as an actual dissociation and applying to it the classical laws of physical chemistry. This was in 1921, and from his theory he derived a formula which has been widely and successfully used in the interpretation of the spectra of the photosphere, the chromosphere and the stars generally. We shall summarise the essential features of Saha's theory and the deductions that can be made from it.

The reversible dissociation of a gas A, a molecule of which splits into a molecule of gas B and another gas C, is denoted by the expression

$$A \rightleftharpoons B + C$$

In the same way, when we are considering an atom of an element, such as calcium, which becomes ionised we may write

$$\text{Ca I} \rightleftharpoons \text{Ca II} + e$$

where Ca I denotes the neutral atom, Ca II the singly ionised atom, and e the electron.

From the laws of physical chemistry the degree of ionisation—i.e. the proportion of ionised atoms, as a function of the temperature T and the pressure P—can be derived providing the energy absorbed in the process of dissociation is known. This energy generally is known, being simply the ionisation potential (usually expressed in electron-volts) of the atom concerned—in this case of the calcium atom. Saha's law relates these quantities to one another and hence permits the percentage of ionised atoms of any element to be calculated when its ionisation potential, temperature and pressure are known.

Conversely, if from the presence of certain lines in the spectrum we can deduce the percentage of ionised atoms whose ionisation potential is known, we can (for the definite temperature range possible in stellar atmospheres) calculate the corresponding pressures; or, given the pressures, the corresponding temperatures can be calculated.

Thus in the case of calcium, for example, Saha's formula yields the figures tabulated below, the ionisation potential of calcium being 6·1 electron-volts; pressures are expressed in atmospheres and temperatures in degrees absolute:

Percentage Ionisation of Neutral Calcium

Temperature \ Pressure	10	1	10^{-1}	10^{-2}	10^{-3}	10^{-4}	10^{-6}
4000°	—	—	—	3	9	26	93
5000°	—	2	6	20	55	90	
6000°	2	8	26	64	93	99	
7000°	7	23	68	91	99		
8000°	16	46	84	98			
9000°	29	70	95				
10,000°	46	85	98				
11,000°	63	93		complete ionisation			
12,000°	76	96					

Saha's formula reveals that the percentage ionisation increases with

(a) increasing temperature,
(b) decreasing pressure,
(c) decreasing ionisation potential.

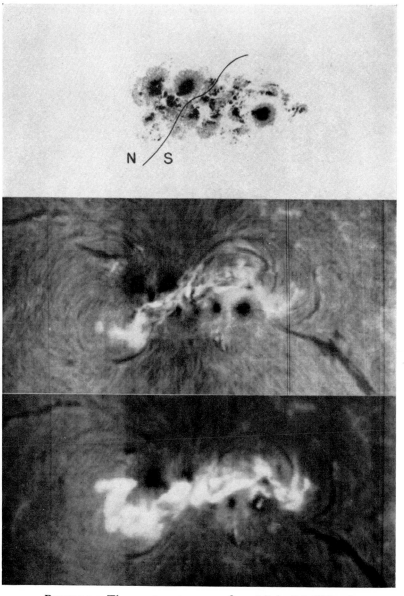

PLATE 107. The great spot group of 1946 July (Mt Wilson).

Upper: Direct photograph, with the polarity of the magnetic field indicated (25^d 13^h 55^m U.T.).

Lower: $H\alpha$ spectroheliograms: 25^d 16^h 5^m and 25^d 16^h 21^m, showing intense flare.

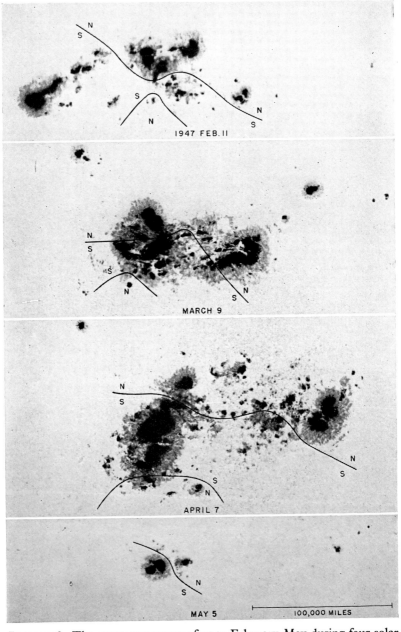

PLATE 108. The great spot group of 1947 February-May during four solar rotations. The areas of opposite polarity are indicated (E. R. Hoge, Mt Wilson).

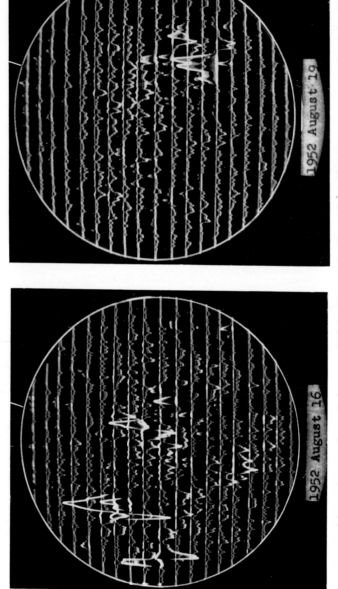

PLATE 109. Magnetic records made by scanning the disc of the Sun. North is at the top, east at the right. For each magnetic trace there is a fiducial line. A deflection equal to the interval between lines is equivalent to about 10 gauss. Upward deflections indicate that the magnetic vector is directed towards the observer (H. W. and H. D. Babcock).

PLATE 110. Equatorial at Meudon Observatory fitted with Lyot's polarising filter. Left to right: M. d'Azambuja, O. Mohler, L. d'Azambuja, B. Lyot.

PLATE 111. The Pic du Midi Observatory (Bagnères de Bigorre, Pyrenees; 9420 feet above sea level).

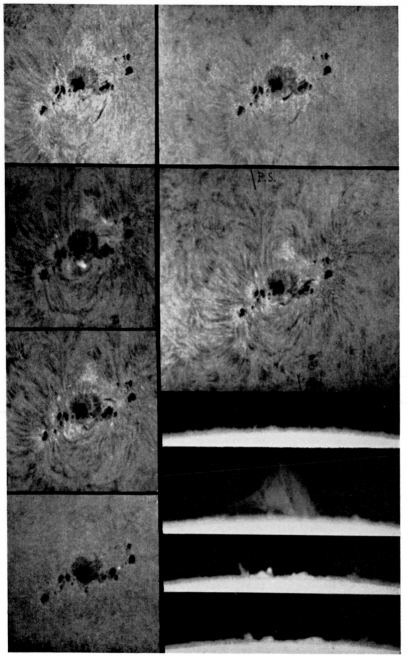

PLATE 112. Ciné film images of the chromosphere obtained by Lyot at the Pic du Midi in 1942 with an equatorial of 15 ins aperture and a polarising filter transmitting a Hα band 1·5Å wide. Exposures, 0·05 secs. Note the flare in the second photograph on the left, and the clearly defined boundary between photosphere and chromosphere in the lower photographs on the right.

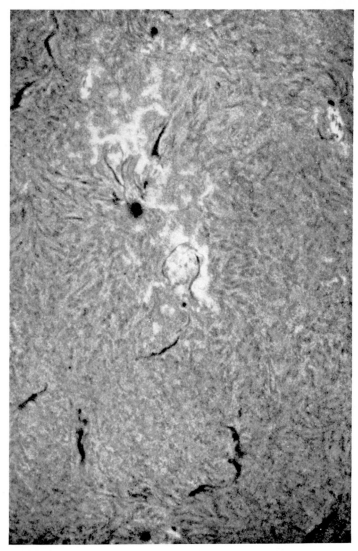

PLATE 113. Spots, flocculi and filaments photographed by Lyot at the Pic du Midi with an equatorial of 4 ins aperture and a polarising filter transmitting a band 0·75Å wide. Exposure, 0·4 secs. (1948 July 27^{d} 8^{h}).

PLATE 114. Plumes of the inner corona photographed by Lyot at the Pic du Midi with a coronagraph and a polarising filter.

Top to bottom: Two simultaneous photographs of the west limb taken with the green and red lines (1941 September 3^d 8^h 10^m).
Green corona at the east limb (1941 September 15^d 11^h 25^m).
Green corona at the west limb (1941 September 14^d 9^h 0^m).

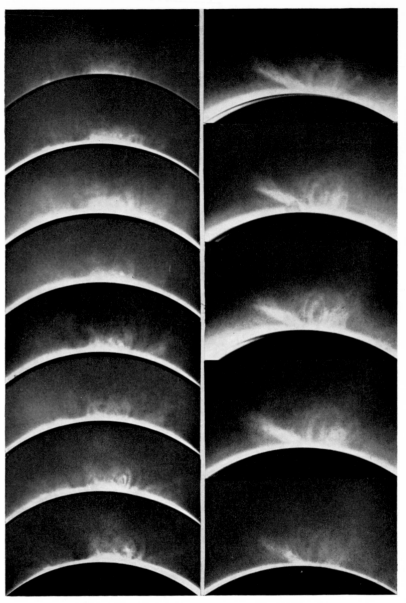

PLATE 115. Changes of the inner corona, photographed by Lyot at the Pic du
Midi with a coronagraph and a polarising filter.

Left (top to bottom): green line at the east limb, 1941 July 30 from $7^h 50^m$
to $17^h 20^m$.

Right (top to bottom): red line at the west limb, 1941 September 2 from
$9^h 15^m$ to $17^h 0^m$.

Calcium has rather a low ionisation potential, and it is interesting to compare the above table with that which follows; the latter refers to atomic hydrogen, with an ionisation potential of 13·5 electron-volts. At the temperatures given in the table the dissociation $H_2 \to 2H$ is complete, so that it is not necessary to consider the molecule.

Percentage Ionisation of Hydrogen

Temperature \ Pressure	1	10^{-1}	10^{-2}	10^{-3}	10^{-4}	10^{-5}
7000°	—	—	—	1	4	12
8000°	—	—	2	5	18	50
9000°	—	2	6	20	63	90
10,000°	2	6	17	49	87	99
12,000°	9	28	68	94		
14,000°	27	65	93			
16,000°	55	90				
18,000°	80	97		complete ionisation		
20,000°	92					

A comparison of the two tables will show that much higher temperatures are required to produce a given percentage ionisation of hydrogen than of calcium, owing to the higher ionisation potential of the former. Caesium, with the lowest potential of any element so far known, would be completely ionised at about 4000° and 10^{-4} atmospheres, while a temperature of about 20,000° at the same pressure would be required to achieve the complete ionisation of helium, which has the highest known ionisation potential (24·4 electron-volts).

These and other consequences of Saha's theory are relevant to the interpretation of the solar spectrum. We have already seen that in the reversing layer and chromosphere the pressures are relatively low and the temperatures between 6000° and 7000°; hence calcium atoms, for example, are found there in both the neutral and ionised states. This explains the simultaneous presence of the 4227Å line of Ca I and the H and K lines of Ca II. With increasing altitude the pressure will drop but the temperature—according to the radiation equilibrium hypothesis and the calculations of Milne—will not fall below 5000°. Under these circumstances the percentage ionisation of calcium must be complete, or almost complete, and hence the highest regions of the chromosphere would be expected to produce none but enhanced lines. It has been established (p. 163) that the H and K lines extend to 9000 miles above the level of the photosphere, while the 4227Å line is visible only to a height of 3000 miles; this can be explained by the fact (predicted by theory) that calcium is completely ionised at altitudes greater than 3000 miles.

The ionisation potentials of strontium (5·7 electron-volts) and barium (5·2 electron-volts) being lower than that of calcium, a given percentage ionisation should be attained at greater pressures for a given temperature, and in the spectrum of the reversing layer the normal lines of these elements do in fact disappear much sooner.

From similar observations it has been possible to evaluate the pressure distribution in the various envelopes of the Sun's atmosphere. Sodium (i.p. 5·1 electron-volts) is completely ionised at pressures below 10^{-3} atmospheres, whence the D lines of the chromospheric spectrum, which are normal lines of the principal series, reach only to about 750 miles. Potassium (i.p. 4·3 electron-volts) should be completely ionised at lower pressures than 10^{-1} atmospheres for a temperature of 7000°, and below 10^{-3} atmospheres at 5000°; hence there will be few neutral sodium atoms in either the chromosphere or the reversing layer. But since the enhanced lines of potassium do not lie in the visible region of the spectrum it would not be observable even if present in considerable quantities. The same may be said of rubidium and caesium, whose ionisation potentials are still lower.

The ionisation potential of magnesium is higher than those of the other alkaline earths, whence the lines of the neutral atom should be visible at relatively high altitudes in the chromosphere, and Mitchell has in fact traced the 3838Å, 3832Å, 3826Å triplet to a height of 4500 miles; at the same time there should be an appreciable density of ionised atoms. On the other hand the 4481Å line reaches only to low altitudes, which at first sight seems anomalous; but Fowler has demonstrated that it belongs to the fundamental series, and however easy its production may be it will nevertheless be more difficult to excite than the enhanced lines of the other series, which lie outside the accessible range.

It also follows from Saha's formula that in the photosphere

molecular hydrogen must be dissociated into atoms. This conclusion seemed to agree well with spectroscopic observations, no
lines of the so-called 'secondary spectrum' of hydrogen having
ever been identified in the solar spectrum. The presence of various
chemical compounds, particularly hydrides, was not considered to
contradict the hypothesis of complete dissociation. Even supposing
the total pressure to be equal to 1 atmosphere, the dissociation of
the H_2 molecule would be complete, not only in the photosphere,
where the temperature is about 5600°, but also in the spots, where
it drops to 4000°.

On the other hand G. Piccardi—using the experimental re-
searches of I. Langmuir on the equilibrium $H_2 \rightleftharpoons 2H$ as his starting
point—has proved that the percentage of molecular hydrogen in
the spots might be anything from 7% to 0·01%, according to the
level involved, and in the reversing layer about 0·8%. In view of
the extraordinary abundance of hydrogen and the enormous
thickness of the solar atmosphere it might be thought that molecular hydrogen should be observable even if present in such
concentrations as these. For a relative abundance of the order of
one thousandth that of hydrogen already represents a very great
abundance on the Sun, greater than that of almost every other
element.

The failure to identify the lines of molecular hydrogen in the
solar spectrum should probably be attributed to the complexity of
the spectrum of bands, often overlapping one another and each
composed of very few lines. In view of these considerations
Piccardi made an accurate examination of the so-called Fulcher
bands of the H_2 molecule, which are of considerable intensity, and
was successful in establishing their probable presence in some
spectrograms of spots taken at the Arcetri solar tower, and also on
the high dispersion spot spectrum map made at Mt Wilson. As
anticipated on the basis of physico-chemical and thermodynamic
considerations, therefore, and in disagreement with the consequences of Saha's theory, the presence of the H_2 molecule appears
to be at least probable, even if not absolutely established.

In view of the important bearing of hydrogen on the composition of stellar atmospheres, H. N. Russell subjected the problem
to a re-examination based on the number and intensities of the
lines identified by Piccardi; he calculated that the relative intensities of the lines of the Balmer series of atomic hydrogen and of
the molecular hydrogen lines are in accordance with the degree of
dissociation derived from thermodynamic considerations. Russell
was also able to show from the intensity of the identified molecular lines that hydrogen, as we shall see (p. 237), must be an even

more abundant constituent of the solar atmosphere, compared with the other elements, than had generally been supposed. The question of molecular hydrogen has also been re-examined from the spectroscopic viewpoint by R. S. Richardson, using spot spectrograms taken at Mt Wilson; his conclusions were in partial agreement with those of Piccardi.

The problem of the identification of the bands is nevertheless extremely difficult, and even the presence of several hundred lines attributable to the secondary spectrum would not in strictness afford a certain demonstration of the presence of the H_2 molecule unless the identification were supported by physico-chemical considerations. When it is further remembered that the bands identified according to the theory are only produced by a high excitation potential it must be acknowledged that the question remains undecided for the time being.

On the other hand, because of the high ionisation potential of the hydrogen atom, its ionisation will in no case be complete. Still less will be that of helium, so that only traces of its enhanced lines are to be found. The absence of the lines of the neutral helium atom from the Fraunhofer spectrum and their presence in that of the reversing layer cannot be deduced from the foregoing considerations; Saha, however, has shown that the lines generally attributed to helium do not belong to the principal series, which lies in the ultraviolet, and will therefore not be absorbed unless a sufficient proportion of the atoms have orbits which exist only under strong excitation.

Thus we see that the theories of ionisation and excitation give satisfactory explanations of the distribution within the solar atmosphere of the various levels producing the different lines of a single element, as well as revealing the temperature and pressure distributions and the composition of the Sun's several atmospheric envelopes.

To arrive at a more exact evaluation of Saha's theory, Russell extended it to the case of mixtures of two or more elements, and found that the relative numbers of ionised and unionised atoms in a mixture of any two gaseous elements is such as to establish a fixed relation between them; this is a function of temperature only, and is independent of pressure, the relative abundance of the two elements, or the presence of other elements. The latter conditions merely affect the degree of ionisation without modifying this proportion. The element with the lower ionisation potential is always the more highly ionised. Russell also considered ionisation states higher than the first, finding that only successive states could be represented at the same time to any considerable extent.

As a result of the theory of ionisation and of what was already known (see p. 159) regarding the distribution and motions of the photosphere and chromosphere, Russell and Stewart were led to envisage the disposition round the solar globe of the chromosphere, reversing layer and photosphere in the following terms.

The chromosphere is a thick stratum situated in the outermost atmospheric envelope, contiguous with the corona; its gases are supported by radiation pressure acting upon their individual atoms. Both the pressure and the density of this stratum increase gradually with decreasing altitude, and gravity begins to assume a more important role than radiation pressure; at its base the pressure may be of the order of 10^{-7} atmospheres. Below this level gravity is the predominant factor in the equilibrium, and the pressure increases rapidly with increasing depth; the temperature, however, remains almost constant in the region of 5000 degrees until the gases are transparent. This is the region known as the reversing layer.

The boundary between the chromosphere and the reversing layer would thus be the level at which single ionisation is practically complete, i.e. the highest level of neutral calcium. As we have seen on p. 154, this corresponds roughly to the level at which the motion of the absorbing vapours around sunspots switch over from efflux to influx, and implies a definite physical state for the chromosphere—the complete ionisation of metallic vapours.

When the pressure reaches 10^{-2} atmospheres the general absorption begins to render the gas opaque. This opacity increases gradually with increasing pressure, and with rather a sudden transition the reversing layer becomes the photosphere; with our means of observation this appears to be completely opaque. As soon as the opacity becomes considerable the temperature rises, in accordance with the theory of radiative equilibrium as developed by Schwarzschild and Eddington. The effective temperature of the photosphere as derived by observation represents a mean value for those layers whose radiation reaches the Earth.

29. Interpretation of the Fraunhofer lines; curve of growth; qualitative analysis of the Sun

We have already seen that the majority of the elements known on Earth have been more or less certainly identified in the solar spectrum. Of the remainder, some have lines so unfavourably situated in the spectrum that we cannot hope to detect them unless the search is pushed into the far ultraviolet or infrared—as has been done in the case of phosphorus, for instance. The spectra of other elements have not been studied carefully enough to permit their certain identification. In the case of some other elements—such as holmium, rhenium, bismuth and radium—the most intense lines occur in accessible regions of the spectrum, yet are absent from the solar spectrum. Probably these elements, if they occur at all in the Sun's atmosphere, are only present in small quantities. Osmium is among the rarest of the rare earths; rhenium likewise is of very rare occurrence on Earth, while radium must, on account of its brief life, be rare everywhere in the universe, so that it cannot be expected that it or any other highly radioactive elements would be found in considerable quantities.

It has already been stated that besides elements in the atomic state, the photosphere and sunspots also contain the hydrides CH, NH, OH, MgH, AlH, SiH, CaH, the oxides AlO, TiO, ZrO, BO, the carbon compounds CN and C_2, silicon fluoride SiF, and probably molecular hydrogen H_2. It is probable that some other of the commoner molecules, such as CO and N_2, occur in the solar atmosphere; but in their normal state they only absorb in the extreme ultraviolet and therefore cannot be identified. It is known that the hydrides are fairly easily dissociated, and their presence is another indication of the great quantities of hydrogen on the Sun. At least one of the constituents of the other compounds so far discovered is known to occur very abundantly on the Sun.

All this tells us something about the qualitative composition of the Sun—or, at any rate, of its outer layers. Interesting work on its quantitative analysis was initiated by Russell and has now arrived at important conclusions.

It must be borne in mind that the Sun has no sharply defined surface. The uppermost regions of its atmosphere tail off imperceptibly into space, as do those of the Earth's atmosphere, but nowhere in its lower layers is a solid surface to be encountered: the gases gradually become more opaque, so that only relatively very thin strata are observable. Stewart, and later Milne, showed that this increasing opacity is caused by the presence of electrons and ions in the gaseous atmosphere. Milne's calculations indicate that the change-over from an extremely low density to opacity occurs within a stratum hardly 20 miles in thickness; this explains the sharp definition of the Sun's limb as seen in even the largest telescopes. The greater part of the absorption producing the Fraunhofer lines occurs in this thin reversing layer, and is produced by incredibly small amounts of the different elements concerned.

More than forty years ago, Lockyer demonstrated by means of direct comparison with a Bunsen flame containing a small quantity of common salt, that the sodium lines in the spectrum of such a flame were more intense than those of the solar spectrum. Modern atomic physics has confirmed this fact, and has furthermore shown how, from the width of an absorption line produced by a rarefied gas, it is possible to calculate the number of atoms taking part in its production for a given unit area of the absorbing layer, irrespective of its thickness.

The width of the more intense solar lines is great enough for their profiles to be measured; this is usually done by means of a microphotometer, which employs a thermopile or photoelectric cell to measure the variations of intensity between the continuous background of a spectrogram and a line, and also across the line itself. In this way the number of atoms spread over a given unit area overlying the photosphere can be determined: it has been found, for example, that for the most intense lines, the H and K lines of Ca II taken together, it amounts to 2×10^{19} atoms per square centimetre; this is equivalent to the number of molecules in a layer of ordinary air some 8 mm thick. In the case of the sodium lines the corresponding number is 900 times smaller, confirming Lockyer's experimental result.

For the thousands of fainter lines the measures would be too uncertain and their significance doubtful, for their widths are influenced by diverse factors, solar, atmospheric and instrumental. The difficulty may however be got round in another way, by utilising modern theories of the origin and formation of spectra.

One may, for example, have two lines of the same multiplet, the intensity of the denser of which is 4 on Rowland's empirical scale and that of the fainter 1; theory tells us that the production of the former would require 40 times as many atoms as that of the latter. Another pair of lines with the same Rowland intensities may indicate a theoretical proportion of 25, another 50, and so on, for it is known that Rowland's estimates are no more than approximate. But since there is a great number of lines to choose from, the mean of them all yields a good determination of the relative number of atoms producing lines of different intensities on Rowland's scale.

In this way Russell, Adams and Moore, of Mt Wilson Observatory, have been able to calibrate Rowland's scale, and with the knowledge of the more intense lines, which have been individually measured, have determined the actual number of atoms whose excitation is necessary to produce a solar line of a given intensity.

It can be calculated that for a line of zero intensity on Rowland's scale (i.e. one barely visible in a spectrum obtained with considerable dispersion) there are 10^{13} active atoms per c.c., equivalent to a layer of gas about $2 \cdot 5 \times 10^{-6}$ mm thick; and, naturally, for still weaker lines correspondingly reduced thicknesses.

It is furthermore possible to estimate how many atoms of each element observed in the Sun's atmosphere are involved in the production of its lines. In estimating the total number, allowance must be made for those atoms which also contribute lines in the invisible regions of the spectrum—the ultraviolet and infrared. This can be done if it is possible to see the important lines which are absorbed in at least one of their energy states, for then the number of atoms at other energy levels can be calculated from thermodynamic theory once the Sun's temperature is known. In this way the numbers of neutral atoms of many elements are deduced.

Accurate measurements of the equivalent widths and profiles of the Fraunhofer lines have, in conjunction with theoretical investigations, led to considerable progress in the interpretation of their origin and of the composition of the Sun. It appears from a vast mass of observations—and particularly from those of Minnaert and his colleagues—that the Sun's spectrum is surprisingly unchanging, indicating a constant temperature; for variations of even a few degrees could be detected by the observational means at our disposal, in the comparisons of lines with different excitation potentials. Variations in the far ultraviolet revealed by certain geophysical observations apparently do not affect the Fraunhofer lines, and it is probable that the ultraviolet radiation originates in the chromosphere. Since it is thus firmly established that the equivalent widths of the lines have fixed, or virtually fixed, values it is possible to make direct comparisons between different observations and to investigate their precision.

Russell, Adams and Moore employed a knowledge of the equivalent widths of lines belonging to multiplets to complete their investigation of the 'curve of growth', which indicates the manner in which the intensity of the lines increases when the concentration of resonating or absorbing atoms is increased. The curve of growth for the solar lines has been gradually established, using ever better material and improved accuracy, by Righini, Menzel, Allen, Minnaert and other investigators; and as a result of their work it is now possible to account in detail for the behaviour of the atoms in the field of the Sun's radiation.

A volume element of the solar atmosphere contains some hundreds of thousands of particles. 'These', in Minnaert's words, 'we have never observed individually; we only hear the ether music emitted by the buzzing swarm, but the refined analysis of these waves reveals each motion, each adventure happening to any single atom. We see before our eyes that there are about 10,000 hydrogen atoms against one metal atom; more uncertain is the abundance of helium, carbon, nitrogen, oxygen, which together perhaps may be put equal to 2000 particles. The metals are for a great part ionised; a few per cent of them are excited. Some free electrons shoot through the swarm, about one to the thousand particles, most of them having been ejected from hydrogen atoms. All are moving quickly by thermal agitation. Moreover there are turbulent motions of the order of 1 km/sec.' The atoms begin to resonate on the arrival of the electromagnetic waves, and these are in consequence deadened, like sound waves in air, though the damping-down is 10 times greater in the case of the Fraunhofer lines than in that of a resonator of the classical type.

Passing on from the consideration of a volume element to that of the solar atmosphere as a whole, it is necessary to investigate the manner in which the interaction of all the unit volumes can explain the Fraunhofer spectrum. At this point the problems of 'transference' in the immense atmospheres of the stars arise, together with the infinitely complicated paths of the radiation and all the accidental encounters and tortuosities which have been simplified by the theoreticians into simple and manageable equations. The whole architecture of the solar atmosphere—its temperature, pressure and ionisation at different levels—and hence that of the other stars, can be studied in detail. According to these investigations a sample of the solar gases should appear markedly bluegreen in colour. This is due to the continuous absorption by some of the negative hydrogen ions, which occur in a proportion of only one to millions of ordinary hydrogen atoms. This gas (H^-), practically unknown on the Earth, was discovered by studying the solar spectrum, and the calculation of its properties rested upon theory only. It is now possible to unravel the relations between temperature and pressure in the successive strata of the Sun, as well as the distribution of its atoms and ions in these strata, and the variation with depth of the damping-down effect and thermal absorption. In the light of these conceptions the 'reversing layer' loses its objective reality: we see the integrated effect of the selective gases to an optical depth of about 2 when we observe the centre of the Sun's disc, and only to 0·5 when observing the limb.

A knowledge of equivalent widths opens the door to the quantitative chemical analysis of the gases at the Sun's surface. If the lines are sufficiently intense and provided with wings the measurement of the equivalent width is an easy matter, but such lines are of relatively rare occurrence in the solar spectrum, the majority having no wings and consisting merely of a nucleus about 0·1Å wide. The determination of the profiles of these weak lines is extremely difficult, even with spectrographs of wide dispersion. Nevertheless the concentration of atoms producing a line can always be deduced from the total energy which it absorbs. The intensity of the continuous spectrum outside the spectral line is taken as unity. If the absorbing atoms are few in number they are able to dispose of all, or nearly all, of the intensity of the continuous spectrum at that particular wavelength. Each atom can absorb independently of the others, and each will absorb the same quantity of energy; hence with low concentrations the total absorption is proportional to the number of absorbing atoms. If the number of atoms increases, practically all the radiation will be absorbed by the nucleus only, through the agency of the Doppler effect, depending on the velocity of the atom. With still further increase in the number of absorbing atoms in the Sun's atmosphere, a very small part of the radiant energy remains available, and hence a given quantity of atoms, which is successively increased in the atmosphere, will produce a considerably lower degree of absorption than that which occurred at the beginning, with the first atoms on the scene. Hence the total absorption increases more slowly. This trend continues until, when the concentration of atoms has increased 10 times, there still remains a 20% increase of the total absorption; in such a case the line is said to be saturated. The process takes still another direction if the concentration of atoms is further increased, when wings begin to appear. When these occupy a spectral interval much greater than that due solely to the Doppler effect, the atoms find more energy available for absorption and hence the total absorption once again increases rapidly with increasing atomic concentration. The curve showing how the total absorption of a spectral line increases with the concentration of the atoms is called a 'curve of growth'. For a given atom the transition probabilities between different levels are different: for example, an atom at the lowest level does not usually show an equal preference for two higher levels. To each line is assigned a number, usually less than unity, which is termed its 'value' or 'f-number', and which indicates this preference. These f-numbers depend solely upon the atomic structure and can be calculated theoretically or determined in the laboratory; they are so defined that the number of absorbing atoms is proportional to the number of atoms multiplied by the f-numbers, which exactly express the probability of the transition corresponding to the line in question. For example, the values of f for the Balmer series, starting with the $H\alpha$ line, are 0·708, 0·125, 0·045, 0·023, 0·012, 0·008. Since all the lines originate from the same level (the second), it can be seen that the number of absorbing atoms Nf falls off rapidly along the series.

Figure 66 shows the curve of growth for the Sun as determined by C. W. Allen at Canberra (Australia). The ordinates express $\log W/\lambda$, where W is the equivalent width of the spectral lines and λ their wavelengths; the abscissae show the quantity $\log X_0$, where X_0 is proportional to Nf.

It is true that the total quantity of a given element is not determined by this means, but only the number of neutral or ionised atoms whose lines it is possible to observe in the spectrum. In the Sun's atmosphere, for instance, the majority of the sodium atoms

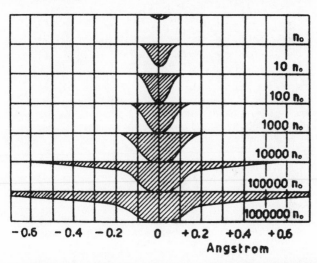

Fig. 65. *Progressive widening of the D_2 sodium line with increasing number of atoms. n_0 represents the minimum concentration (Waldmeier).*

are ionised, and the lines of these are unobservable since situated in the ultraviolet. Saha's formula, as we have seen, relates the percentage of ionised to neutral atoms with the number of free electrons and the temperature. When the spectrum contains as many lines of neutral as of ionised atoms—as is the case with solar calcium, for example—Saha's formula allows the calculation not only of the number of free electrons but also the amount of the ionised element. Thus is derived the total quantity of the element from the analysis of the observable spectral lines.

By this method it is possible to establish the quantity of a large number of elements in the solar atmosphere, though only of the metals; for the lighter elements, so important on the Sun, the method is not applicable. The results of a recent analysis by D. H. Menzel and his collaborators at Harvard, so far as the more abundant elements are concerned, are summarised below.

Quantities of the Elements in the Sun's Atmosphere

Element	Percentage (by volume)	Mass (milligrams per cm²)
H	81·76	1200
He	18·17	1000
C	0·003	0·5
N	0·01	2
O	0·03	10
Na	0·0003	0·1
Mg	0·02	10
Al	0·0002	0·1
Si	0·006	3
S	0·003	1
K	0·00001	0·003
Ca	0·0003	0·2
Ti	0·000003	0·003
V	0·000001	0·001
Cr	0·000006	0·005
Mn	0·00001	0·01
Fe	0·0008	0·6
Co	0·000004	0·004
Ni	0·0002	0·2
Cu	0·000002	0·002
Zn	0·00003	0·03

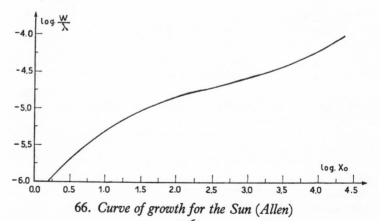

66. *Curve of growth for the Sun (Allen)*

The second column gives the percentage quantity in terms of the number of atoms contained in a column of atmosphere vertical to the photosphere, whose cross section measures 1 sq. cm.

Since the Sun is a gaseous sphere the atoms are in constant movement from one region to another: at one time an atom will be in the outermost layers and at another in one of the lower, so that the solar material is in a constant state of agitation and mixing. But this mixing occurs slowly, by diffusion, and in any case one must suppose that the heavy atoms are more abundant at the centre of the Sun. Convection currents nevertheless exist, similar to those encountered on Earth: these can be observed at the Sun's surface, while those at deeper levels are deduced from theroretical considerations.

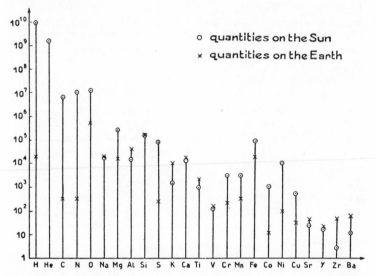

Fig. 67. Comparative quantities of the elements on the Sun and on the Earth (Menzel).

The quantities of the light elements are more difficult to determine and are correspondingly less certain. Nevertheless the investigations of various workers—e.g. B. Strömgren, P. ten Bruggencate, J. Houtgast, Menzel, Unsöld—indicate that the three light elements Li, Be and B are very rare on the Sun, while H, He, C, N and O are very abundant, particularly hydrogen. It appears that about 80% of the atoms of the Sun's atmosphere are hydrogen, which explains why the lines of hydrogen are visible over a wide temperature range in the spectra of stellar atmospheres.

It will be noticed that despite the great intensity of the lines of ionised calcium the abundance of this element is certainly not remarkable, compared with other elements. This is explained by the fact that the H and K lines originate in the lowest energy level, at which most of the atoms exist. In consequence, nearly all the atoms of ionised calcium contribute to the absorption of these lines. Similar very intense lines of magnesium have, as already stated, been photographed recently in the ultraviolet region from above the Earth's ozone layer.

It is interesting to compare these results of the quantitative analysis of the Sun's atmosphere with that of the Earth's. In Figure 67 the symbol ⊙ indicates the relative solar quantities of the various elements on an arbitrary scale, and × the corresponding terrestrial quantities. These should be understood to represent the number of atoms, and not the total weight of the material. The solar quantities are taken from the work of Minnaert, Hunaerts and Unsöld; the terrestrial values from that of Washington and Clarke, and refer to the Earth's crust.

It can be seen from this Figure that whilst the lighter elements—and especially hydrogen and helium—are much more abundant on the Sun than on the Earth, the percentage distributions of the metals (e.g. calcium, iron, titanium, nickel) on the two bodies are roughly the same. The quantity of helium is admittedly very uncertain since its value is extremely sensitive to small errors in temperature. Leaving helium out of account, one can say that the Sun's atmosphere is composed essentially of pure hydrogen. This, however, is not spectroscopically pure hydrogen, for there are sufficient though minute quantities of the other elements to produce the Fraunhofer lines as well as those of hydrogen in the solar spectrum.

The presence of various molecules in the Sun's atmosphere remains to be considered. Russell has attempted the quantitative analysis of its molecular composition, and his results, so far as the principal molecules whose bands are visible in the spectrum are concerned, are as follows:

Molecule	Mass (gms per sq. metre of photosphere)
CN	0·004
C_2	0·00005
CH	0·0012
NH	0·0002
OH	0·0015
BO	0·00006

It will be seen how much less abundant are these chemical compounds than the free atoms of the elements; the total mass of the most numerous molecules in the Sun's atmosphere is 7×10^{-7} gms/cm², whereas that of the atoms amounts to 10^{-2} gms/cm².

30. PHYSICAL CONDITIONS IN THE CHROMOSPHERE

The composition of the chromosphere, the distribution of the elements within it, and its equilibrium under the action of the different forces that must there be operative, have given the theoretical astrophysicists much to think about. It might reasonably be supposed that above the reversing layer—where the most turbulent regions, with their ascending and descending currents, come to an end—the elements would arrange themselves in strata according to their atomic weights, as has happened to a large extent in our own atmosphere. But the presence of calcium at considerably greater altitudes than hydrogen, whose atomic weight is much smaller, suggests that at the chromospheric level there must be forces other than that of gravity, and that these must act differentially upon the various elements present.

Milne, who devoted much thought to this subject, worked out an interesting theory which seems to give the most satisfactory explanation of the observational facts. The non-gravitational force is the pressure that light exerts upon any body absorbing or reflecting it. When an atom absorbs a given radiation it also absorbs the momentum that the radiation possessed on leaving the Sun's surface, so that it receives a slight outward-directed push. In this way the atoms of the chromosphere remain suspended at a certain level above the Sun's surface, sinking a little and then rising again under the influence of radiation pressure, like scraps of paper floating in the air and occasionally sent aloft by wind eddies. Of all atoms, those most likely to be found floating in the chromosphere are naturally those most capable of absorbing large quantities of radiation in comparison with their weight.

Let us consider a particular atom in the solar atmosphere, and a particular frequency which it is capable of absorbing or emitting. The Fraunhofer spectrum will contain an absorption line of this frequency, and the line will have a certain residual intensity.

The atom will be subject to the downward-directed force of gravity and also to radiation pressure acting in the opposite direction; the latter will be proportional to the residual intensity of the line. If the radiation pressure is weaker than gravity, equilibrium will be maintained by the pressure gradient of the gas, which increases towards the interior. If, therefore, the force of radiation pressure is greater than that of gravity the atom will be driven upwards. The process of expulsion will continue until a state of equilibrium is attained, with the atom suspended at a great altitude by the balanced forces of radiation pressure and gravity; the density will here be so low that the occurrence of collisions, and therefore the pressure of the gas, will be negligible.

There is reason to believe that the highest gases observed in the flash spectrum during eclipses are in equilibrium of this sort, and that what we term the chromosphere is simply an atomic atmosphere completely, or almost completely, supported by radiation pressure. In the stable state such an atmosphere will be in radiative equilibrium, but since the radiation is restricted to the spectral lines of the gases composing it, Milne considered the ideal case of a gas which radiates and absorbs a single frequency. The radiative equilibrium is then monochromatic, and the theory applies only to the intensity in the frequency of this radiation.

The case of the solar H and K lines of Ca II is particularly interesting. The excitation orbit of the ionised calcium atom is only slightly larger than the normal orbit, so that the electron is able to move between these two orbits without running much risk of relapsing spontaneously. With other elements, on the other hand, the first available orbit is relatively much larger, and the energy required to reach it is not much less than that required for the electron to escape altogether. In the case of these elements, therefore, it is not easy to maintain a continuous source of light capable of inducing orbital transitions without the loss of the electron.

It is the great difference between the energy of excitation and the energy of ionisation of the calcium atom that enables it to exist at high levels in the Sun's atmosphere. The mean time required by the electron to pass from one orbit to the other is one twenty-thousandth of a second, and according to Milne's calculations it remains in the outer orbit for a mean interval of one hundred-millionth of a second before relapsing spontaneously towards the nucleus. During this short time the electron makes something like a million revolutions of the nucleus in the outer orbit.

The excitation of the ionised calcium atom occurs with the particular wavelengths corresponding to the lines of the Fraunhofer spectrum denoted by the letters H and K. These lines are not completely dark, but have a certain residual intensity sufficient to maintain the ionised calcium atoms in suspension despite the Sun's gravity: as soon as the outward flow of light is weakened to a level at which it can no longer support the atoms it emerges into space with this limiting intensity. The measurement of this residual in-

PLATE 116. The Arosa station of the Zurich Observatory (6730 feet above sea level).

PLATE 117. The solar station of the Harvard and Colorado Universities at Climax, Colorado (11,480 feet above sea level).

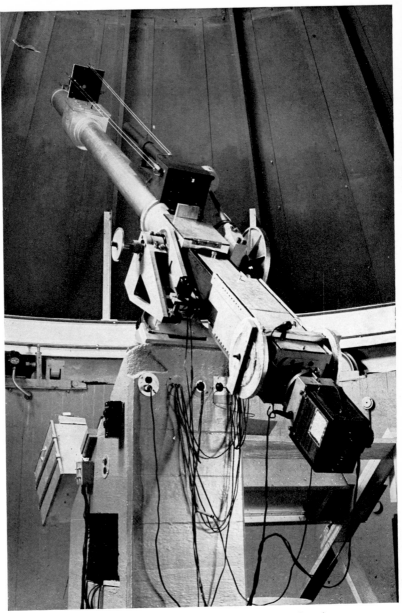

PLATE 118. The coronagraph at Climax, Colorado.

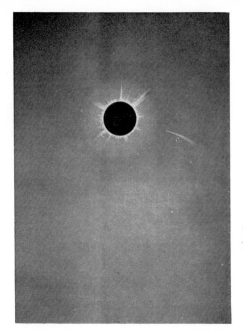

PLATE 119. Drawing of the solar corona made by P. Tacchini in Egypt during the eclipse of 1882 May 17.

PLATE 120. The corona of 1932 August 31. Equatorial type (W. H. Wright, Lick Observatory expedition).

PLATE 121. Station of the Italian expedition for observing the eclipse of 1936 June 19 at Sara (Orenburg district, U.S.S.R.).

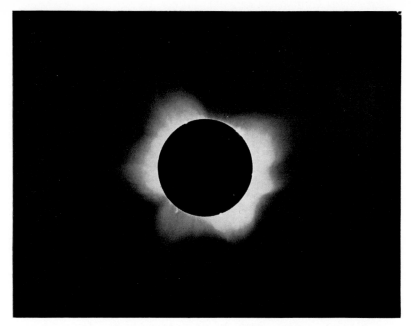

PLATE 122. The corona of 1936 June 19. Intermediate type. (Italian expedition to Sara, U.S.S.R.)

PLATE 123. Drawing of the corona of 1936 June 19 (L. Taffara, Italian expedition to Sara, U.S.S.R.). From the different pictures taken during the eclipse all the details of the inner and outer corona were revealed, variable intensity not being taken into account.

PLATE 124. The corona of 1937 June 8 photographed at Canton Island (Pacific Ocean) by the expedition of the National Geographic Society and the U.S. Navy. Exposure, 14 secs.

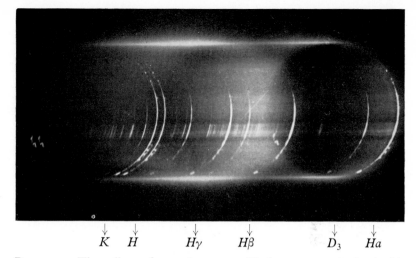

$\underset{K}{\downarrow}$ $\underset{H}{\downarrow}$ $\underset{H\gamma}{\downarrow}$ $\underset{H\beta}{\downarrow}$ $\underset{D_3}{\downarrow}$ $\underset{Ha}{\downarrow}$

PLATE 125. The eclipse of 1914 August 21. Flash spectrum obtained with an objective prism by the Italian expedition to Theodosia (Crimea) towards the end of totality. The continuous spectrum of the corona can be seen at top and bottom.

North

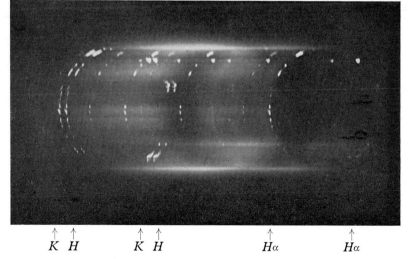

st

$\underset{K}{\uparrow}$ $\underset{H}{\uparrow}$ $\underset{K}{\uparrow}$ $\underset{H}{\uparrow}$ $\underset{H\alpha}{\uparrow}$ $\underset{H\alpha}{\uparrow}$

PLATE 126. The eclipse of 1926 January 14. Spectrum of the chromosphere and prominences obtained with an objective prism by the Italian expedition to Italian Somaliland; beginning of totality.

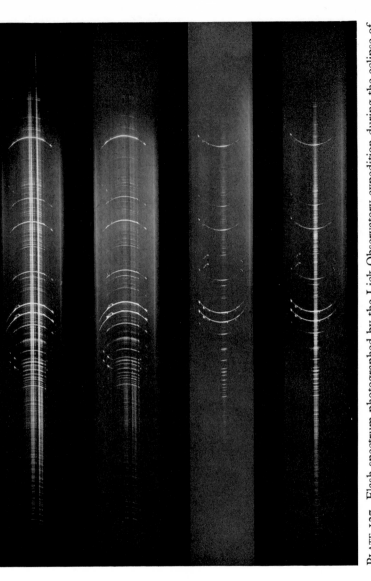

PLATE 127. Flash spectrum photographed by the Lick Observatory expedition during the eclipse of 1932 August 31 at Fryeburg, Maine (U.S.A.).

tensity has permitted the calculation of the constants of the calcium atom and of the atom's mean length of life in the excited state.

The equilibrium of the chromosphere has been shown by the work of Milne and others to be extremely delicate, and the smallest departure from the precise conditions of equilibrium can have catastrophic results. Such unstable conditions can, on the one hand, lead to a slow collapse of the atmosphere into the Sun— exemplified by the descending currents observed by St John for all the lines of the upper chromosphere (p. 165); on the other hand, to counterbalance these currents, we have local disturbances in which the gases are being expelled at high velocities. These manifest themselves as the flocculi and prominences which are continuously being formed in the upper layers of the solar atmosphere.

R. Wildt, searching for a theoretical interpretation of the altitudes of the chromospheric lines measured during various eclipses, noted that the density gradient of hydrogen in the chromosphere was exponential up to an altitude of 10,000 miles. The same gradient was also revealed by comparing the electronic density at the base of the chromosphere with that at a height of 10,000 miles, as derived by Baumbach from the absolute intensity of the continuous spectrum of the solar corona: for almost all the free electrons are produced by the ionisation of hydrogen, which, as we have seen, is the predominant element in the solar atmosphere.

The relative quantities of Na, Mg, Al, Ca, Fe, Cu and Sr in the chromosphere derived for the above-mentioned altitudes and transition probabilities, are in agreement with those deduced from the Fraunhofer spectrum. An acceptable theory of the equilibrium of the chromosphere is still awaited, but in the meantime it is interesting to note that at the eclipse of 1940, R. O. Redman found that the line-of-sight velocities of the atoms were confined between 8·5 miles/second for hydrogen, and 1·0 miles/second for lanthanum.

The distribution of velocities in relation to atomic weight, and also the profile of the hydrogen lines, suggest that the kinetic temperature of the chromosphere is of the order of 35,000 degrees; this is also confirmed by Wildt on the basis of the density gradient of hydrogen. The fact that the density gradients of the metals up to about 1200 miles are some five times greater than that of hydrogen argues against the existence of any chromospheric turbulence other than thermal motions, i.e. motions affecting all atoms equally, and independently of atomic weight. In the chromosphere underlying the corona—where, as we have seen, the kinetic temperature must be extremely high—indications of a high temperature in a more or less isothermal atmosphere are already beginning to be detected. Such a temperature must not, however, be confused with the excitation temperature of the lines; the relative intensities of the chromospheric lines in fact correspond to an excitation temperature of 4600 degrees, i.e. the intensities of the lines are appropriate to the excitation that would be experienced in a region which is in thermodynamic equilibrium at this temperature. The width of the profiles associated with real velocities of the particles argues against a temperature of the order of 35,000 degrees.

Another consequence of the particular distribution of the elements in the chromosphere is the appearance of the Sun's limb. According to the formulae of hydrostatic equilibrium the intensity of the solar disc decreases from 1 to 0 for a difference of level of about 370 miles; in fact, however, this brightness difference occurs in about 1250 miles, corresponding to about 2".5. The solar limb is thus not sharply defined—as has been proved by Lyot's photographs of the chromosphere taken without an eclipse, and by B. Lindblad's observations during the 1945 eclipse—but fades gradually over a distance of about 1200 miles.

Although the phenomena of the chromosphere are but little understood, according to Van de Hulst it may be accepted that below 2500 miles the hydrogen is in a neutral state and its ionisation, dependent upon collisions or on radiation, follows the law formulated in Saha's equation. Above the 4000-mile level hydrogen is strongly ionised. Its free electrons determine a flow of heat downward from the corona with a consequent considerable temperature gradient in its lower layers.

31. SUMMARY OF THEORIES OF THE SUN'S CONSTITUTION

From the account so far given in this book of the extremely complex observations of the Sun it will be guessed that, notwithstanding the richness of the available material, there are numerous difficulties in the way of explaining them in terms of a general theory. When it is remembered that the observed phenomena belong only to the relatively shallow layers external to the Sun's surface, and that its interior is quite inaccessible to observation, it will be understood that the many theories that have been proposed at different times are not of a sort capable of giving a complete picture of the Sun's mechanism.

The suggestion that the Sun has a solid or liquid core, made by the older theories, is difficult to reconcile with the observed value of the Sun's mean density, which is only one quarter of the Earth's, and since the time of Secchi and Lockyer it has been realised and repeatedly confirmed that the Sun is a wholly gaseous globe.

But the Sun's visible surface phenomena are: an equatorial acceleration of the various strata, the existence of spots, eruptions, flocculi and prominences, and their periodic variation. Many theories have been proposed to account for these phenomena, but it has to be admitted that so far none has proved to be satisfactory or complete. Here we shall briefly outline the fundamentals of some of them.

According to Wilsing the Sun's equatorial acceleration springs from the fact that it is in a transitional stage between a nebula and a solid globe. Its rotation would tend towards uniformity, which would finally be achieved when the relative motions of its different parts had been unified through the action of internal friction. It is probable that they have already been ironed out in the Sun's interior though they still persist in or near its surface. However, their disappearance is a slow process, requiring very long epochs for its completion, and for this reason they would appear to be constant over relatively short periods of a century or two.

Wilsing further sought a reason for the periodicity of the Sun's activity in the supposition that the operation of existing laws in a rotating system would produce displacements of mass as a result of the gradual cooling and for other reasons. These would produce a shift in the axis of symmetry, which in consequence would no longer coincide with the present axis of rotation, as is necessary for the maintenance of rotation about a constant axis. Fluid material would then be forced to smooth out this rotational disturbance and bring the two axes back into coincidence. The realisation of this new equilibrium will, however, be retarded by the internal friction of the fluid and gaseous material, and the disturbance may grow to considerable proportions. But only when it has reached a sufficient size to overcome the resistance of friction will equilibrium be restored through a shift of mass. The periodicity of this process is suggested as underlying the 11-year cycle. In this way, also, an explanation might be found of the relatively rapid increase of spot frequency during the early stages of the rise of solar activity.

A great advance in our theoretical understanding of the Sun's constitution was achieved by Emden, whose hydrodynamic investigations of gaseous spheres are directly applicable to the solar globe.

Material at the Sun's surface emits heat, becomes denser, and consequently must sink towards the interior. If the Sun were not in rotation, then, for the supposed equilibrium state these masses would sink to the Sun's centre where they would displace an equal quantity of material which would then replace them at the solar surface. This formation of currents is completely altered by the rotation of the Sun. For reasons of symmetry, the surfaces of equal pressure are surfaces of rotation; the forces of pressure intersect the Sun's axis, and the sinking masses which have become cooler must maintain their rotational momentum.

As they approach the solar axis these gaseous masses will rotate ever more quickly, maintaining their internal heat, while the outgoing material will conserve its smaller rotational momentum and lag ever further behind.

It is thus clear that we are concerned with masses of gas, of differing densities and rotational velocities, which may give rise to successive and well defined surfaces of discontinuity. Emden attributes to these surfaces the conditions for the formation of very extensive waves. These will increase progressively in a direction parallel to the Sun's axis, and their accelerating motion will break them up with the formation of a vast vortex in which will be established the equilibrium of the rotational momenta and energies of the different strata. This mixing process is discussed by Emden, who concludes that the supposed surfaces of discontinuity must be such that as we pass over them we move towards the exterior of the Sun and at the same time recede from its axis.

The consequences to be drawn from this theory are in agreement with some of the facts of observation. The angular velocities of the equatorial regions must be greater than those of the polar. In fact, if the Sun were not rotating, the convection currents could be generated freely, and would mix the material at all depths; the Sun would thus grow cooler, as was supposed to be the case by the older solar theories.

The rotation has no effect on those currents which move along the axis towards or away from the poles. But the nearer the equator is approached, the more the formation of convection currents is obstructed by that of the Emden surfaces, and the less deeply these currents penetrate the body of the Sun. They can only form inside each individual stratum between two consecutive surfaces of discontinuity. Thermal losses will consequently be more difficult to recover at the equator than at the poles, and the Sun's surface should be hotter in the polar than in the equatorial regions. The fact that the chromosphere is characteristically deeper at the poles than at the equator (p. 121) may be an observational confirmation of this conclusion.

Similar considerations may serve to explain the differing angular velocities observed at the equator and the poles. The outer layers of the Sun contract through cooling, and their angular velocity increases, so that they gain ground over the underlying layers. The convection currents, which in the polar regions reach undisturbed to greater depths, bring about an equalisation of the angular velocities. But the nearer the equator is approached, the more rapidly the currents will be damped down by the surfaces of discontinuity, and the more slowly will the increasing angular velocities of the exterior be transferred to the interior, owing to the continuous new formation and revolution of these surfaces. Thus the angular velocity of the Sun's surface layers should be greater in equatorial than in polar regions.

The formation of spots may also, according to Emden's theory, be explained in terms of the mutual frictions between the solar strata. We have seen that between two contiguous layers vortical waves are generated, the direction of whose rotation is the same as that of the Sun. These, like the cyclones in our own atmosphere, produce a reduction of pressure and a suction effect in the direction of the axis. The initial causes of the spots may be none other than these small local vortices, and hence there will be a depression in the photosphere when they are formed near the surface.

The photospheric material drawn downward by the rotation tends to sink into this depression, giving rise to an irregular crater. The more central gaseous masses taking the place of those sucked into the spot generate prominences and faculae in the spot's vicinity. If the vortices form near the surface, the directions of the rotary motions of spots in the two hemispheres will be opposite to one another.

The shape of the surfaces of discontinuity shows that in the vicinity of the equator there must be a zone in which spots cannot be formed; only exceptionally can such a surface be asymmetrical and thus give rise to a spot in this region. In the neighbourhood of the poles the surfaces of discontinuity can moreover only be formed with difficulty, and only at great depths are the differences in linear velocity such as can produce vortices. Sunspot formation will therefore not occur in the equatorial or polar regions, but will be limited to median latitudes, as is in fact observed to be the case.

It must however be recorded that this theory of Emden gives no account of the formation of bipolar spots which, as we have seen, are the most frequently occurring feature of the 11-year cycle. Regarding the appearance of spots in high latitudes after a minimum of solar activity, and their subsequent drift towards the equator, it may be supposed that during the minimum the surface layers are cooled to a greater degree before sinking towards the centre, and that the internal currents no longer contribute so effectively to the re-establishment of thermal equilibrium.

For the same reason—the comparatively undisturbed condition of the solar material—the surfaces of discontinuity are more easily able to be formed at great depths and in high latitudes. The spots then have a greater tendency to occur in these regions, but as the solar activity increases so the unstable equilibrium of the cooling surface material will be more rapidly upset, and the less strongly heated material should in consequence sink more rapidly, giving rise to stratification and the formation of spots in ever lower latitudes.

Emden's theory, like many others, ignores the magnetic fields in sunspots and the other phenomena connected with this discovery. These have created an entirely new situation as regards the formation of the spots and the constitution of the Sun generally.

As has already been pointed out (p. 186), it is the hydrodynamic hypothesis that gives the most satisfactory explanation of the motions and currents that develop in disturbed regions of the solar surface. A notable attempt to apply hydrodynamic and thermodynamic principles by terrestrial analogy has recently been made by W. Bjerknes to explain the circulating system which must be seated in the upper layers of a gaseous sphere such as the Sun, the formation of spots, their lower temperatures, their periodicity, bipolar structure, etc. The attempt is doubly noteworthy in that the great majority of the observed phenomena are covered by a relatively simple theoretical picture whose development inspires belief in its outstanding importance to solar physical research.

Since the origin of the solar phenomena is the Sun's radiation, it follows that the light and heat radiation will be responsible for the dynamics of its interior, and also for the eventual emission of electrically charged particles.

Since the upper layers of the photosphere are subject to cooling the conditions of equilibrium will be upset. The heat thus lost by the photosphere is made good through the agency of internal radiation, and by convection and conduction from the underlying layers. Internal radiation is probably the dominating factor, especially in the deep layers of very high temperature. But a sufficient percentage remains to produce powerful convection currents, whose importance increases in the vicinity of the surface where, because of the lowered temperature, the internal radiation is relatively less important. The Sun's rotation tends to distribute the various phenomena in a generally symmetrical manner about the rotational axis.

While Bjerknes evolved no theory to account for the magnetic fields in sunspots, he assumes that the spots themselves are vortices and that these fields are linked with the vortical motion in such a manner that the magnetic polarity switches over when the direction of the motion is reversed. He compares the spots with tropical cyclones on the Earth, and thus demonstrates that when the vortical motion involves horizontal currents whose intensity increases upward, there must be a nucleus of cooled gas at the centre of the vortex. The vortex will in fact produce a suction effect and cause the gaseous masses to rise upward, cooling adiabatically in the process.

Bjerknes derived a formula for the temperature gradient from the centre of the vortex to the exterior, as a function of the increase of angular velocity of the current with height, and the angular velocity of the vortex at its surface. Applying this formula to the case of a sunspot—regarded as a vortex at the photospheric surface —it may be conceded that the vortex will reach some distance below the surface and that the vortical velocity, starting from zero at this depth, will increase linearly with increasing altitude. It follows from the formula that the temperature drop is proportional to the depression formed in the photospheric surface, and it is found that a vortical depression amounting to only one-tenth of the thickness of the stratum will be sufficient to cause a temperature drop of 1100 degrees; and the larger the depression, the greater the fall in temperature.

The velocities required to produce a given depression are found to be of the same order as those observed, and which are possible under the conditions existing on the Sun: in fact, in the case of a vortex whose diameter is ten times its depth, the velocity required to produce a depression of one-tenth is 3·4 miles per second at a distance of 6200 miles from the centre of the vortex, and 11·0 miles per second at a distance of 62,000 miles. With increasing temperature drops the velocities increase.

The theory of vortices thus provides a simple explanation of the increased absorption in the umbrae and penumbrae of spots. Under the intense flood of radiation coming from lower levels the cooled masses forming at any moment the core of the vortex will be unable to maintain their low temperature unless, whilst becoming heated, they are also replaced by new material sucked up from below, which will flow radially outwards over the photospheric surface. This process will continue until there is sufficient energy available to produce the suction effect. During the movement towards the exterior the circulation around the centre of the spot will diminish rapidly and the radial component will become dominant.

At the level of the reversing layer the outward radial motion produces a subsidence, with a corresponding radial flow inwards at the highest levels. Owing to the Sun's rotation this flow will assume a spiral form, and this may explain the particular appearance of the hydrogen and calcium in spectroheliograms.

Since this spiral form is dictated by the direction of the Sun's rotation and not by that of the underlying photospheric vortex, the direction of these spiral structures will not change when the magnetic polarity changes at the onset of a new solar cycle.

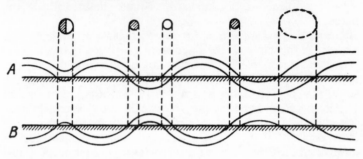

Fig. 68. Formation of sunspots, according to Bjerknes' hypothesis.

If each spot constituted an individual vortex, the appearance of bipolar spots would be a matter of accident: to explain the frequent occurrence of these systems Hale had already suggested that they must be formed of a type of ring, the two spots representing its intersection by the photosphere. Half the ring belongs to the chromosphere, while the other half, dynamically the more important, forms a link between the spots below the level of the photosphere. Bjerknes developed this idea, and put forward the suggestion that all spots may belong to a single zonal vortex surrounding the Sun and lying approximately parallel to the equator; this is supposed to give rise to a spot wherever it passes from the photosphere into the reversing layer, or vice versa. This hypothesis can be expressed in two different ways: the zonal vortex may be regarded as belonging almost wholly to the solar atmosphere, and occasionally plunging below the photosphere from one spot to the other of a bipolar system; or, conversely, as lying almost wholly below the photosphere and occasionally rising into the atmosphere from spot to spot of a bipolar system.

The idea of a zonal vortex has the advantage of explaining at once the most notable features observed in the spots:

(*a*) the spots of a single cycle appear within a limited latitude zone, and are generally of the bipolar type;

(*b*) the axis of each bipolar system tends to be parallel to the equator;

248

(c) the majority of bipolar systems belonging to the same cycle show the same succession of polarities;

(d) groups at their first appearance are frequently bipolar;

(e) a single spot usually represents the final stage of a bipolar group, in which one component has broken up and disappeared before the other;

(f) the companion of a single spot appears behind (i.e. following) it if the polarity of the original spot is that of the particular cycle in question, and ahead of (i.e. preceding) it in the opposite circumstances.

This theory also has the advantage of reducing the progress of the spot phenomena, from higher to lower latitudes, to the periodic motion of the whole zonal vortex, while the reversal of polarities from cycle to cycle can be explained by a reversal of the rotation of the zonal vortex. An occurrence of this sort might come about if there existed on the Sun a general circulation from the poles to the equator at photospheric level; this would appear to be plausible if strata of different densities already existed in the Sun's interior. The simplest example of stratified circulation is that shown in Figure 69; here it is supposed that the circulation in the uppermost stratum takes place from the poles to the equator close to the surface, and from the equator towards the poles at its lower levels; the next lower stratum would then circulate from the equator to the poles in its upper regions, and from the poles to the equator in its lower; and so on.

Bjerknes points out that such a circulation is thermodynamically possible, since the motive force is furnished by radiative cooling of the photosphere, by heating in the lower layers due to radiation from the interior, and by contact with the first internal stratum. The photosphere may be thought of as functioning like a heat engine.

On the Earth the currents flow from the equator to the poles at the upper levels and from the poles to the equator at the lower, the principal source of heat being located at ground level along the equator. On the Sun, it is difficult to foresee what the direction of the circulation will be, but once it has started it will continue in the same direction. Assuming that the circulation in the upper levels of the photosphere takes place from the poles to the equator, and in the next lower stratum from the equator to the poles, it can at once be deduced what effect the Sun's rotation will have on it.

The great internal bulk of the Sun on both sides of the equatorial plane and around the axis of rotation (the shaded area in Figure 69) will evidently take little part in the general circulation and will move almost as a rigid body. The masses participating in the circulation, on the other hand, will obey the same law that we find operating on Earth, and hence those moving from the poles towards the equator will lag behind, whilst those moving in the opposite direction will gain ground on the rigid or virtually rigid core. Of the strata involved in the circulation, therefore, the uppermost should according to this hypothesis move with increasing retardation from the equator to the poles, thus providing an explanation of the equatorial acceleration—which, however, should more properly be called the high-latitude retardation.

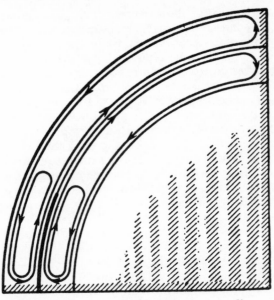

Fig. 69. Circulation in the solar hemispheres, according to Bjerknes' hypothesis.

During its slow movement from the poles towards the equator the material forming the surface of the photosphere must gradually cool. The temperature of the Sun should therefore be maximal at the poles and minimal at the equator. Such differences of temperature must be relatively small, but the possibility of greater differences cannot be ruled out—if, for example, the Sun's internal stability were increased, so that the depth of the vortices and of the individual strata participating in the circulation were to diminish. It will be remembered that Emden's theory also led to the conclusion that the Sun is hottest at its poles.

To sum up, the sunspots would appear to depend upon intense

local circulations, and the equatorial acceleration upon a slow general circulation. It remains to be seen whether the two hypotheses can be combined in such a way as to explain the occurrence of spots in mid-latitudes and their characteristic periodicity. In this connexion it should be noted that the greatest temperature differences will occur on either side of the equator, where the cooled photospheric material (which has been radiating steadily ever since it left the poles) descends and encounters the hot ascending material of the circulating stratum immediately beneath.

This state of affairs sets up favourable conditions, both because of the concentration of the general circulation in low latitudes (as indicated by the curves in Figure 69) and also because of the formation of other vortical zonal rings producing spots. If these rings survive for a reasonable length of time they may be set in rotation by the general circulation in low latitudes, and the polarity reversal with each new cycle may be explained by assuming the existence of two zonal vortices, with opposed directions of rotation, which are carried along by the general circulation (Figure 70).

If the circulation from the poles to the equator occupies several years—as, according to this hypothesis, it may well do—then a period of 22 years for the complete revolution of the zonal vortices is reasonable.

This mechanism—which, as Bjerknes points out, is dynamically and thermodynamically plausible, and will be more satisfactorily treated in a more fully developed theory—is in good agreement with the facts of observation: the spots of a new cycle, with reversed rotations and polarities, will make their appearance in high latitudes, while those of the old are making their final exit in the vicinity of the equator.

When the zonal vortex dives below the surface and disappears from sight at the equator, the only remaining spots will be those of the new cycle, which thereafter will attain its full development. The vortex of the latter having in its turn reached equatorial regions, the former will reappear in high latitudes to produce the reversed-polarity spots of the new cycle, and so on.

We have also seen (p. 140) that the latitude drift of the spots is not the only indication of the presence of general circulatory currents in the external atmosphere of the Sun, but that the filament-prominences and the corona likewise exhibit periodic displacements away from and towards the poles. It is reasonable to suppose that at the onset of a new 11-year cycle the Sun's internal disturbance seeks to break through the surface in about latitude $\pm 40°$. That section of the circulatory movement which, according to

Bjerknes' hypothesis, begins to ascend in lower latitudes, succeeds in producing spots whose size and activity are greater in medium latitudes. Possibly because of reduced energy in the circulating material, the section which rises in the polar regions does not succeed in producing spots, but only eruptions of gas which are visible as filament-prominences.

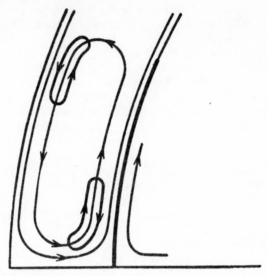

Fig. 70. *Formation of zonal vortices with opposed directions of rotation (Bjerknes).*

Unsöld, modifying the hypothesis of Bjerknes, returned to the idea originally put forward by Hale that the spots are formed from small U-shaped vortices detached from the main vortex, somewhat resembling a single vortex cut in half by the solar surface. The open ends of the U-vortex behave like rotary pumps, cooling the gas by expansion and producing spots of opposite polarity. Unsöld showed that such vortices would be more stable than those of Bjerknes' type, which would manifest themselves in forms different from those actually observed.

New theories, based to a greater extent on the presence of magnetic fields, have been developed by H. Alfvén and C. Walén. According to these Swedish astrophysicists, the intense magnetic fields in sunspots cannot be generated by high-level vortices, and hence one must rather suppose that the spot results from the magnetic field of the solar atmosphere. Since the magnetic fields of the spots could not be produced near the solar surface it is supposed that their origin must be sought near the Sun's centre, whence they are transmitted towards the exterior along the lines of force of the Sun's general magnetic field in the form of a new type of wave, which has come to be known as a 'magneto-hydrodynamic wave'. This wave, according to Alfvén and Walén, is propagated at a velocity of the order of 1 metre per second; in about forty years it

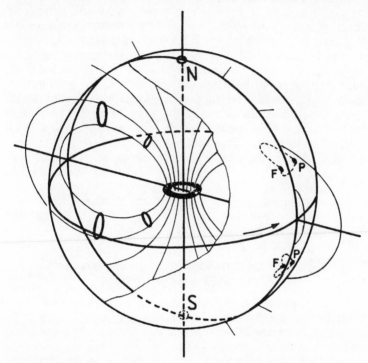

Fig. 71. *The Sun's internal circulation, according to Walén's hypothesis.*

would therefore reach the Sun's surface, where it would produce strong magnetic fields. The wavefront cuts the solar surface in high north and south latitudes, and then gradually closes on the equator—as is observed. The velocity of the spot zone is in good enough quantitative agreement with the theoretical velocity of this wavefront. The theory shows that if the magneto-hydrodynamic waves are generated by hydrodynamic vortices in the equatorial plane near the Sun's centre, the characteristic magnetic polarities observed in the spots can be explained. In order to do this, the theory assumes that the Sun's magnetic field resembles that produced by a circular current in the equatorial plane, not very far from the centre. The lines of magnetic force through the spot then intersect the equatorial plane in a region near the centre of the Sun. If a vortical ring whose plane coincides with the equatorial plane is formed in this region, it will split in two, one half moving northward and the other southward along the lines of force of the field. The vortical magnetic fields are of opposite direction in these two rings. When they finally cut the solar surface they generate magnetic fields at these two intersections, with the resultant formation of two spots of opposite polarity constituting a bipolar group. Since the magnetic fields of the north and south rings are of opposite directions the polarities of bipolar spots in the south hemisphere are reversed with respect to conditions in the north hemisphere. In this way the mysterious law of polarity reversal every eleven years might be explained. In Figure 71 the letters P and F at the right-hand side of the north and south hemispheres indicate respectively the preceding and following components of a bipolar group; the arrow shows the direction of the Sun's rotation.

The theories that we have been glancing at are still speculative, and it cannot be said that a complete explanation of the complex phenomena of the Sun has yet been evolved.

32. SUMMARY OF THEORIES OF THE CONSTITUTION AND STRUCTURE OF THE CORONA

If little can be said in explanation of the constitution of the body of the Sun, it is still more difficult to frame a theory of that of the corona or to explain how it comes to surround the Sun. If the corona in any way resembled our atmosphere the resultant pressure at the Sun's surface would be enormous, yet we find extremely small pressures even in the reversing layer. Apropos of the tenuity of the material composing the corona (of which we have already spoken—see p. 213), Newcomb, recalling how the great comet of 1843 had passed within 3' or 4' of the Sun's surface, and therefore actually through the corona, observed that at this time the comet's velocity was nearly 350 miles per second, and at that velocity it traversed 300,000 miles of the corona without experiencing any observable perturbation or deceleration.

To form some idea of what would have happened had the comet encountered even the most rarefied atmosphere it is only necessary to reflect that meteors are completely and almost instantaneously vaporised by the heat that develops when they encounter our atmosphere at altitudes of 60 to 100 miles, where it is so tenuous that it no longer scatters the Sun's light. The velocity of meteors varies from about 20 to 40 miles per second. Bearing in mind that the air resistance and the heat developed increase at least with the square of the velocity it is not difficult to imagine the fate of a body (or a collection of bodies, in the case of a comet) passing through many hundreds of thousands of miles of even a highly rarefied atmosphere at a velocity exceeding 300 miles per second. The great comet of 1882 also passed very close to the Sun's surface, and was so much brighter than the corona that it was visible in broad daylight (see Plate 119).

It must therefore be concluded that the corona cannot be regarded as a true atmosphere surrounding the Sun. Yet we know from the examination of its spectrum that it is composed of highly ionised gases producing emission lines, although a continuous spectrum is also shown by the inner corona and Fraunhofer lines by the outer.

Numerous theories have been proposed in the past, such as the 'electrical' theory of Huggins, the 'magnetic' theory of Bigelow, the 'electromagnetic' theory of Ebert, and the 'mechanical' theory of Schaeberle—to mention only a few. Nowadays, with the help of modern knowledge of atomic physics and of radiation pressure, it is certainly possible to throw a clearer light on the problem of the existence of the corona. Since it must consist of free electrons and ionised gases it is feasible to suppose that (as suggested by Schwarzschild) the corona consists of an electron gas—i.e. a gas with very long free paths, which is capable of reflecting and polarising light. If then it is supposed, as in Störmer's theory, that the electrically charged particles move under the influence of the Sun's magnetic field, the various forms assumed by the coronal petals at the poles and the equator throughout the solar cycle can also be explained.

According to S. Mitchell, who also came to the conclusion that the corona consists largely of electrons, it might be thought of as resembling those nebulae that are rendered luminous by the radiation of the stars embedded in them.

J. Anderson has calculated on the basis of convective equilibrium the effective molecular weight of the coronal material, and has found good agreement with the atomic weight of the electron. The thermal radiation of the inner corona is naturally greatest near the Sun's surface, as is the intensity of the photospheric light reflected by the electrons. It thus seems probable that the coronal radiation has an electronic origin, while the radiant energy owes its origin to two sources: (a) thermal radiation resulting from collisions, and (b) reflection and diffraction of photospheric light.

The complex appearance of the coronal spectrum, both internal and external, can thus be explained. The collisions would occur between electrons and protons or atoms once or several times ionised. The latter will naturally be more numerous at the Sun's surface, the few that occur in the outer corona giving rise to forbidden lines.

Regarding the corona's changes of shape during the course of the 11-year cycle, it has already been remarked that the coronal petals are extremely sensitive to photospheric and chromospheric disturbances, and hence to the presence of spots, flocculi and prominences, whose vicissitudes they follow closely. The coronal rays would simply be the trajectories followed by electrons under the impulse of the Sun's magnetic field, and the variations of their form, which are linked to the 11-year cycle, would be caused by the emission of swarms of electrons from the spots or from the nearby active regions.

The very high temperatures that various lines of enquiry show to exist in the corona, prominences and chromosphere (compared with that of the photosphere) complicate the problem of the constitution and structure of the corona. The probable existence of hydrodynamic-electromagnetic waves issuing from the inner layers of the Sun, and chance variations of the electric fields, may excite the chromosphere and corona. While the discovery of the emission lines and the possibility of the continuous observation of their intensities and of the motions and form of the inner corona open up new vistas of theoretical research, we are still far from explaining their occurrence and their various phases. The same must be admitted of the other classes of phenomena exhibited by the Sun.

Recent observations have demonstrated the existence on the Sun of particles endowed with enormous energy. According to Alfvén, we can reach a theoretical understanding of how these particles are produced. The prominences can be explained as electrical discharges; the motion of the solar material in the magnetic fields of the Sun must set up differences of potential between different points on its surface, and it can be shown that under certain circumstances these can give rise to discharges on the Sun's surface. Calculation indicates that the e.m.f. may reach 10^7 volts, so that if the charged particles are normally accelerated by only a small fraction of this potential they will attain high energies. This process is very conspicuous in the prominences, where, consequently, a very intense production of high-energy particles should

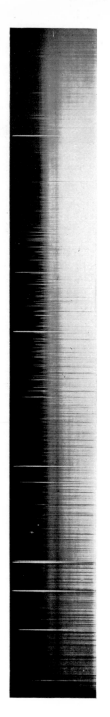

PLATE 128. Spectrum of the solar limb and chromosphere photographed by Campbell's moving plate method at Alhama, Spain, during the eclipse of 1905 August 30.

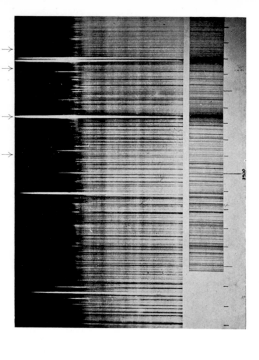

3900 A   K   H H_ϵ

PLATE 129. Enlargement of the left-hand section of Plate 128, with the spectrum of the photosphere (below) added for comparison.

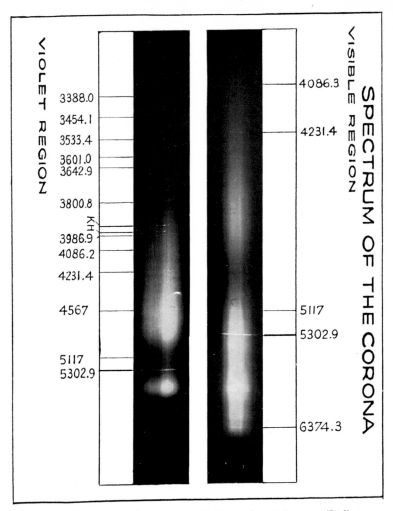

PLATE 130. Spectrum of the corona. Eclipse of 1936 June 19 (Italian expedition to Sara, U.S.S.R.). In the original photographs the emission lines from which the wavelengths were derived are visible.

5117 Å   Mg   5303 Å

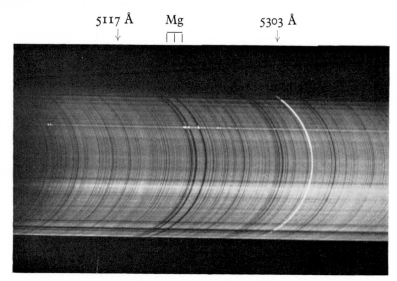

PLATE 131. Coronal emission lines photographed by Lyot in full sunlight
(the short emission lines are due to a prominence).

6374 A   Hα   6704 A

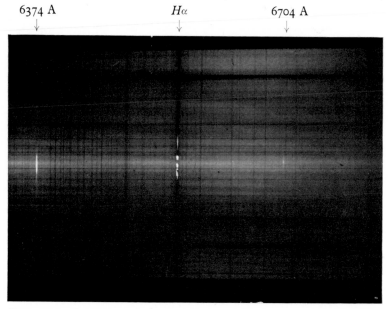

PLATE 132. Coronal emission lines photographed by Lyot in full sunlight
(1935 August).

PLATE 133. Spectra of the corona and of prominences photographed by Lyot in full sunlight.

1. Lines 5303Å and 5694Å.   2. Lines 7059Å, 7065Å (He), 7254Å (O I).
3. Lines 7775Å (O I), 7892Å, 8024Å.
4, 5. Lines 10747Å, 10798Å, 10830Å (He), 10938Å (H).
6. Distribution of the coronal lines at the Sun's west limb, 1937 July 18.
7, 8. Infrared lines of ionised calcium and Paschen's series.
9, 10. *H* and *K* lines, and Balmer series.

PLATE 134. Silver disc pyrheliometer (Smithsonian Institution).

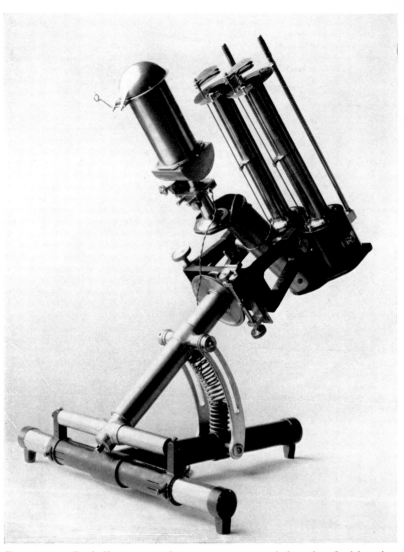

PLATE 135. Pyrheliometer and pyranometer used by the Smithsonian Institution of Washington.

PLATE 136. Smithsonian Institution station at Montezuma (Chile).

PLATE 137. Smithsonian Institution station at Bruckaros (South West Africa).

be observed. If, as appears from observation and has been considered by Unsöld, the chromosphere is composed of a multitude of small prominences, it is likely that the production of high-energy particles occurs everywhere on and above the Sun's surface.

Alfvén supposes that the corona consists of high-energy particles of this sort, which is equivalent to saying that its temperature is extremely high. Assuming that the corona is an electrically neutral atmosphere, composed of ions and electrons in equilibrium under the action of the Sun's magnetic and gravitational fields, and applying the laws of thermal equilibrium, he found that the electronic density calculated by Baumbach yielded a coronal temperature of the order of 10^6 degrees, which agrees with the values found by other methods. The flood of energy required to raise the temperature of the corona to this level would be provided by the prominences and by cumulative action of the chromosphere. The total energy required to maintain this very high coronal temperature is small (about 10^{-5} of the total energy radiated by the Sun), since the radiation losses from so highly rarefied an atmosphere are negligible. The spiral trajectories of the ions and electrons wind themselves round the lines of force of the field; the radius of curvature for the electrons is of the order of one centimetre in the inner corona and several metres in the outer, where the intensity of the magnetic field must be about 10^{-2} gauss. Even in the case of the heavy ions the radius of curvature is always much smaller than the mean free path, and hence the number of collisions is very small: one per second in the inner corona, and one per 10^{-3} seconds in the outer.

These facts relating to the electromagnetic effects present in the different layers of the Sun's atmosphere assume special importance in view of the discovery of the origin of the emission lines in the coronal spectrum.

As to what the corona actually is, the words of Van de Hulst may be quoted: 'It is a hot gas, virtually isothermal at a temperature of the order of a million degrees, in which most atoms are highly ionised. Its distribution shows certain structural details that keep changing continuously by small but definite streaming motions. The gas is made visible by the light scattered by the free electrons and by the spectral lines emitted by the ions, while superposed on these is the inner zodiacal light and the skylight. The light scattered by electrons is 99 per cent of the total light, has the same colour of the Sun, and is partially polarised.'

The problems of the origin of the corona, of its equilibrium, and of its variations with the cycle of solar activity—all these still remain unsolved.

33. INTERIOR OF THE SUN, AND THE SOURCE OF SOLAR ENERGY

Knowing that the stars are gaseous spheres with well determined surface temperatures, Eddington employed the findings of atomic physics to develop a theory of the internal constitution of the stars and, *ipso facto* therefore, of the Sun. Russell has based on this theory a picture of the actual conditions in the Sun's interior, and has considered what theories of the origin of its emitted energy are the most plausible.

The pressure, density and temperature of a gaseous sphere whose surface is very hot must increase steadily towards its centre; and because the density of its outer layers is much less than that of water, while its mean density is greater, it follows that the density towards its centre must be considerably greater than that of water. Given the weight of the overlying material, it can be calculated that the central pressure must be of the order of a million tons per square centimetre, while the central temperature—assuming that, as seems to be the case, the gas laws are still applicable—must exceed ten million degrees absolute. It is not possible to reproduce this temperature in our terrestrial laboratories in order to study the behaviour of matter under such conditions; but this can nowadays be done indirectly, for it is possible to produce falls of potential in vacuum tubes which result in the electronic bombardment of atoms as violent as that produced by collisions in a gas at temperatures greater than a thousand million degrees. The behaviour of atoms under these conditions gives us some idea of what is happening in the interior of the Sun.

In this way it has been found that despite the high pressures in the internal layers, the matter must remain everywhere gaseous; furthermore the atoms must be so highly ionised as to have been stripped of almost all their orbital electrons. In view of these conditions of temperature and pressure that must characterise the centre of the Sun, and knowing also the ionisation potentials concerned, it can be deduced that the atoms with atomic numbers below 6 or 7 (i.e. up to carbon and nitrogen) must have lost all their orbital electrons and have been reduced to bare nuclei. Calcium atoms (At. No. 20) will have retained only two of the innermost electrons, and iron (At. No. 26) only two or three.

Eddington's theory then reaches the important conclusion that such highly ionised matter continues to behave as a perfect gas, because the volume of the stripped atoms and the free electrons is always small compared with the total space that they occupy. On the other hand the atoms, though denuded of their electrons, retain their own characteristics, since the collisions occurring in the Sun's interior are not violent enough to transform one element into another; they are therefore incapable of making the nuclei lose their identities. One must therefore suppose that, if it were possible to extract the nuclei from the centre of the Sun, they would recapture those electrons that were theirs before they were ionised.

Radiant energy floods the interior solar gas in all directions, by means of electrons and ions, and since the laws governing the radiations of a black body are applicable beneath the photosphere, these laws can be used without modification to interpret the conditions in the Sun's interior. One of these well-known laws, that of Wien, states that the wavelength of the zone of maximum intensity of a perfect radiator (e.g. a black body), multiplied by the absolute temperature, is equal to a constant. When the constant is known it can immediately be calculated that at a temperature of ten million degrees the wavelength of the radiation must be extremely short—of the order of 3 angstroms, or what the physicist terms soft X-rays.

Another law—that of Stefan—states that the total energy emitted by a perfect radiator is equal to the fourth power of its absolute temperature multiplied by a constant. At 10^7 degrees the flux in all directions is 8×10^{12} times greater than that emanating from the photosphere. It is thus radiation of an intensity quite inconceivable to us, which makes its way slowly towards the exterior of the Sun in a series of absorptions and re-emissions by the atoms that it encounters.

The application to the solar globe of Emden's theory of a gaseous sphere permits the calculation of the physical characteristics (pressure, density and temperature) at the centre and at varying distances outward from the centre. If R is the solar radius, r the radii of successive spheres between the Sun's centre and its surface, M the total mass of the Sun, and M_r the mass of a sphere of radius r, then, according to Waldmeier, we have the following data:

r (miles)	r/R	Pressure (atmos.)	Density (gm/cm^3)	Temperature (deg. absol.)	M_r/M
0	0	$1 \cdot 2 \times 10^{11}$	76·5	$1 \cdot 9 \times 10^7$	0·00
125,000	0·29	$1 \cdot 4 \times 10^{10}$	15·1	$1 \cdot 1 \times 10^7$	0·52
250,000	0·58	$2 \cdot 3 \times 10^8$	0·7	$4 \cdot 0 \times 10^6$	0·95
375,000	0·86	$0 \cdot 5 \times 10^6$	0·01	$8 \cdot 0 \times 10^5$	1·00
433,000	1·00	—	—	—	—

At $r/R = 0.28$, $M_r/M = 0.52$: that is to say, half the Sun's mass is contained within a sphere whose radius is one-third that of the Sun, though the volume of this sphere is only about 4% of the total volume of the Sun. It follows that the material of which the Sun is composed is strongly condensed towards its centre. Yet despite the great density at the Sun's centre—greater than that of any metal—the material must still be in a gaseous state, owing to its extremely high temperature.

The temperature of the photosphere depends upon the speed with which the heat can escape from the interior of the Sun, and this in turn depends on the opacity of the matter at the base of the photosphere, which prevents the intense internal radiation from escaping more quickly.

The problem of discovering the origin of such vast outpourings of energy as the Sun now produces—unstintingly and constantly (or almost so) in all directions, and over so long a period of time—has been many times discussed. Knowing the value of the so-called solar constant (p. 271), we can calculate that the Sun radiates about 90,000 cals/cm²/min, or 84,000 horsepower continuously for every square metre of its surface.

The old theories that the Sun's heat is replenished by the fall of meteorites into it, and the contraction theory suggested by Helmholtz, have now been superseded: they were soon recognised as quite inadequate to account for the vast quantities of energy radiated by the Sun at the present time—as well as for the long past epoch which we can estimate and the future epoch which we can predict. The amount of energy required is certainly hundreds of times greater than could be supplied by the potential gravitational energy of the Sun. Its temperature is still so high that a great part of its energy must still be locked away in its interior, while the remainder if released at a present-day rate would keep it shining for too short a time to satisfy the demands of the geologists.

It can today be demonstrated that the great quantity of energy released by the Sun has its origin in atomic nuclei. We know that subatomic forces are colossal, and it has been discovered that the radioactive elements liberate (during their transformation, with the ejection of electrons and high-speed α-particles) great amounts of energy.

We now know that the solar globe must, in radiating, lose a certain amount of its mass. This loss must involve some of its atoms, with the liberation of a corresponding quantity of energy. The transformation of hydrogen into other elements liberates energy, when electrons and protons come together to form the nucleus of a heavy atom, since the atomic weight of the latter is always less than that of the hydrogen atoms which according to theory went to its making.

The atomic weight of hydrogen is 1·008, while almost all heavier atoms have integral atomic weights; in the formation of an atom of atomic weight X, a mass of 0·008 X will be transformed into energy by X hydrogen atoms. The mass of the Sun being 1·98 × 10³³ gms, most of which is hydrogen, only 0·8% of its mass can be transformed into energy—i.e. 1·6 × 10³¹ gms. According to the theory of relativity, a mass loss of m gms corresponds to the liberation of mc^2 ergs (c being the velocity of light), or 9·00 × 10²⁰ ergs per gm. The Sun thus radiates 1·4 × 10⁵² ergs. The solar constant, S, being 1·94 cal/cm²/min., we have for the Sun's total radiation (putting R for the Earth's mean solar distance),

$$E = \frac{4\pi R^2 S}{60} = 9 \cdot 1 \times 10^{25} \text{ cal/sec} = 3 \cdot 8 \times 10^{33} \text{ erg/sec}$$

whence the supplies of energy available in the Sun will last

$$0 \cdot 4 \times 10^{19} \text{ sec} = 1 \cdot 3 \times 10^{11} \text{ years.}$$

The formation of heavier elements than hydrogen can thus, if it proceeds without interruption, account for the life history of the Sun.

In 1939 H. A. Bethe considered what possible nuclear relationships could occur under the conditions prevailing in the Sun's interior. This work led him to the conclusion that only two nuclear reactions could be operative in the production of solar energy: H+H, and the C−N cycle. The simplest of all nuclear reactions—assuming that the Sun consisted originally only of monatomic hydrogen—is the combination of two protons with the formation of heavier elements, according to the formula

$$^1_1\text{H} + {}^1_1\text{H} \rightarrow {}^2_1 D + e^+$$

where D indicates the deuteron (^{2}H); the lower left-hand index, the characteristic number of the nucleus; the upper left-hand index, the mass of the nucleus; and e^+, a positive electron. The probability of this reaction occurring at the temperatures obtaining at the centre of the Sun is extremely small, whilst becoming very great when the temperature approaches 100 million degrees. But when this occurs, the deuteron very rapidly captures a proton, with the formation of an isotope of helium of atomic weight 3:

$$^2_1 D + {}^1_1\text{H} \rightarrow {}^3_2\text{He}$$

Helium in this form is capable of being transformed in various ways, with the cooperation of light elements, such as Li and Be, to produce $_2$He; hence one may conclude that if this transformation is occurring under present conditions in the Sun's interior, only helium is being produced from hydrogen. Heavier nuclei will be formed only in very small quantities.

The C—N cycle is the one most probably occurring on the Sun, since it comes into operation at a temperature of about 18 or 20 million degrees. The normal carbon atom is transformed and a remarkable process sets in, which leads anew to the production of helium from hydrogen. Carbon of atomic weight 12, bombarded by a proton, becomes radioactive nitrogen of atomic weight 13, with the release of a positive electron. Subsequent collision with another proton transforms carbon 13 into ordinary nitrogen of atomic weight 14 with the emission of radiation. The nitrogen atoms, when bombarded with protons, emit radiation and become radioactive oxygen of atomic weight 15. This is unstable, and disintegrates into nitrogen 15 with the release of a positive electron. When the heavy nitrogen atom is bombarded by a proton it disintegrates into an α-particle and the original carbon, atomic weight 12. During this cycle, four hydrogen nuclei are converted into one helium nucleus, and the original carbon atom reappears. The carbon, which behaves like a chemical catalyst, can be used over and over again until all the available hydrogen has been converted into helium. Remembering that the normal atoms are

$$_1^1\text{H}, \ _2^4\text{He}, \ _6^{12}\text{C}, \ _7^{14}\text{N},$$

we have the cycle:

$$_6^{12}\text{C} + _1^1\text{H} \rightarrow _7^{13}\text{N}$$

$$_7^{13}\text{N} \rightarrow _6^{13}\text{C} + e^+$$

$$_6^{13}\text{C} + _1^1\text{H} \rightarrow _7^{14}\text{N}$$

$$_7^{14}\text{N} + _1^1\text{H} \rightarrow _8^{15}\text{O}$$

$$_8^{15}\text{O} \rightarrow _7^{15}\text{N} + e^+$$

$$_7^{15}\text{N} + _1^1\text{H} \rightarrow _6^{12}\text{C} + _2^4\text{He}$$

That the cycle is re-entrant shows that the carbon is completely regenerated and that from four $_1^1\text{H}$ we arrive at $_2^4\text{He}$.

It is possible to gain some idea of the quantity of helium that has been produced by the Sun. The $4H \rightarrow 1He$ transformation is associated with a difference of mass equal to 0·028, since the masses of the nuclei of ^1_1H and ^4_2He are respectively 1·008 and 4·004. Hence one gram of hydrogen produces, in the transformation to helium,

$$0·007 \times (3 \times 10^{10})^2 = 6·3 \times 10^{18} \text{ ergs.}$$

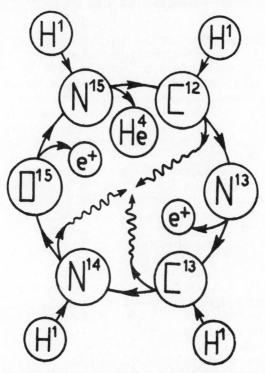

Fig. 72. Hypothetical cyclic nuclear reaction involving carbon and nitrogen, as the source of solar energy (according to Bethe).

During its probable life of 2×10^9 years the Sun has emitted $2·4 \times 10^{50}$ ergs, whilst $0·4 \times 10^{32}$ gms, or 2% of the Sun's mass, have been transformed from hydrogen into helium. Assuming that there were originally only negligible quantities of helium on the Sun, the quantity of this gas should today amount to about 2%, which appears to be in agreement with observation.

Chapter VI

RADIATION AND TEMPERATURE OF THE SUN

34. How the intensity of the Sun's radiation is measured

The quantity of radiant energy received on Earth from the stars is in general extremely minute, so that only with the most powerful instruments can it be measured—and then only in the case of the brighter stars. The Sun, on the other hand, pours down on us radiation of great intensity, and since it is of the utmost interest to humanity to discover whether this is constant or variable with time, instruments and techniques were long ago developed to measure it and thence to deduce the effective temperature of the photosphere.

Since these measurements are made at the Earth's surface they must be freed from the effects of the terrestrial atmosphere. This done, the intensity of the solar radiation which would be received by the Earth at mean solar distance can be derived: that is, the quantity of solar energy that would be received in unit time by unit area of a surface situated outside the Earth's atmosphere and inclined perpendicularly to the incident rays.

The instruments employed in this work are variously termed pyrheliometers, bolometers, spectrobolometers and radiometers, according to the principles of their design and also to whether their function is to measure the integrated radiation or the intensity of selected regions of the spectrum.

As long ago as 1837 Pouillet had constructed his celebrated pyrheliometer, which consisted of a copper vessel with a flat bottom painted black, filled with water containing a thermometer bulb.

In order to measure the Sun's radiation the instrument is first placed in the shade and the change of temperature of the water in a given interval of time is noted; it is then turned towards the Sun and its temperature rise due to the heating effect of the Sun during the same interval of time is noted. The observation in the shade is then repeated so that the mean temperature rise per minute in sunlight can be corrected for the mean loss of heat as indicated by the shade readings. Thus is obtained the rise in temperature per minute of a mass of water and copper of known heat capacity, due to the Sun's radiation falling perpendicularly on the instrument and being absorbed by the bottom of the vessel, whose area likewise is known. A further correction of 2·5% must be added to allow for radiation wasted by reflection from the blackened surface.

The radiation so measured has been weakened by its passage through the Earth's atmosphere, which—from the practical viewpoint of estimating this absorption—may be taken as extending for some 90–125 miles above the Earth's surface; its thickness is therefore inconsiderable compared with the radius of the Earth. If we write l for the length of the path of the Sun's rays through the atmosphere, h for its thickness, and z for the Sun's zenith distance at the time of observation, then providing that the Sun is not less than about 15° above the horizon, we may say with sufficient accuracy that

$$l = h \sec z$$

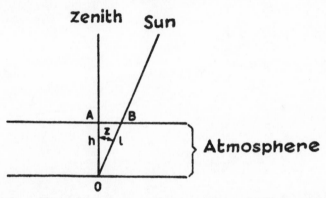

Fig. 73. Absorption of solar radiation in the Earth's atmosphere.

Bouguer and Lambert in 1760 showed independently that when a ray passes through a transparent homogeneous medium of thickness s, its original intensity I_o is weakened according to the law expressed in the equation

$$I = I_o \alpha^s$$

where I is the intensity after passing through a thickness s, and α is a constant representing the proportion of the radiation that is transmitted by unit thickness. Pouillet applied this formula to his own observations, taking as unit thickness the zenithal depth of the atmosphere, whence he derived

$$I = I_o \alpha^{\sec z}$$

265

Taking logarithms, this becomes

$$\log I = \log I_o + \sec z \log \alpha.$$

A graph can now be drawn (Figure 74), taking values of sec z as abscissae and the corresponding values of log I as ordinates; the result is a straight line, the ordinate of whose origin is the logarithm of the solar constant I_o.

Pouillet drew the straight line which best fitted his experimentally obtained points, and deduced a value of 1·76 calories per square centimetre per minute for I_o. We shall see (p. 271) that this value is lower than those subsequently obtained by more accurate methods. In fact the observational data actually lie on a curve, which yields a higher value of I_o, since the Bouguer-Lambert formula is only valid for monochromatic radiation, and it cannot be assumed that α is invariable.

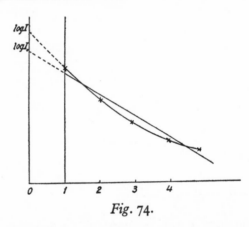

Fig. 74.

Innumerable instruments of ever-increasing perfection have been constructed since Pouillet's time, some of the more important of which will be described here. They can be divided into two categories, relative and absolute: the former make relative measurements from which absolute values may be derived by reference to a standard instrument, while the latter are used to make absolute measurements and provide results expressed directly in calories.

To the first type belong Pouillet's pyrheliometer, described above, and Tyndall's silver disc pyrheliometer which is simply a modification of it, the copper box of water being replaced by an iron box containing mercury. This instrument has been widely used, notably by Abbot and his collaborators at the Astrophysical

Observatory of the Smithsonian Institution of Washington for their classical measures made in many parts of the world.

The second type is exemplified by the compensating pyrheliometer, first constructed in 1896 by Ångström; this also has been very extensively employed. It consists of two thin manganin plates of known area, blackened on the side that is turned towards the Sun; at the back of each is mounted a thermocouple to determine its temperature. A known electric current is passed through one plate at the same time as the other is exposed to the Sun, and when the galvanometer connected to the thermocouples indicates the equality of their temperatures it is assumed that the known quality of heat introduced by the electric current is equal to that absorbed by the plate exposed to the Sun's rays.

In order to improve the balance of the readings the two plates are then reversed, so that the plate through which the current passed is now the one exposed to the Sun, and the mean taken. After a correction has been applied for losses due to reflection, the result is immediately deducible in calories per square centimetre per minute. The instrument is mounted in such a way that it can be directed easily at the Sun and maintained in this position despite the Sun's apparent motion.

One source of error in pyrheliometers of this type is particularly difficult to allow for, since it varies according to the varying conditions of the observations: part of the solar heat absorbed by the blackened surface is returned to the air or re-emitted as radiation of longer wavelength. Such heat naturally has no effect on the thermometer or thermocouple and is therefore lost. Various alternative types of absolute pyrheliometer have been designed, notably by Abbot, to eliminate this source of error.

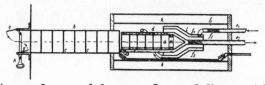

Fig. 75. Layout of the water-flow pyrheliometer (Abbot).

One of these is the water-flow pyrheliometer, which seeks to realise as closely as possible the conditions of a black body in the receiving unit. The radiation absorbed by this instrument is not measured direct; it is allowed to raise the temperature of water circulating round the receiver, and it is this rise of temperature which is measured. The general characteristics of this type of pyrheliometer are shown in Figure 75. The cover *gh* being opened, the radiation is allowed to pass down the blackened tube b past a number of baffles c. The outer cover of the calorimeter, k, encloses the receiving unit, a, which is a blackened cylindrical tube with a conical end. Between the wall of a and an outer wall, d, flows a current of water which enters by the tube e_1 and leaves by tube e_2.

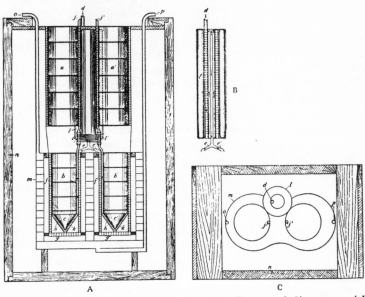

Fig. 76. Layout of the standard water-flow pyrheliometer with double compensating chamber (Abbot).

A differential electric thermometer composed of four strips of platinum, f_1, f_2, f_3 and f_4, is connected to a Wheatstone bridge which is in turn connected to a very sensitive galvanometer. The pyrheliometer is protected from external variations of temperature by enclosure in a Dewar vacuum flask. This pyrheliometer was subsequently modified so as to eliminate various other small sources of error, and finally, in its perfected form (Figure 76), led to the establishment of an absolute scale (the 'Smithsonian revised scale') to which all estimates of the solar constant, made with any absolute or relative instrument, are referred.

Following the demonstration by Macedonio Melloni in 1842 that heat radiation is of the same nature as visible radiation, and that in the study of long wave radiation use can profitably be made of rock-salt prisms, Langley in about 1880 designed a very sensitive electric thermometer; this was given the name of bolometer—

or spectrobolometer if used in conjunction with a spectroscope—
and by its means important results were obtained regarding the
energy distribution of the solar spectrum.

The plan of the instrument, with which Langley succeeded in
observing the solar spectrum as far as 28,000Å, is shown in
Figure 77. The sensitive element of the bolometer consists of two
blackened platinum plates b, b'. These constitute the two branches
of a Wheatstone bridge, which is so balanced that the needle of a
galvanometer in circuit remains at rest. When solar radiation is
allowed to fall on one of the plates its resistance is increased, with
a resultant deflection of the galvanometer needle which is proportional to the heat produced by the radiation.

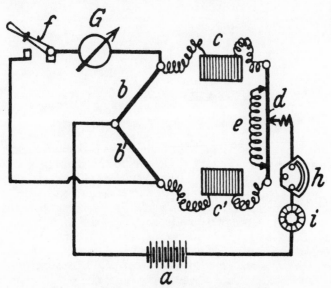

Fig. 77. Diagram of Langley's bolometer.

In Figure 77, c and c' are two coils of manganin wire which
constitute the resistances of the other two branches of the bridge.
The exact balance of the bridge is effected by the two resistances
e and d, a represents a storage battery, and G the galvanometer.
The current, of the order of 0·1 amp, is indicated by the milliammeter h and is regulated by the resistance i.

A great improvement was obtained by enclosing the receiving
element of this bolometer in a vacuum: with a sensitive galvanometer it is possible to measure temperature variations of the order
of 10^{-8} degrees.

In order to investigate the radiation in different regions of the spectrum the bolometer is used in conjunction with a spectroscope, as illustrated in Figure 78. The radiation passes through the slit S and falls first on the rock-salt prism P and then on the mirror Sp_1. The concave mirror Sp_2 reflects the radiation of different parts of the spectrum to the bolometer B.

The galvanometer readings may either be observed visually or else registered automatically on a photographic plate which is moved vertically by clockwork at the same time as the spectrum is moved across the receiving unit of the bolometer. In this case the instrument is termed a 'bolograph.'

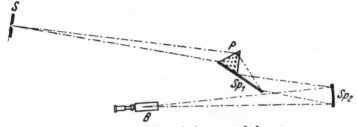

78. *Layout of Langley's spectrobolometer.*

To derive information about the Sun's radiation outside our atmosphere it is necessary to determine the transmission coefficients of this atmosphere. The serious difficulties encountered in this work have suggested the adoption of another instrument: this is the 'pyranometer', commonly used by meteorologists for the measurement of the radiation from the day and night sky.

By combining the readings of this instrument with those obtained simultaneously with a spectrobolometer it is possible to make the observation with the Sun at only one zenith distance and thus to utilise days when the sky is not completely clear.

The pyranometer consists of a flint glass hemisphere closed by a metal disc; at the centre of the hemisphere are situated four small plates, alternately blackened and whitened with magnesium oxide and zinc oxide. Behind these strips are fixed thermocouples connected to a galvanometer. When the instrument is exposed to the Sun a temperature difference develops, since the black strips are more heat-absorbent than the white, and hence a deflection of the galvanometer needle is observed. If the instrument is then removed from the sunlight it will be necessary to pass a compensating current, controlled by a resistance, through the white plates in order to make the galvanometer needle return to its zero position. The radiation may reasonably be taken to be proportional to the square of the current intensity, which is indicated by a milliammeter.

After various improvements had been incorporated in the pyranometer it was extensively used at the stations established by Abbot in California, Chile and Africa for the measurement of the solar constant and of its variations.

Although this instrument certainly permits more accurate determinations of the absolute solar constant to be made, it is nevertheless too much to hope that we have yet exactly evaluated the absorption due to water vapour, however precisely the intensities of its bands in the infrared may have been measured. The same is true of the atmosphere's transmission coefficients in other wavelengths; and hence the results so far obtained cannot be accepted as applying strictly to the Sun's radiation outside the terrestrial atmosphere.

35. THE SOLAR CONSTANT AND ITS VARIATIONS

As already stated (pp. 264–5) the solar constant is the quantity of solar energy which is received outside the terrestrial atmosphere by a surface 1 cm square, perpendicular to the Sun's rays, at the Earth's mean solar distance, in 1 minute. It is expressed in gram-calories, whose value in absolute units is

$$1 \text{ gm cal cm}^{-2} \text{ min}^{-1} = 0.01667 \text{ gm cal cm}^{-2} \text{ sec}^{-1}$$
$$= 6.977 \times 10^5 \text{ erg cm}^{-2} \text{ sec}^{-1}$$

Naturally the higher we ascend in the atmosphere the nearer we approach the true value of the solar constant. The following table gives an idea of its variation as a function of altitude, and it can be seen that its value outside the atmosphere must be in the neighbourhood of 2 calories.

Place of observation	Height above sea level (feet)	Energy (cal cm⁻² min⁻¹)
Sea level	0	1·40 approx.
Davos	5,250	1·59 ,,
Jungfraujoch . . .	11,350	1·63 ,,
Mount Whitney . .	14,500	1·72 ,,
Free balloon . . .	65,000	1·89 ,,

If the different strata of the atmosphere were equally transparent it would be possible to derive the solar constant from such data by extrapolation; but experiment has shown that in order to obtain a tolerable result the observations must be made from the same station, with the Sun at a variety of altitudes above the horizon.

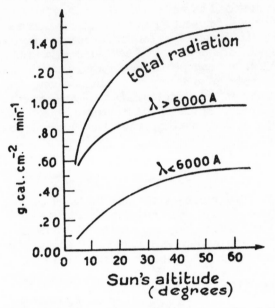

Fig. 79. *Dependence of solar radiation upon the Sun's altitude* (*Götz*).

The variation of the Sun's radiation as a function of its altitude above the horizon can be seen in, for example, Figure 79, which plots the measurements made by F. W. Götz at Arosa (Switzerland) during the month of June. This variation is given not only for the total radiation but also for radiations in the spectral regions $\lambda > 6000\text{Å}$ and $\lambda < 6000\text{Å}$. The trend of the curves indicates that when the Sun is near the horizon the radiations of shorter wavelength are strongly or almost completely absorbed by the atmosphere, and that in any case, when the Sun is high in the sky, the greater part of the total radiation always consists of the red and infrared radiations.

The problem of reducing all the observations, made at various solar altitudes, to the Sun's maximum altitude, has been treated by various authors (such as A. Bemporad, for example) who have computed tables relating the observed radiation in a unit mass of air as though the Sun were always at the zenith of the place of observation.

In order to arrive at the solar constant it is also necessary to determine the coefficient of transmission, α, i.e. the loss suffered by the total radiation in passing through a unit mass of air (p. 265). Many investigations have been undertaken with this purpose; a complication is introduced by the fact that α is dependent on wavelength, the shorter wavelengths having correspondingly smaller values of α.

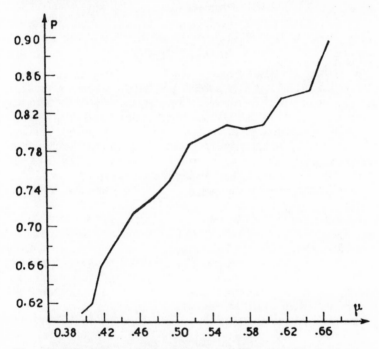

Fig. 80. *Variation of transmission coefficient with wavelength (expressed in microns).*

G. Müller made one of the earliest determinations of the selective absorption of the atmosphere in the visible region of the spectrum:

for $\lambda=4500$Å, $\alpha=0\cdot72$
for $\lambda=5500$Å, $\alpha=0\cdot81$
for $\lambda=6500$Å, $\alpha=0\cdot87$.

Wilsing, Müller and Kron's determination of the mean trend of the coefficient of transmission for various wavelengths from the violet to the red, is represented in Figure 80. The drop in the curve around 5800Å is caused by absorption in the ozone layer situated between the terrestrial troposphere and stratosphere.

It may be noted that for wavelengths of less than 4000Å:

(*a*) the decrease of atmospheric transparency with decreasing wavelength is considerably more rapid than in the visible region of the spectrum;

(*b*) the short-wave region is much more sensitive to diurnal variations of atmospheric transparency than the long-wave;

(*c*) the atmospheric transparency in the ultraviolet region increases more rapidly with increasing altitude above sea level than in the radiations of the visible spectrum.

In making the extrapolations necessary for the determination of the solar constant it is thus necessary to take account of many disturbing factors and to establish the transmission coefficient for different regions of the spectrum. On the other hand the derived value of the solar constant cannot be the true one unless the measures comprise the total radiation of the Sun. And this is not possible, since solar radiation below 2850Å cannot reach us on account of absorption by terrestrial ozone, and that above 25,000Å is largely absorbed by the bands of water vapour and carbonic acid.

We have learnt that the first value of the solar constant (1·76) was obtained by Pouillet. With the invention of the spectrobolometer Langley established the value as 1·92 calories, later confirmed by Wilsing at Potsdam. The extensive measures made by Abbot and his collaborators at Washington and at stations expressly chosen for their altitude and clarity of atmosphere in widely separated parts of the world (California, Chile, South Africa) yielded a mean value of

$$S = 1 \cdot 94 \text{ gm cal cm}^{-2} \text{ min}^{-1}$$
$$= 1 \cdot 35 \times 10^6 \text{ erg cm}^{-2} \text{ sec}^{-1}$$

for the epoch from 1905 to 1930, with an estimated mean error of $\pm 0 \cdot 02$, allowance also being made for the small quantity of ultraviolet and infrared radiation which escaped measurement for the reasons given above.

Such precision in the determination of the solar constant raises the problem of ascertaining whether, owing to causes inherent in the Sun and in its variable activity, the constant may have a more or less long-period variation. The problem is complicated by all the disturbing factors introduced by the terrestrial atmosphere.

Various investigators have concerned themselves with the problem, but the most extensive and continuous investigation has been that undertaken by the Astrophysical Observatory of the Smithsonian Institution. Its results suggest that one may assert the existence of variations in the value of the solar constant which are connected with the 11-year period of solar activity, as well as variations of short period.

On the other hand Bernheimer and Marvin have found in the monthly averages of the solar constant deduced from the Smithsonian Institution observations, a strict relationship with the coefficients of transmission determined at the same time. The trend of the monthly means may be represented by a sine curve with a period of one year, the maximum occurring during the summer and the minimum during the winter. The cause of this periodicity is evidently to be sought in the variation of the coefficient of transmission and hence of the particular conditions of the terrestrial atmosphere. This may perhaps spring from incomplete knowledge of the absorption due to water vapour. It is therefore difficult to establish a reliable correlation between variations of the solar constant and the 11-year period of solar activity.

The difficulty of proving these small variations in the solar constant over relatively long periods is exaggerated when we attempt to establish their existence over short periods—for example, from day to day. With the most exact modern methods of observation and reduction, and using stations chosen in particularly favourable localities so as to reduce the mean errors, it has been found that the deviations of the results from a mean value have grown smaller in recent years, and particularly since the introduction of the pyranometer.

For the time being it may be said that the observed diurnal variation averages 0·012 gm cal cm^{-2} min^{-1}, i.e. 0·60% of the Sun's mean energy throughout a year; this variation is of an order of magnitude comparable with the margin of inaccuracy in the pyranometer measures. On the other hand the possibility of short-period variations—dependent on special solar conditions such as the transit of large spots across the central meridian, eruptions, etc—cannot be excluded. Thus Abbot believes that the smallest amplitudes of the short-period variations amount to 0·45% and the largest to 2·5%, and that furthermore they are related to the trend of terrestrial temperatures and barometric pressures (p. 296).

Discussion of the measures of solar ultraviolet radiation which still reaches the lower levels of the Earth's atmosphere also indicates that the variations observed during the course of time are caused by its variable transparency.

36. ENERGY DISTRIBUTION IN THE SPECTRUM AND ON THE DISC OF THE SUN

When one wishes to investigate the way in which the Sun's radiation is distributed over the different regions of the spectrum one naturally encounters the same difficulties as those described in the last section, which are caused by the terrestrial atmosphere.

As regards the Fraunhofer lines, it has been pointed out that those belonging to the Sun's atmosphere may be easily distinguished from those belonging to the Earth's by seeing whether or not they are displaced by the Sun's rotation; but when one is concerned with the distribution of energy in the continuous spectrum, or with the limits of the spectrum in the ultraviolet or infrared, the problem is more difficult. Here again it is necessary to obtain bolograms with the Sun at a variety of altitudes above the horizon. These allow the transmission coefficients for individual regions of the spectrum to be obtained, and finally the energy of the spectrum is derived as though it were observed from outside the atmosphere.

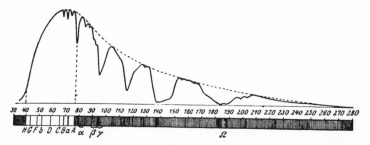

Fig. 81. *Distribution of solar energy in the normal spectrum, between* 3000Å *and* 28000Å *(Langley).*

From Langley's measurements, reduced to the normal spectrum, the distribution of solar energy is as shown in Figure 81. The conspicuous depressions in the infrared are all due to the bands of water vapour, carbon dioxide and other molecular compounds.

When determining the energy of the solar spectrum these depressions must be taken into account; corrections must also be applied for the bands, partly due to ozone, in the extreme infrared and ultraviolet. The effect of these ultraviolet bands—which are particularly noticeable between 2900Å and 3150Å—has been studied by Fabry and Buisson, and other investigators. They are due to the presence in the Earth's atmosphere of a quantity of ozone equivalent to a variable thickness in the neighbourhood of 3 mm at an altitude of from 15 to 20 miles.

The molecule of this triatomic form of oxygen (O_3) is unstable, and can be made to relapse into the ordinary diatomic state by various means, such as temperature changes, collision with fast moving particles, and ultraviolet radiation; other agencies, conversely, can promote the synthesis of ozone from oxygen. The interaction of these two antagonistic classes of radiation in the upper atmosphere, both deriving from the Sun, results in the establishment of an equilibrium between the ozone that is formed and that which is broken down.

The exploration of wavelengths shorter than 2900Å is, as we have seen, nowadays rendered possible by means of spectrographs shot to great heights in the Earth's atmosphere by rockets, far above the ozone layer. By means of V2 rockets launched at White Sands, New Mexico, the Fraunhofer spectrum in the ultraviolet as far as 1900Å has been photographed with relatively low resolving power and small dispersion. The existence of solar radiation in the extreme ultraviolet at shorter wavelengths than 1350Å, extending as far as the X-ray region, has also been established by means of rockets. It appears that a part of the X-radiation occurs in the form of 'bursts' or 'impulses' and that these coincide with sudden disturbances in the ionosphere.

The spectrobolographic investigations of the long infrared wavelengths by Langley and Abbot have since become classic. In 1881 the

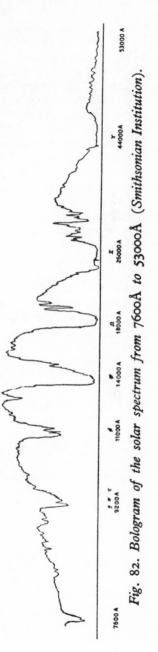

Fig. 82. Bologram of the solar spectrum from 7600Å to 53000Å (Smithsonian Institution).

former succeeded in plotting the energy distribution of the solar spectrum as far as 38,000Å by establishing his instrument on Mt Whitney at an altitude of 14,500 feet above sea level. Subsequent measurements carried out at Washington extended the range to 53,000Å. The characteristics of the infrared spectrum are represented in Figure 82; the conspicuous depressions, denoted by Greek letters, are due to molecular substances in the terrestrial atmosphere, as already explained.

More recently (1949) R. McMath and L. Goldberg of the McMath-Hulbert Observatory have recorded the solar spectrum in the infrared from 14,000Å to 36,000Å by means of a Cashman lead sulphide (PbS) spectrometer linked to an amplifier. It can be seen from Langley and Abbot's map that the solar spectrum is almost wholly absorbed in the bands Ψ, Ω and X, due to the molecules of water vapour and carbon dioxide. But between these bands it is possible to see the solar spectrum, and it is through these 'windows' that the researches in question have been carried out. With this new apparatus it has been possible to identify, among the strongest telluric bands, eight due to ordinary carbon dioxide and a further five originating from the isotopic molecules $C^{13}O_2^{16}$ and $C^{12}O^{16}O^{18}$. In addition, confirmation was obtained of the presence of five bands of methane (CH_4) and three of nitrous oxide (N_2O), originally detected by A. Adel and M. Migeotte. Some 400 new solar lines were identified on McMath and Goldberg's microphotograms; among the most intense are those due to the neutral atoms H, Mg, Si and Fe, whose ionisation potentials are about 5 electronvolts.

Comparisons made between the intensities of N_2O bands obtained in the laboratory and those of the solar bands lead to the conclusion that the quantity of N_2O in the Earth's atmosphere is equivalent to a thickness of about 4 mm at atmospheric pressure and a temperature of 20° C. The quantity of CH_4 in the terrestrial atmosphere amounts to about 12 mm at atmospheric pressure. The quantities of carbon dioxide and its isotopes are now being accurately determined, and the possibility of seasonal variations studied.

The energy distribution of the normal solar spectrum, as established by the determinations of numerous investigators, is represented by the broken curve in Figure 83. It will be seen that there is a very pronounced energy maximum at 4700Å, with a gentler diminution on the long-wave side than towards the violet. The continuous curves represent the amounts of energy emitted by a perfect radiator, or 'black body', in all wavelengths. The areas enclosed by the curves give the total quantities of energy radiated at the various temperatures; these quantities are proportional to the fourth power of the temperature (Stefan's law). It will be noticed that the maxima of the various curves are displaced progressively towards the shorter wavelengths as the temperature rises (Wien's law). The solar curve approximates closely to that of a black body at the temperature of 6000° K.; the missing region in

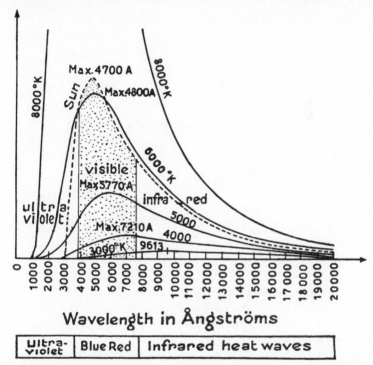

Fig. 83. *Energy distribution of the Sun and of a black body at different temperatures. (The area beneath any curve represents the total amount of energy radiated at the temperature in question. As the temperature increases, the maxima of the curves are displaced progressively towards the violet.)*

the ultraviolet is, as we have seen, the result of absorption by ozone in the Earth's atmosphere. The intensity curve of the Sun's radiation in the ultraviolet at altitudes of about 20 and 35 miles above sea level, as derived from recent work with rockets, is shown in Figure 84, together with that of a black body at 6000° K. for comparison. It has already been pointed out (p. 60) that the Sun's disc is not uniformly bright, but diminishes in intensity rather rapidly from the centre towards the limb, and that this must be due to the fact that rays leaving the photosphere obliquely are more heavily absorbed by the solar atmosphere. Since, moreover, this absorption is selective (as in the case of our own atmosphere), the darkening of the limb will not be the same in all wavelengths.

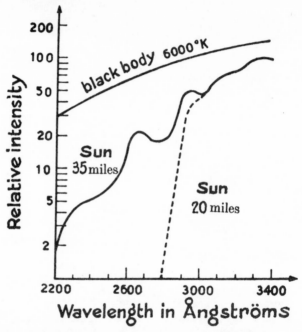

Fig. 84. Distribution of solar energy in the ultraviolet at different heights in the Earth's atmosphere.

The theoretical researches of Schwarzschild and others into the phenomenon of the limb darkening have shown that the Sun, being a gaseous sphere in radiative equilibrium, must both absorb and radiate with the same intensity. Moreover the comparison of the spectra of the centre of the disc and of the limb forces us to conclude that at the centre the rays emerge from hotter and deeper layers, whilst those from the limb are radiated by relatively cool and high-altitude levels. In other words, we see more deeply into the Sun's atmosphere at the centre of the disc than at the limb, where, observing obliquely, we find that the lower levels are hidden by the outer layers of inferior temperature and pressure.

One of the problems of astrophysics is to devise a model atmosphere which, obeying the laws of physics, would reproduce the characteristics of the Fraunhofer spectrum. Regions of the Sun at all depths down to the level at which the gases become opaque contribute to the emitted radiation. Once the mechanism of the production of this opacity was understood it became possible, from observations of the limb darkening, to devise models of the solar atmosphere in which increase of pressure and temperature corresponds to the observed effects. Various investigators have in fact calculated and discussed models of this type, which are associated with the discovery of the negative hydrogen ion as the originator of the opacity.

Determinations of the total intensity of a restricted region at the centre of the Sun's disc, and at successive positions along one of its radii from the centre towards the limb, had already been carried out by a variety of methods at the hands of the early observers. For various reasons, the results obtained were not in particularly good agreement with one another; chief among these reasons were the variety of instruments used and the diffusion of the Sun's light by the terrestrial atmosphere, leading to confusion of the radiations from different parts of the disc. Nevertheless it can be said that if the intensity of the radiation from the centre of the disc is put at 100, then the following figures represent average values:

0·50 of the distance from centre to limb					93·4
0·75	,,	,,	,,	,,	78·8
0·98	,,	,,	,,	,,	49·0
1·00	,,	,,	,,	,,	c. 39

In order to reduce the effects of diffusion Julius tried making these observations during total eclipses of the Sun, obtaining the value of the limb darkening from determinations of the intensity at different points along the radius as the Moon's disc moved across that of the Sun. By this method he and others obtained higher values of the limb darkening than those quoted above.

A more satisfactory method of investigating the darkening of the limb is to make similar measurements in the light of different wavelengths. As long ago as 1872 Vogel had measured the decrease in intensity from the centre of the disc to the limb, and had shown it to be more rapid in the short-wave regions of the spectrum; a more recent investigation by Schwarzschild and Villiger was carried as far into the ultraviolet as 3000Å with the aid of optical materials transparent to these radiations.

More extensive measurements were made later still by Abbot,

who allowed the Sun's image to trail across the slit of a spectro-bolometer, so that the energy radiated in a restricted spectral region could be recorded. The results of these measurements, together with more recent ones obtained by other workers, are shown in Figure 85: the intensity at the centre of the disc is taken as 100 (ordinates) and the solar radius as unity (abscissae). It can be seen that while there is very marked limb darkening in the violet, in the infrared it is almost nonexistent.

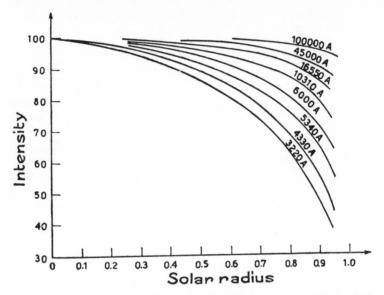

Fig. 85. Darkening of the Sun's disc from its centre towards the limb, for different wavelengths.

The following table also reveals the energy distribution in different regions of the spectrum, expressed on an intensity scale which is uniform for all wavelengths. The horizontal lines again show the progressive darkening of the limb in different regions of the spectrum, and in addition the vertical columns give the energy distribution in the normal spectrum (from outside our atmosphere) for selected points along a solar radius.

It can also be seen in the Table that the region of maximum intensity is displaced progressively towards the red as the limb is approached. We shall see later that these maxima can be used to determine the effective temperature of the photosphere in different regions of the Sun's disc.

Values of the Limb Darkening (according to Abbot)

Wavelength (Å)	$R_\odot$ 0·00	0·40	0·75	0·95
3220	144	129	99	49
4330	456	423	333	205
5340	463	440	366	254
6990	307	295	258	195
10310	111	108	99	81
16550	40	39	37	32
λ of maximum energy (Å) .	4580	4670	4780	5050

According to some theories of the Sun's constitution (p. 242) there should be a more pronounced limb darkening in the east-west direction (i.e. along the solar equator) than in the direction perpendicular to it (i.e. along the axis of rotation). Abbot's investigations lead to the conclusion that if such a difference exists it is too small to be perceptible with the observational means at our disposal.

Minnaert has also determined the region of the solar disc, in various colours, at which the predominant radiation is equal to the mean radiation over the whole disc. He derived a value of $R=0.75$, virtually constant in all regions from the violet to the red, with a slight increase to $R=0.77$ in the infrared.

37. TEMPERATURE OF THE PHOTOSPHERE AND SUNSPOTS

The investigations described in the last section, which supplied information regarding the solar constant, the energy distribution in the solar spectrum, and the darkening of the limb, also provide data on the temperature of the photosphere; they can at any rate yield an approximate overall value—for it will be evident from what has so far been said that its radiative capacity must vary with wavelength, with the part of the disc examined, and with the quiescence or disturbance of this region.

Different temperatures will be derived from the observational material according as to whether the well-known Stefan-Boltzmann formulae, Planck's law, or other indirect methods are used. Since, as we have seen, the Sun does not radiate like a black body, it is natural that the various methods should yield different values.

The so-called 'effective temperature' or 'bolometric temperature' is that derived from the Stefan-Boltzmann law, which states that the total energy radiated by a black body is proportional to the fourth power of its absolute temperature:

$$S=\sigma T^4$$

where
$$S=1\cdot94 \text{ gm cal cm}^{-2} \text{ min}^{-1}$$
$$\sigma=1\cdot37\times10^{-12} \text{ cal cm}^{-2} \text{ sec}^{-1} \text{ deg}^{-4}$$

This gives the value
$$T=5770^\circ \text{ K.}$$

Wien's displacement law states that the product of the effective temperature and the wavelength of the intensity maximum in the observed energy curve is equal to a constant:

$$T \cdot \lambda_{max}=C$$

Putting $\lambda=4740\text{Å}$ (see Figure 83) and $C=0\cdot2884$ cm deg
$$T=6050^\circ \text{ K.}$$

Since it is difficult to determine the wavelength of the intensity maximum with precision, this is not one of the best methods of determining the Sun's temperature.

The discrepancy between the two results is considerable, and Milne, who sought the explanation of it, came to the conclusion that the Sun's energy distribution (the Sun being regarded as a gaseous sphere in radiative equilibrium) corresponds to that of a black body displaced towards the longer wavelengths: hence its temperature as determined from its total radiation will be lower than that derived from Wien's law. This discrepancy may also be thought of as arising from the fact that the measures of the total radiation, in contrast to those of individually observed spectral regions, will also include radiations over the whole wavelength range, originating in higher and therefore cooler levels of the photosphere.

Numerous investigations of the temperature of the photosphere have also been based on the application of Planck's energy equation. This equation gives the energy of a particular radiation emitted by a radiating body, as a function of its wavelength and of the absolute temperature; it can therefore be used to determine the latter when the energy radiated in different wavelengths is known.

From Planck's law—which is the most general one, including those of Stefan-Boltzmann and Wien as special cases—the temperature corresponding to each spectral region in which the photosphere's energy is measured can therefore be calculated: these so-called 'colour temperatures' will only be equal if the photosphere radiates as a black body. We have seen that this is only approximately true of the Sun, the observed energy distribution being fairly well represented by the curve of a black body at a temperature of 6000° (Figure 83, p. 279).

Mulders has calculated the colour temperature of the photosphere and finds that for the violet region from 3000Å to 4000Å it is 4850° K, and for the region between 4100Å and 9500Å, 7140° K. This considerable difference is partly to be explained by the presence of very numerous Fraunhofer lines in the ultraviolet, which introduce conspicuous modifications in the continuous spectrum of the Sun. Arnulf, Chalonge and Déjardin, indeed, obtained a value of 6200° K using only the narrow sections ('windows') of the spectrum that, between 3000Å and 4500Å, are free of absorption lines.

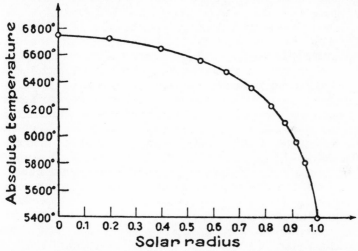

Fig. 86. *Distribution of mean photospheric temperature across the Sun's disc.*

More recently H. Kienle has compared the absolute values of the radiation from the centre of the Sun's disc with that from the positive electrode of a carbon arc. The colour temperature of the photosphere as determined from the gradient between the two 'windows' at 3300Å and 4316Å works out as 7540°±200° K. The temperature gradient becomes increasingly steep with increasing depth in the Sun's atmosphere.

Wilsing, using Abbot's figures for the limb darkening (p. 283), derived the values shown in Figure 86 for different points on the disc, showing a difference of about 1400 degrees between the levels observed at the disc centre and at the limb. In fact, as we shall see, the wavelength of the intensity maximum increases steadily from the centre towards the limb; hence, as stated by Wien's law, the temperature falls from the centre to the limb. Radiation from upper levels is eliminated more by diffusion when it comes from the limb than when it comes from the centre of the disc, owing to the former's oblique sight-line to the Earth.

We have already seen (p. 282) that the darkening of the limb is more pronounced in violet light than in red, either because the reduction of temperature reduces the short-wave radiation more than the long, or because molecular diffusion is greater for the violet rays than for the red, so that at the limb the effective violet-radiating stratum is situated higher above the photosphere than the red. The reversing layer is thus relatively cooler at the limb than at the centre.

The theory of ionisation also permits the calculation of the Sun's temperature on the temperature scale of the fixed stars, which can be established from the maximum intensity of the absorption lines in their spectra. Thus from the examination of the spectra of the spots and faculae it can be deduced, on the basis of this theory, that the former are cooler than the photosphere and the latter hotter.

Also based on the theory of ionisation, a new method for the precise evaluation of the Sun's temperature has been developed by R. v. d. R. Woolley, using his own observations of the intensities of the Ca I line at 4227Å and the Ca II line at 3933Å (the K line), made at Cambridge. From the widths of these lines he deduced the relative numbers of ionised and neutral calcium atoms per cubic centimetre at a given optical depth; knowing the electron pressure, he was able to derive a temperature of 6180 degrees from the integrated light of the whole disc.

On the other hand Russell, employing the theory of ionisation and the relative intensities of lines in the spectra of the photosphere and of spots, derived a temperature of between 4000 and 4500 degrees for the spots.

Pettit and Nicholson have determined the relative intensity of spots and photosphere in different wavelengths, using a thermocouple attached to a monochromator mounted in the focal plane of the larger solar tower at Mt Wilson. If the spots radiate like a black body, assuming the Sun's temperature to be 5955 degrees, then the relationship discovered by these authors yields a temperature of 4860 degrees for the spots. This value has also been confirmed by measures of the total energy of the umbra of a spot compared with that of the photosphere, likewise made with a thermocouple. The relation between them was found to be 0·47:1·00, which agrees well with the value derived by comparing the areas enclosed respectively by the energy curve of the spot and that of the photosphere.

Recent investigations by Richardson, likewise at Mt Wilson, of the bands produced by molecular carbon have led to a new determination of the temperature of the reversing layer and of the spots. From a comparison of the theoretical temperature and that determined by himself from the lines of the Swan bands of C_2 (so called after their discoverer) at 5165Å, and from the position of the intensity maximum of these bands, he calculated that the temperature of the reversing layer is 5300 degrees and that of spot umbrae 4500 degrees.

The following table summarises these various results.

Temperature of the Photosphere and of Sunspots

Method	Region of Sun	Temperature (°K)
Colour temperature:	photosphere	
according to Mulders . .	3000–4000Å	4850
according to Mulders . .	4100–9500Å	7140
according to Arnulf, Chalonge,		
Déjardin	3000–4316Å	6200
according to Kienle . .	3300–4316Å	7540
Effective radiation . . .	photosphere	5770
Visual radiation		
according to A. Brill . .	photosphere	6050
Photographic radiation		
according to A. Brill . .	photosphere	5895
Wien's law	photosphere	6080
Ionisation temperature . .	photosphere	6180
Thermocouple . . .	spot umbrae	4860
C_2 band intensity . . .	{ photosphere	5300
	{ spot umbrae	4500

Chapter VII

THE SUN AS A STAR

38. THE PHYSICAL CHARACTERISTICS OF THE SUN AND THE STARS COMPARED

Having reached this point in our exposition of present-day knowledge of the Sun, it is permissible to enquire whether the Sun can be considered as a star and whether we can assign it to its proper position in the classification and evolutionary sequence of the stars. And when this is done we shall realise the importance of being able to establish, in the case of at any rate one star, so many details and phenomena of a sort that may legitimately be supposed to apply in different forms and under different aspects to every star in the sky.

In order to form some conception of the apparent brightness and luminosity of the Sun, compared with other stars, we must imagine it as being removed to a distance from the Earth comparable with those of the stars in the immediate vicinity of the Solar System. Therefore, in order to compare the stars, not only with the Sun, but also with one another, it is usual to refer them to a standard distance and to determine from their apparent brightness what their brightness would be at this distance. The latter is termed the 'absolute magnitude' of the star, to distinguish it from the apparent magnitude which is determined directly by means of photometers.

By convention, the absolute magnitude of a star is defined as the magnitude it would have if it were situated at a distance of 10 parsecs—i.e. at such a distance that its parallax would be 0″.1.

The Sun's apparent visual magnitude on the scale ordinarily employed for the stars is, according to the most reliable determinations, $-26\cdot72$, and its apparent photographic magnitude $-25\cdot93$ (see p. 60). From these figures it can be calculated that its absolute visual magnitude is $4\cdot85$, and its photographic $5\cdot64$. Transported to a distance of 10 parsecs (32·6 light years), therefore, the Sun would be nearly at the threshold of naked-eye vision (6th magnitude).

Among the more familiar stars, Sirius (α Canis Majoris) has an apparent visual magnitude of $-1\cdot6$, whence, its distance being known, its absolute magnitude can at once be calculated as $+1\cdot3$. Converting magnitude to luminosity by means of the well-known

288

relationship linking these two quantities, it is found that Sirius is 27 times more luminous than the Sun (p. 60). Rigel (β Orionis), whose apparent visual magnitude is +0·3, but which is considerably more remote than Sirius from the Solar System, has an absolute magnitude of −5·5: i.e. it is 14,000 times more luminous than the Sun. Barnard's star, on the other hand (named after the discoverer of its relative proximity to the Solar System, its parallax being 0."54), which is only visible with a telescope, has an apparent visual magnitude of 9·7, and hence an absolute magnitude of 13·3, corresponding to a luminosity of only four ten-thousandths that of the Sun.

Even from these figures, which by no means represent the limits, it can be seen that the range of stellar luminosity is enormous—21 magnitudes, so far as is at present known; this represents an intensity difference of 1 :200,000,000. The Sun lies near the middle of this vast gamut, being neither one of the most nor the least luminous stars. From the viewpoint of stellar evolution, however, the Sun rates as a 'dwarf'.

The difference between the Sun's photographic and visual magnitudes—its so-called colour index—is +0·79, which agrees well with the colour index of those fixed stars having similar spectral characteristics; it can, in fact, be classed with the yellow stars.

The second of the spectroscopic classes into which Fr Secchi in 1869 classified the stars is, in his own words, 'that of the yellow stars, such as Capella, Pollux, Arcturus, etc. Their spectra are altogether similar to that of the Sun, i.e. they are composed of very fine and closely packed lines occupying the same positions as those of the solar spectrum.'

Draper's more detailed and recent classification, which has replaced that of Secchi, employs letters of the alphabet in the following manner:

Draper classification		Secchi's classes
O, B, A, F	. .	I. bluish-white stars
F, G, K	. .	II. yellow stars
K, M	. .	III. orange and red stars
R, N, S	. .	IV. red stars

The letters are accompanied by a number indicating the decimal division of each type; the Sun is classified as G0 or somewhat earlier, in type F7.

The various types constitute a linear spectroscopic sequence; the characteristics of each type are determined by the physical conditions of the stars belonging to it, i.e. by the degree of excitation of the atoms comprising their atmospheres. In stars of type O the majority of the lines are produced by doubly or trebly ionised atoms, despite the enormous energy necessary to produce this condition. The level of ionisation decreases steadily in types B and A, while in F the lines of neutral atoms make their appearance and become ever more important in classes G and K. Bands due to chemical compounds appear in type M, where at the same time the *raies ultimes* of the arc spectrum, characteristic of low excitation, are intense; the same may be said of types R, N and S.

The factor determining these variations of the spectra is temperature, which is also responsible for the general colour of the star and therefore for its colour index also. It is thus possible to state that the Sun occupies a well-defined position in the stellar spectral sequence, since all stars of about type G must have the same surface physical characteristics of temperature and pressure as are encountered on the Sun.

As to size, while many stars are of about the same dimensions, and also mass and density, as the Sun, there are others which are very much larger and very much smaller. Barnard's star, already referred to, which is a red star with a temperature of 3000 degrees, has a radius $R=0.2$ times that of the Sun, and a mass $M=0.2$, while its density (taking that of water as unity) $D=45$. In the case of Sirius, a bluish-white star with a temperature of 11,200 degrees, $R=1.8$, $M=2.4$, $D=0.4$.

These two stars, and also the Sun, belong to what, in connexion with stellar evolution as understood today, is termed the 'Main Sequence', which is composed entirely of dwarfs as opposed to giants, which are very much larger yellow or red stars. A typical giant is Capella (α Aurigae), whose spectrum resembles that of the Sun and which therefore belongs to type G; but although its temperature is the same as the Sun's, $R=12$, $M=4$ and $D=2\times10^{-3}$. Another example is Antares (α Scorpii), a red star with a temperature of 3100 degrees and $R=480$, $M=30$, $D=3\times10^{-7}$. It can be seen from these figures that the enormous sizes of the last two stars (and also of others of the same kind) are due rather to their low densities than to the amount of matter they contain.

In Figure 87 are shown those of the brighter and nearer stars whose absolute magnitudes and spectra it has been possible to compare with the Sun. It is a picture of the different stages through which a star may pass, and we can arrange them in a convenient

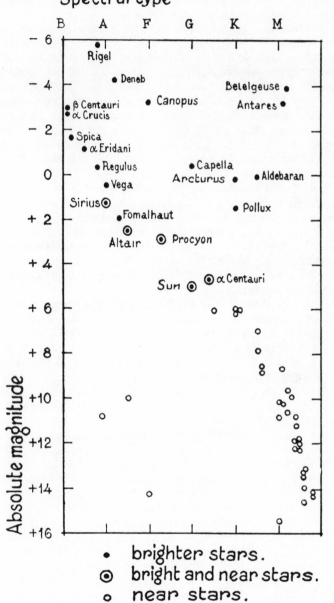

Fig. 87. *Absolute magnitudes and spectral types of the brighter and nearer stars.*

manner for understanding its evolution and hence the present state of the Sun.

It is nowadays generally believed that a single star may pass through almost all the known spectral types: starting out as a giant of considerable mass and passing through different stages with ever increasing temperature, it reaches the main sequence as a type B star (blue-white) and then moves down the sequence as far as type M, all the time contracting, becoming increasingly dense, and cooling. According to this hypothesis the Sun may once have been the equal of Sirius in mass, luminosity and temperature, and earlier still it may have been as gigantic as Capella now is. In the distant future it may contract to a red dwarf as faint as Barnard's star.

The time scale opened up by this conception of stellar evolution is, according to Russell's calculations, of impressive extent. Even allowing for the fact that the Sun would have radiated more rapidly when it was more massive, the time required for it to attain its present mass, assuming it was twice as massive to start with, would be 5×10^{12} years. To lose half its present mass would require a further 4×10^{13} years, and to attain a mass only one-fifth of its present mass, a period twenty times as long.

The geological history of the Earth shows that in the past the Sun has radiated at the same rate as that which we measure today. The temperature of the Earth's surface is controlled almost entirely by solar radiation. If the so-called solar constant had been different, or had changed appreciably with time, all forms of life would have been wiped off the Earth by excessive heat or excessive cold. But the geology of the Earth, and the fossils found in its crust, prove that since pre-Cambrian times there has been a steady evolution of organic forms; it may reasonably be assumed, therefore, that since this epoch the Sun's radiation has not altered to any great extent, or at least has never suffered any interruption. During this period, which can be calculated to be several hundred million years, we must assume that the Sun has poured upon the Earth the same quantity of energy as we receive at the present day.

It may yet be asked what is the standing of the Sun among the stars, and what is its origin. Given the identification of the Sun with a particular and very numerous class of stars, its origin must clearly be the same as that of its immediate neighbours in space.

The Sun is embedded in the Milky Way, which constitutes an organic system of stars, and very nearly traces out a great circle about the star sphere. It is composed of stars of all the spectral types referred to above, and also of cosmic material which appears in the form of bright and dark nebulae. Stars of all types (but

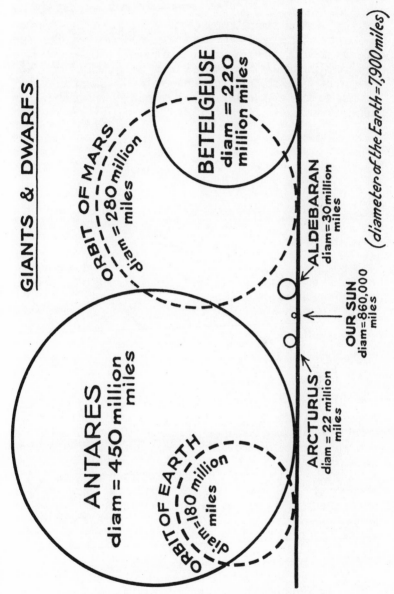

Fig. 88. Examples of stellar giants and dwarfs.

293

particularly those of types O and B) crowd about the great circle marking the fundamental plane of the Galaxy; a similar crowding is shown by the open clusters, novae, Cepheid variables, and gaseous nebulae. Globular clusters and spiral nebulae are more numerous in regions far removed from the galactic plane. The volume of space occupied and defined by the globular clusters appears to coincide approximately with that occupied by the galactic system.

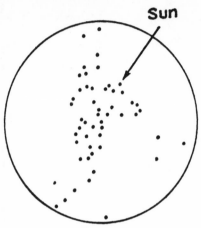

Fig. 89. *Distribution of the globular clusters, and relative position of the Sun (Shapley).*

It was formerly believed, on the authority of Herschel and Kapteyn, that the centre of the galactic system must lie in the vicinity of the Sun, but more recent research has displaced the Sun from the centre; the latter is now believed to lie among the extensive star clouds of the constellations Ophiuchus and Scorpio at a distance of about 30,000 light years from the Sun. If the positions of the known clusters are plotted on a diagram as they would appear to an observer situated out in space at one of the galactic poles, the Sun would occupy the position shown in Figure 89; the radius of the circle is equivalent to a distance of about 75,000 light years.

The Sun in its eccentric position appears to belong to what Shapley has named the Local Cluster, which consists of bright stars in the Sun's neighbourhood. This has the same elongated and flattened form as the main stellar system, but is very much smaller; its median plane does not coincide exactly with that of the Milky Way, being inclined to it at an angle of about 12°. It appears that the Sun is situated close to the central plane of the Galaxy, at a distance of about 100 light years to the north of it (Figure 90).

According to recent work by Oort, Plaskett, Lindblad and others, the whole galactic system is rotating in a manner analogous to that of the planets round the Sun—i.e. its inner parts revolve more rapidly than its outer. The axis of this gigantic system passes through the centre of the system of globular clusters as well as through the centre of the Galaxy. In the vicinity of the Sun the Milky Way completes one revolution in about 230 million years; this implies that the stars in the Sun's neighbourhood have a velocity of more than 200 miles per second, due to this rotation alone.

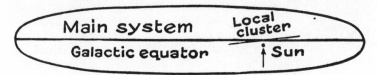

Fig. 90. Cross-section of the Milky Way.

From theoretical considerations concerning the formation and radiation of the stars, Jeans has set an upper limit of 8×10^{12} years on the Sun's age. This takes us back to the remote epoch when, according to current ideas, the Galaxy was being formed from a primordial nebula of extremely low density. Gravitational instability would cause innumerable condensations to separate out of this nebula, as can be seen happening at the present time in many of the extragalactic nebulae in different stages of evolution. The more tenuous the original gas, the heavier would these condensations be, and masses millions of times greater than that of the Sun might be attained. With contraction, the density of these condensations would increase until, when their rotation resulted in the emission of gaseous material, this would form condensations comparable with the Sun in mass—i.e. stellar nuclei, either single or multiple.

According to this hypothesis the Sun might have been formed in such a manner; the Local Cluster perhaps represents one of the masses that condensed out of the parent nebula. The Local Cluster is certainly dependent on, and an integral part of, the Milky Way; the ill-defined frontiers of this star cloud probably fade imperceptibly into the general galactic star field.

Chapter VIII

THE SUN AND THE EARTH

39. *CORRELATIONS BETWEEN SOLAR PHENOMENA AND DISTURBANCES OF THE IONOSPHERE, TERRESTRIAL MAGNETISM AND AURORAE

The study of the Sun's electromagnetic influence on the Earth—whether continuous or, depending on the varied phenomena occurring on the Sun, sporadic—may be said to have been put on a scientific footing when, in 1850, it was discovered almost simultaneously by R. Wolf in Switzerland, Gautier in France, I. Lamont in Germany and E. Sabine in England that there is a connexion between the 11-year solar cycle and that of the variations in the Earth's magnetism.

Although this chapter deals more with geophysics than with astronomy it is nevertheless of interest in relation to what has already been said of the Sun's constitution, as indicating the manner in which its influence can be propagated, and under what conditions and with what velocity it is transmitted to the Earth, where it manifests itself in the form of magnetic and other disturbances.

Since 1850 much experimental and theoretical research has been, and still is being, devoted to this important problem; much progress has been made, including certain developments which may have repercussions on our everyday life. In order to coordinate this research an International Commission was formed in 1924, consisting of members who were specialists in solar physics, astrophysics, geophysics, meteorology, radio communication and allied sciences.

Between 1924 and 1954 the Commission has published, under the auspices of the International Council of Scientific Unions, eight reports on the progress made during these years in the field of terrestrial phenomena which are dependent, or are suspected of being dependent, on solar events. They thus contain the most up-to-date information regarding this important problem.

The relations between solar and terrestrial phenomena can be broadly classified as follows:

(1) variations of terrestrial magnetism,

(2) polar aurorae and the luminosity of the night sky,
(3) the ionosphere,
(4) ozone,
(5) high-frequency radio waves originating in the Sun,
(6) effects on terrestrial meteorology,
(7) effects of terrestrial life.

The first three relationships have now been thoroughly confirmed. The variability of the ozone layer is very probable, but requires further investigation. The fifth, only recently discovered, is already well established. The meteorological effects are extremely problematical, owing to their complexity and to the difficulty of relating them to solar causes; nevertheless it is certain that the influence of the Sun is not negligible. Continued research into this problem is of great importance, since it is clear that its solution would facilitate long-term weather forecasting. Nothing definite is known about the seventh relationship, but it may be noted in this connexion that all the phenomena of nature exhibit cyclic trends. Much work has been done in this field, though it has to be admitted that its scientific value has been small; for the record it may be noted that as far back as 1801, W. Herschel drew attention to the relationship between the price of wheat and solar activity, besides discussing the effects on the weather.

While it is true that we observe on the Sun several classes of phenomenon of which a terrestrial counterpart can be found, it is also true that others are to be found on the Earth (especially as regards its magnetism) for which no corresponding solar happening can be identified. The question therefore arises whether, with the observational means at present available, we may be able to discover or suspect any other categories of phenomena connected with the Sun's activity.

It should be emphasised that until a few years ago the only disturbances that we were able to observe on the Sun were the spots and the faculae, which have been described and counted since Galileo's day. Later, Wolf's relative numbers were introduced, providing a more precise means of evaluating the area of the Sun's surface covered by spots and faculae (p. 73).

Since it was discovered that the limb prominences could be observed in broad daylight with the spectroscope (p. 123), the records of their frequency and extent have provided another valuable index of chromospheric activity. Since 1869 a continuous series of such observations has been accumulating, at first only visual but later photographic also. Finally, the invention of the spectroheliograph and spectrohelioscope opened the way to the study of the calcium and hydrogen distribution in the chromo-sphere, and of the flares, greatly increasing our knowledge of solar storms and their development.

At the 1928 meeting of the International Astronomical Union held at Leyden, it was decided to produce a three-monthly *Bulletin* dealing with solar activity, published regularly by the Zurich Federal Observatory. Its purpose was to provide up-to-date news of the state of the Sun's activity, combining observa-tional data submitted by observatories in all parts of the world, and at the same time to compare these with the observations of terre-strial phenomena reported in geophysical publications. In the course of time the data given in the *Bulletins* have been modified in various ways, so as to suit them better to the advances of the observational work and the research on correlations with ter-restrial phenomena.

At the present time the *Bulletin* gives the following information: (1) the relative spot numbers, (2) the history and development of spot groups—their coordinates, time of central meridian transit, times of appearance and disappearance, the classification of the groups on the Zurich scale, (3) a list of the flares observed with spectroheliographs or spectrohelioscopes (coordinates and inten-sities on a scale of 1 to 3), (4) a list of active regions, (5) the inten-sity of the corona in monochromatic light (i.e. the lines at 5303Å and 6374Å) observed at 5° intervals from high-altitude stations, (6) the radio-frequency radiation of the Sun, and finally (7) a diagram showing the effective hours of spectroheliographic and spectrohelioscopic observation of the Sun from day to day at all the internationally-cooperating observatories.

As an example of such a summary, that relating to the second quarter of 1948 is reproduced in Plate 138; the effective hours of observation, expressed in U.T., are shown by thick horizontal lines. Diagrams are also given showing the intensity of the coronal line at 5303Å, at different position angles; these are based on observations made at the Pic du Midi (France), Arosa (Switzer-land), Climax (U.S.A.) and Wendelstein (Bavaria). Other pub-lications are issued from time to time by other observatories, con-taining data relating to the various solar phenomena. Last-minute news is also given by radio.

One physical cause of the Sun's influence on the Earth is obvious: its ultraviolet and corpuscular radiation. In the past the relative spot numbers have been the fundamental data for the study of correlations of solar with terrestrial events, and it is beyond doubt that magnetic, ionospheric and auroral disturb-ances are more frequent during periods of maximum solar activity than around minima. This is clearly shown when annual averages are used, but becomes confused in the monthly averages and disappears in the daily. This may be because we cannot follow the solar phenomena with sufficient continuity, or because there is a certain lag between the solar cause and the terrestrial effect (due to the lapse of time required by the swarms of particles to reach the Earth), or again because the spots are not the only motivators of these disturbances.

The outstanding fact is that these terrestrial disturbances are repeated after a period equal to that of the Sun's synodic rotation, proving that there are certain zones only (i.e. the disturbed regions of the Sun) which, on coming into a favourable position, are capable of affecting the Earth; hence not only are the spots taken as indices of the Sun's activity, but also the faculae, flocculi, filaments and prominences. Spectroscopic indices and variations in the Sun's ultraviolet emission may also be important.

The magnetic fields of sunspots would not appear capable of producing the observed disturbances at so great a distance as that of the Earth, though it is possible that the lines of magnetic force may provide the trajectories along which ions and electrons escape from the Sun and reach the Earth; charged particles do in fact tend to spiral round such lines of force. The prominences, especially those of the eruptive type, reveal the manner in which considerable quantities of matter can be expelled from the Sun and are then permanently lost to it. Quiescent prominences, on the other hand, appear to be regenerated on the spot, later to fall back into the Sun's surface. At these times, as we have seen, they assume a characteristic filamentous form and expand into a great arch which increases steadily in size and ends by disintegrating, while the matter of which it was composed is lost into space. The difference between bright flocculi and filaments is probably due only to differences of altitude, excitation and absorption, dependent on the temperature and density, probably with a strong augmentation of ultraviolet radiation from the intensely luminous and therefore highly excited material. The thick flares seen in profile on the disc as the extremities of relatively thin columns of very intense hydrogen and calcium, which in the neighbourhood of spots are rapidly renewed in the same position or thereabouts, and which sometimes extend over considerable areas, may represent regions from which an intense flood of ultraviolet is being emitted.

One of the present-day problems in the study of the relationships between solar and terrestrial phenomena is our inability to identify with certainty the precise region of the Sun responsible for the terrestrial disturbances. The recurrence of magnetic storms after about 25–27 days suggests that active areas must be situated on a certain part of the Sun's surface in order to affect the Earth. For if the disturbance could arise from any point whatever on the Sun, the rotation period would not be so sharply indicated. The fact that the disturbances may arise from a zone in high or in low latitudes is another complication. On the other hand it is noticeable that magnetic storms intensify at the time of the equinoxes; at such times the latitude of the centre of the disc is maximal, so that at the equinoxes the zones most favoured by the spots are placed in the most favourable position for influencing the Earth.

The recently discovered radio disturbances originating in the Sun are most conspicuous between 30 and 3000 Mc, with a maximum at about 175–200 Mc. At these frequencies the mean intensity of the noise, if it is assumed to emanate from the whole disc, is equivalent to that of a black body at a temperature of the order of 10^6 degrees. A fluctuating noise is sometimes superimposed on this emission, termed descriptively a 'burst', whose source is small compared with the total area of the Sun. The regions responsible for these bursts seem to be associated with those disturbed by solar storms. It has been calculated that if the origin of the noise were only thermal, the temperature would have to be of the order of 10^9 degrees.

Although, as we have seen, our atmosphere absorbs almost all the ultraviolet radiation reaching it from the Sun, it is nevertheless possible to base predictions of the presence of monochromatic radiations in these regions on the laws of spectroscopy, partially confirmed by spectra obtained at great altitudes with rockets. It seems to be generally accepted that these radiations are responsible for the ionospheric disturbances, while the magnetic and auroral disturbances are caused by slowly moving charged particles whose velocities do not exceed about 1200 miles per second. Both these radiations are betrayed by the ionisation and excitation of the gases in the atmosphere, and their action is so similar that it is sometimes almost impossible to distinguish the effects of one from those of the other.

The velocity of escape from the Sun's gravitational field of those atoms that are expelled from it has a sharply defined threshold, which Milne has calculated to be approximately 1000 miles per second in the case of ionised calcium; with such a velocity a particle would be capable of reaching the Earth and penetrating its atmosphere. The order of size of this limiting velocity is the same for the atoms of some other elements, such as H, He, Ti II, Sr II, Mg and any others whose condition enables them to be supported in the chromosphere by radiation pressure.

It is thus necessary to postulate the existence of a 'permanent radiation', emitted continuously by the Sun, and a 'local radiation', associated with solar storms. To distinguish between ultraviolet and corpuscular radiation it should be noted that:

(1) ultraviolet radiation is propagated linearly, and therefore affects only the daylight hemisphere of the Earth; corpuscular radiation, on the other hand, is deflected by the Earth's magnetic field and can also reach the night-time hemisphere;

(2) during total solar eclipses the ultraviolet radiation is cut off at the same time as the visible radiation; the corpuscular radiation behaves differently (corpuscular eclipse) owing to the velocity of the particles being much smaller than that of light;

(3) the local ultraviolet radiation is usually emitted in all directions; therefore its action is independent of the storm's position on the solar disc; corpuscular radiation, on the contrary, shows itself only when the emission comes from more restricted zones of the disc, and its effects are felt for relatively short periods. Moreover, when the solar storm has a long enough life (and even after it has apparently vanished) the corpuscular radiation can reappear at intervals of one solar synodic rotation (27 days).

Although the permanent ultraviolet radiation creates and maintains the ionosphere, the local ultraviolet radiation is manifested by irregular disturbances of this same ionosphere—the so-called fadeouts of radio transmission. As long ago as 1927 Guglielmo Marconi, speaking about beamed radio communication, cited two instances of interference with the transmission of signals, on 20 September and 14 October of that year, which coincided with the appearance of large sunspots and intense aurorae. At the same time it was noticed that telegraph lines and submarine cables were rendered unusable. In 1930 Mögel drew attention to the fact that short-wave signals sometimes faded out or weakened for short periods (30^m to 60^m), then gradually returned to normal. In 1935 J. H. Dellinger, after examining data from several stations, came to the following conclusions. Fadeouts are only experienced if the radio stations are situated in the hemisphere which is in daylight at the time. The fading is both longer and more sudden, the smaller the distance between the line joining the transmitting and receiving stations and the region of the Earth's surface having the Sun at its zenith. Simultaneously with the fading, weak but characteristic disturbances of the terrestrial magnetic field are experienced, their geographical distribution being similar to that of the radio fadeout.

These facts make it clear that the disturbing radiation must be electromagnetic in origin, for if it were composed of charged particles the part of the Earth in shadow would also be affected, owing to the action of the magnetic field. It is generally agreed that this irregularly disturbing radiation is violent—such as might be ascribed to chromospheric flares which, as we have already seen, involve restricted zones of the Sun while at times achieving very considerable intensity. The main reaction to it seems to develop in the lowest reflecting and conducting layer of the ionosphere—that denoted by the letter D—situated at a height of about 30 miles above the Earth. Owing to the highly ionised condition of this layer the energy of the electromagnetic waves, on the arrival of the ultraviolet radiation emitted by the flare, is dissipated through collisions between the electrons, set in oscillation by the field of the radiation, and the atmospheric atoms and molecules. The resultant complete absorption of all frequencies renders long-distance reception impossible.

The propagation of the electromagnetic waves from flares and other disturbed solar regions takes place at the velocity of light, so that it is after a brief delay that they produce radio fadeouts and the characteristic disturbances of the Earth's magnetic field which show themselves on the diagrams giving a continuous trace of its variations: these are the so-called 'magnetic storms'. They consist typically of a more or less conspicuous 'crochet', indicating a sudden drop in the intensity of the elements of the terrestrial magnetic field. This diminution usually takes several minutes to attain its maximal value, and the subsequent return to normal occurs slowly and without oscillations. It thus appears possible to affirm that there is a connexion between flares, fadeouts and crochets, and that a certain intensity of electromagnetic radiation is necessary in order to provoke the latter. Indeed, when the Sun is low and the ionisation of the ionosphere is weak, crochets are not observed. Nevertheless, it cannot be said that such correlations are always clear and well-defined.

That the Sun's ultraviolet radiation varies with the 11-year cycle has been proved by E. V. Appleton and R. Naismith. In fact, the 'characteristic number'—i.e. the 'critical frequency' expressed numerically in megacycles per second—for the E and F_1 regions of the ionosphere (heights respectively 60 and 120 miles) during the 1933–38 solar cycle varied continuously and in step with the Sun's activity; that is to say, with an increase in the ultraviolet radiation there would be an increased production of electrons, which was minimal at sunspot minimum (1933.8) and maximal at sunspot maximum (1937.5). The ratio of maximal to minimal electron production in the two regions E and F_1 was respectively 2.25:1 and 2.45:1. It follows that the ultraviolet radiation whose absorption is responsible for the formation of the E and F_1 layers varies enormously during the course of the solar cycle.

Coming now to the corpuscular radiation, it is difficult to distinguish between the phenomena produced by the permanent radiation and that by local; to the former may perhaps be attributed aurorae and the 'ring current', while magnetic storms are certainly due to local radiation.

The theoretical researches of C. Störmer have thrown some light on the problem of the paths followed by charged particles moving in the Earth's magnetic field. These are of two types: trajectories surrounding the Earth, which describe a kind of ring in a plane parallel to that of the equator, and trajectories which encounter the Earth in two zones contained within a double cone whose axis is the Earth's magnetic axis. Trajectories of the former type give rise to the ring current, while those of the second type are the paths followed by particles producing the polar aurorae. Theoretical considerations suggest that protons are largely responsible for the generation of aurorae, whose mean altitude above the Earth is about 60 miles.

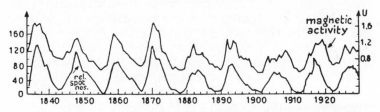

Fig. 91. *Terrestrial magnetic activity* (*u*) *and relative spot numbers from* 1840 *to* 1930.

Magnetic storms are recorded at geophysical observatories by means of appropriate instruments, using the three components of terrestrial magnetic field: the horizontal component H, the vertical component V, and the declination D. They manifest themselves as irregular perturbations of greater or smaller amplitude and duration, which are superimposed upon, and thus modify, the diurnal and seasonal variations due to movements of the ionosphere, amounting normally to about 1%. H and V are measured in the conventional unit $\gamma = 10^{-3}$ gauss, and D in degrees and minutes.

Magnetic storms are classified into four groups: violent, with

303

variations of H exceeding 330γ and of D exceeding $60'$; strong; moderate; and weak, with barely perceptible variations. While the crochet due to electromagnetic radiation may be geographically restricted, these other disturbances of the magnetic field involve the whole world, and occur at night as well as during the day.

The correlation between solar and magnetic storms also shows itself clearly in the 11-year cycle, as can be seen by comparing the curve of the relative spot numbers with the characteristic numbers of terrestrial magnetic activity. In general outline the latter exactly follows the solar vicissitudes, though the correlation is complicated by the mode of emission of the corpuscular radiation by the Sun, and of its entry into the Earth's magnetic field (Figure 91).

Past maxima of solar activity have provided many observations illustrating the connexion between the passage of large spot groups across the Sun's disc and magnetic storms on the Earth. As a typical example, the case is here described of the storm produced by an unusually large group that crossed the Sun's central meridian on 1941 September 17. A very strong flare developed (precisely at $9^h\ 27^m$ U.T.—Figure 92), as so often happens in such groups when at their greatest development, and lasted for over an hour. The traces of the three field components were suddenly distorted by characteristic crochets; on the following day at $5^h\ 48^m$ U.T. began the notable disturbances which lasted throughout the 18th and 19th. It is clear that two characteristic features of terrestrial magnetism are caused by the eruptions: the first—of short duration, synchronous with the flare—caused by ultraviolet radiation, and the second caused by a stream of particles, which, starting in this case about 20 hours later, achieved its greatest intensity between 30 and 41 hours afterwards. In this instance the particles emitted by the Sun with the highest velocities travelled to the Earth at more than 1000 miles per second, the majority at between 900 and 600 miles per second, and the slowest at about 450 miles per second. The central position of this particular spot group was particularly favourable for the encounter between the corpuscular radiation and the Earth. During the night 18–19 September there was, in addition to the magnetic storm, an imposing auroral display, observed under optimum seeing conditions by M. Waldmeier at Arosa Observatory.

Magnetic storms and aurorae are therefore two different effects of the same cause—irruptions of corpuscular radiation into the Earth's atmosphere. The corpuscular swarm, investing the Earth and strongly disturbing the equilibrium of the ionosphere, enters the terrestrial magnetic field and suffers deviations whose principal

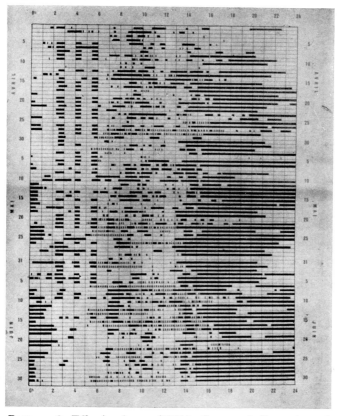

PLATE 138. Effective hours (U.T.) of spectrohelioscopic and spectroheliographic observation of the Sun during the second quarter of 1948 (d'Azambuja).

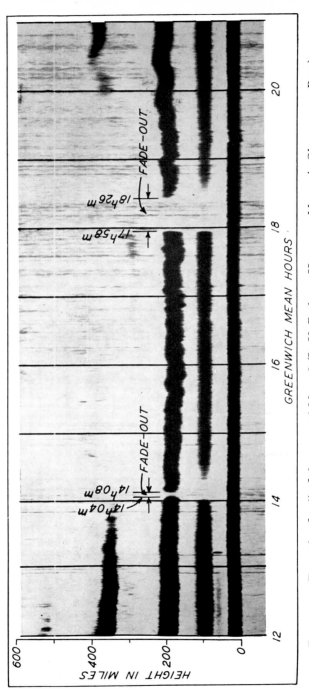

PLATE 139. Example of radio fadeout, 1936 May 28 (L. V. Berkner, Huancayo Magnetic Observatory, Peru).

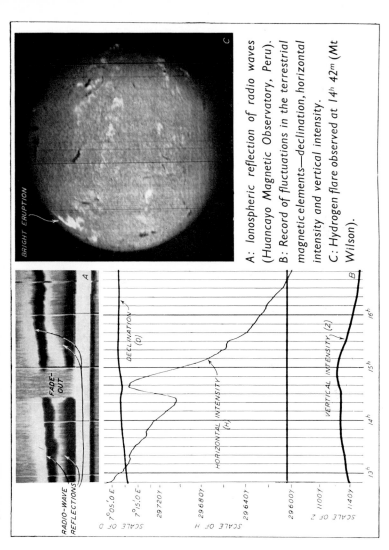

A: *Ionospheric reflection of radio waves (Huancayo Magnetic Observatory, Peru).*

B: *Record of fluctuations in the terrestrial magnetic elements—declination, horizontal intensity and vertical intensity.*

C: *Hydrogen flare observed at 14ʰ 42ᵐ (Mt Wilson).*

PLATE 140. Variations of terrestrial magnetism and interruption of radio reflection from the ionosphere caused by a solar flare, 1937 August 28 (A. G. McNish).

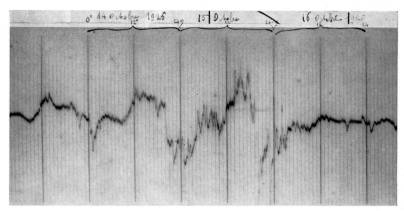

PLATE 141. Variations of magnetic declination recorded at Meudon during the magnetic storm of 1926 October 14–15.

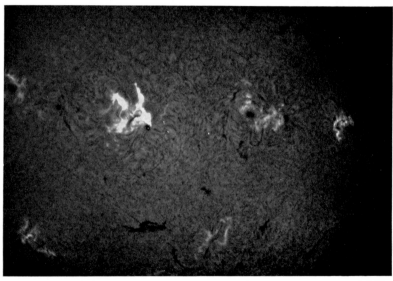

PLATE 142. Hydrogen flare observed on 1926 October 13 at 13^h 15^m U.T. (Meudon).

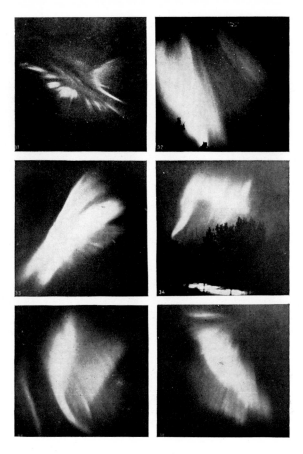

PLATE 143. Different types of aurora polaris (Störmer).

PLATE 144. Sections of conifers (*Pinus silvestris*) from Eberswalde, showing increased annual growth during sunspot maxima.

PLATE 145. Section of the conifer *Pinus Pinea* from Ravenna (U. Buli).

PLATE 146. Parabolic antenna at the Radiophysics Laboratory, Sydney (Australia), for receiving radio waves emitted by the Sun and stars.

PLATE 147. 250-ft radio-telescope at Jodrell Bank (Manchester University).

effect is to concentrate it in the regions of the magnetic poles where, on reaching the atmosphere, it gives rise to aurorae and variations in the magnetic field. It is for this reason that both magnetic storms and aurorae are normally encountered in high latitudes, and only in cases of very exceptional solar activity in lower latitudes.

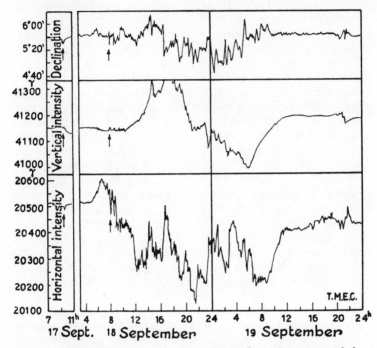

Fig. 92. Magnetic storm of 1941 *September* 18–19 *recorded at Regensberg Observatory (F. Götz).*

The northern zone of maximum auroral frequency is bounded by a line running from North Cape along the northern coast of Nova Zembla (the extreme north-east point of Siberia), through Hudson's Bay, Labrador, and the southern parts of Greenland and Iceland. This zone includes both the geographical and magnetic poles; the same is the case in the southern hemisphere.

For the record, let us recall that it was G. B. Donati who, on the occasion of the great aurora which was observed from all parts of the world during the night of 1872 February 4–5, for the first time stated definitely that this phenomenon must be dependent on causes located in the Sun. A particularly notable sunspot maximum had occurred two years previously, and the Sun was still in a thoroughly disturbed condition, as was shown by the large number of spots observed in that year. The February aurora was observed from localities scattered all over the Earth; an admirable description of it was given by Fr Secchi in the meteorological bulletin of the Observatory of the Collegio Romano.

Donati collected as much information as possible about the circumstances of the aurora by means of a questionnaire sent to all Italian consuls, and in his memoir (the first and last that he wrote at Arcetri before his premature death) he discussed all the reasons for believing that the aurora was of cosmic, or rather solar, origin. Comparing the times at which the aurora appeared in different localities, he concluded that 'The luminous phenomenon of the great polar aurora which was observed over vast areas of the world during the night of 1872 February 4-5 was first seen in the east and later in the west; and it was observed at each place at about the same local time, though with an east-to-west tendency to appear rather earlier.' Having thus established the fact that the appearance of the aurora was connected with the apparent motion of the Sun, and could therefore not have a terrestrial meteorological origin, he affirmed the necessity of invoking a new 'cosmic meteorology'. 'The phenomena of sunspots,' he wrote, 'as well as all the other phenomena occurring on the Sun do indeed lie outside the domain of the old meteorology, and if aurorae are related to solar events we are forced to the conclusion that they are dependent not only on meteorological causes, properly so called, but also on cosmic causes.'

Since Donati's time, the cosmic origin of aurorae having finally been put beyond all doubt, many observations and experiments have been made, and theories propounded, to account for their formation. This has particularly been the case in Norway, where, as we have seen, the aurorae can be observed with greater frequency; simultaneous photographs have been taken from different stations with a view to determining their heights, and their emission spectra have been investigated.

In 1896 Birkeland discovered that a magnetic pole acts upon a beam of cathode rays in the same way as a lens upon a beam of parallel light, focusing it to a point. He therefore concluded that aurorae are due to cathode rays from the Sun experiencing a similar effect in the Earth's magnetic field. By means of a spherical electromagnet and a beam of cathode rays he was able to reproduce the principal features of aurorae experimentally.

Störmer, who has carried out much theoretical and experimental work in this field, assumed that the relative motions of the Sun and Earth may be neglected and that the Earth's magnetic field is similar to that of a uniformly magnetised sphere; on this basis he was able to calculate the trajectories of electrified particles emanating from the Sun. The results obtained were very satisfactory, and he extended his investigation to cover the trajectories of both positively and negatively charged particles moving with different velocities. In this way he was able to account for the observed appearances and heights of the aurorae, the latitude of the zone of maximum frequency, and the fact that aurorae extending to low latitudes are always accompanied by magnetic storms. According to Störmer's theory, the cathode rays are curved in towards the Earth while still a very great distance from it, thus approaching the polar regions where they produce aurorae on the side of the globe not illuminated by the Sun; many other trajectories also encounter the Earth, especially in antarctic regions.

The gas constituting this corpuscular swarm ejected from the Sun will be predominantly hydrogen, but owing to its high degree of ionisation it will not be observable spectrographically. Calcium will be present in the form of Ca II ions, and should therefore be observable, since it would give rise to an absorption band displaced slightly towards the violet from the H and K lines. This additional absorption, of the order of 1%, appears to have been observed on several occasions. Following the outbreak of one violent magnetic storm H. A. Brück and F. Rutlant, for example, detected a small depression in the violet wings of the H and K lines at the critical moment, indicating a cloud of particles moving at a velocity of about 460 miles per second.

Satisfactorily though the correlation between solar storms, magnetic storms and aurorae may appear to have been established, it must nevertheless be admitted that many magnetic storms occur for which no corresponding solar event can be traced. But it is to be observed that magnetic storms show a strongly marked tendency to repeat themselves after an interval equal to the Sun's synodic rotation period, namely 27 days.

It is necessary to make a distinction between great magnetic storms—such as that of 1941, already referred to—which originate in a solar eruption (flare) of exceptional intensity, and weak magnetic storms: whereas the former develop with great violence, and may not be repeated after 27 days, the latter show a marked tendency to repeat after 27, 54, 81 etc. days. This suggests that from certain special regions of the Sun, where nothing out of the ordinary is visible to the eye, streams of corpuscles are ejected like jets of water for weeks or even months on end; these are directed towards a certain point in space, and whenever the Earth encounters their trajectory it will become invested in a swarm of particles.

Such special and well-defined regions, termed 'M-regions' by J. Bartels, can thus only be identified through the disturbances of the Earth's magnetic field that they cause. Though their duration is limited it generally exceeds the lifetime of spot groups, and may be as long as ten or more solar rotations. Research carried out at Arcetri, based on spectroscopic images of the solar limb and synoptic charts, suggests that the M-regions may be identified with the filament-prominences, which, as we have seen, are often long lived; this result was later confirmed at Zurich.

Another phenomenon needing further investigation and clarification is the general increase of solar activity around the times of the equinoxes, when a corresponding increase in terrestrial magnetic activity is experienced. In this connexion it may be remarked that at the equinoxes the inclination of the Sun's axis to the Earth-Sun direction has its greatest positive and negative values, and hence the preferred zone of the spots is in the most favourable position for affecting the Earth.

As regards the regions of the Sun that are involved, it should also be noted that the very variable intensity of different regions of the corona is nowadays under continuous observation at a number of high-altitude observatories. It seems that these very active regions—which may have no counterpart disturbances whatsoever in the photosphere or chromosphere—may be connected in some way with the M-regions.

Since, as Waldmeier pointed out, the most clearly marked 27-day sequences occur immediately before spot minimum, when the corona assumes its equatorial form, it is permissible to suppose that, hidden from our eyes beneath the Sun's surface, those processes are in preparation which later will break through the surface and give rise to the observable phenomena.

40. *THE SUN'S RADIO-SPECTRUM

The name 'radio-spectrum' may be given to the long-wave radiation that is emitted by the stars—long, that is, compared with the 'optical spectrum' with which we have so far been dealing; it lies beyond the long-wave end of the latter spectrum, and is separated from it by a wide zone of absorption due principally to the numerous bands of water vapour in our atmosphere. At the low-frequency end the stellar radio-spectrum extends as far as the 'short waves', and there comes to an end owing to ionospheric absorption. Its limits may be set approximately at $\lambda = 100$ m on one side and $\lambda = 0.5$ cm on the other. If, within this range, the radiated energy had a purely thermal origin, its distribution in the radio-spectrum would be regulated by the black body laws, but from experiments so far carried out in a narrow section of the spectrum, it appears rather that there is a preponderance of non-thermal and still unknown processes involved in its production, similar to those which we have already had occasion to study in connexion with the corona and the prominences.

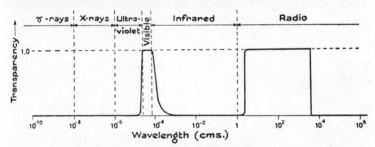

Fig. 93. Transparency of the Earth's atmosphere to electromagnetic radiations of different wavelengths.

In 1916 Marconi reported to the Accademia dei Lincei that the naturally produced electrical waves termed 'interference' or 'atmospherics' could not be wholly atmospheric in origin, and that the latter appelation was probably inaccurate. He further stated that 'it is still uncertain if these waves are produced by very distant electrical discharges, either by electrical disturbances in the Earth's interior or disturbances situated outside the Earth and its atmosphere. Simultaneous observations made over a period of several years at the long-distance radiotelegraphic stations in Europe and America have proved that in many cases the same disturbance is experienced at the same time—i.e. at the identical instant—and with the same intensity on both sides of the Atlantic. This would lead one to believe that these waves originate at a great distance, compared with the distance of about 2500 miles separating the transatlantic stations.'

A specific source of extraterrestrial signals, coming from the Milky Way, was discovered in 1931 by K. G. Jansky of the Bell Telephone Company: while investigating the origin of interference on the 15-metre wavelength he noted that an increase in background noise occurred when the aerial was directed at the Galaxy. Later research, carried out in England by E. V. Appleton, J. S. Hey and their collaborators, has shown by means of radar tuned to

5 metres that the origin of this 'galactic noise' is to be found in the Scorpio-Sagittarius region, i.e. in the direction of the centre of the Milky Way.

During the summer of 1942 radar employed in the defence of the coasts of Britain was prevented from functioning by a continuous 'noise' of mysterious provenance. At first it was thought that an enemy anti-radar device was responsible, but scanning of the sky very soon proved that the responsibility for the interference lay with the Sun—on which, at that time, several notable storms were raging. On this occasion, also, it was possible to distinguish between 'permanent' and 'sporadic' radiation. The former probably originates from the whole disc as well as from outside it, in the chromosphere and corona, while the latter is produced by the active regions in a manner which is still not clear.

Observations of the radio-spectrum are today being made by a variety of receiving methods in all parts of the world. Many types of antenna have been experimented with as receivers of the solar radio waves in different wavelengths. The commonest consists of a parabolic lattice which acts like an optical parabolic mirror, although, obviously, it does not demand the degree of precision with which optical reflectors are made. While the surfaces of the latter must be worked to 0·1 micron, the required precision for the reflectors of radio-telescopes is of the order of 1 to 10 cms, according to the wavelength. The lattices are constructed of metal and are mounted in such a way as to allow movement in azimuth and altitude; alternately, and more conveniently, they have an equatorial mounting which allows the Sun to be followed in its apparent diurnal motion across the sky. Different dipoles, mounted at the focus of the lattice, enable different wavelengths to be received. Many such telescopes have already been built and are in operation in all parts of the world. At the Jodrell Bank station of the University of Manchester a radio-telescope with a lattice 250 feet in diameter is under construction; this will permit the recording of low-intensity radio waves with great resolving power.

While the galactic radiation shows only small-scale variations—not exceeding 10 to 15% of the normal value—that of the Sun sometimes reaches very high values when exceptional storms are in progress on the Sun. One of the earliest well established observations was that made by Hey in 1942: this radio storm maintained a high intensity throughout the daytime of 27 February, disappeared completely at sunset, and reappeared the following morning immediately after sunrise. It was thus clear that direct solar radiation was involved, and not, as had also been suggested, a secondary radiation produced in the ionosphere by solar excitation. During these particular days a spot group, whose area

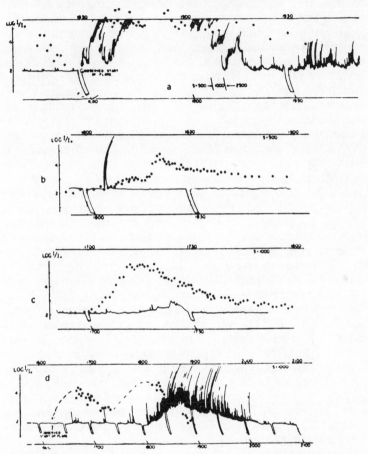

Fig. 94. Examples of 200 Mc/sec radiation associated with flares. Light curves for the flares (series of dots) are superimposed on the radio records. (a) Major burst, 1950 May 20. (b) Minor burst, 1950 October 17. (c) Small rise in base level, 1949 June 22. (d) Series of bursts, 1950 June 1. (Abscissae, Universal Time; ordinates, intensities of flares and of bursts on 200 Mc/sec.)

measured more than 1500 millionths of the disc, was crossing the central meridian, and intense flares were observed at Arcetri, Greenwich and Sherborne. 28 February was marked by a complete fadeout in short-wave radio transmission, and 24 hours later a violent magnetic storm disturbed the magnetometer records. Hey considers that the radiation responsible for radio noise of this intensity must have a temperature of 10^8 degrees K.

In the 1–10 metre band (300–30 Mc) the intensity of the radiation is enormously greater than the heat energy one would expect at these wavelengths. G. Reber, in the United States, describes in the following terms a violent interference experienced during the afternoon of 1946 November 21, the occasion also of numerous solar flares: 'The loudspeaker produced hissing sounds very similar to those which normally constitute the thermal background noise. But instead of maintaining a constant acoustic level their intensity fluctuated rapidly, producing an effect similar to that of the wind whistling through leafless trees. Now and then more intense hisses were superimposed on the variable background noise; the crackling noises characteristic of atmospherics were entirely absent. When the antenna was pointed at 90° from the Sun, the background noise disappeared, and was only to be heard from time to time, and then much weakened. At times the noise of the interference attained 400 times the normal value of the background noise; the whistles certainly exceeded the mean value by several thousand times. During the following night very weak noises, similar to those of the daytime, were heard; louder hisses, lasting about a quarter of a second, were, however, distinctly heard at irregular intervals of from one to two minutes. Often these hisses were accompanied by a faint rasping sound.' It is important to note that while Reber was making these observations on the 6-metre wavelength, at the nearby laboratory of the Bell Telephone Company nothing abnormal was heard on a wavelength of 1·25 cm. The phenomenon is thus only to be encountered on the metre wavebands, vanishing on the cm wavebands; nor is it observable on wavelengths longer than 30 metres, owing to ionospheric absorption.

The observations of Appleton and Hey have shown that no direct proportionality exists between the areas of the sunspots and the volume of the noise. All that can be said at the present time is that the larger the spot, the more intense the noise. The continuous emission of the spots is extremely variable, being at some times relatively constant and at others fluctuating continuously and rapidly. It has also been noted that active spots produce a sharply defined maximum of radio noise when in the vicinity of the central meridian, indicating that the interference is propagated as a beam roughly perpendicular to the spot. True 'bursts', of the kind associated with flares, are superimposed on the background radio noise; in this case, also, no proportionality with the intensity of the flare can be observed, though the brighter it is the greater is the probability of an associated burst. It seems, however, that the bursts dependent on flares do not exhibit the characteristic of well-defined direction which is shown by the radio noise produced by sunspots, because a sharp maximum simultaneous with the phenomenon is not observed in the case of flares occurring near the Sun's central meridian. The bursts are generally registered over a wide waveband, and they are sometimes of very spectacular intensity.

The mean observed emission is equivalent to a radiation temperature of the order of 10^6 degrees K, with wide fluctuations. When the radio noise is at its loudest it approaches a temperature of 10^{12} degrees K, comparing the emission to that of a black body the same size as the solar storm.

Although this research into the solar radio waves is still in its infancy it has been possible to establish the fact that when the Sun is undisturbed we receive signals of constant intensity on various frequencies, originating in (a) the chromosphere, with a temperature between 10,000 and 40,000° K, extending from the photosphere to an altitude of 6000 miles, (b) the corona, at a temperature of a million degrees, extending from the chromosphere for a distance of several solar radii.

When the Sun is disturbed, very striking variations of the radio noise are recorded, and these have no counterpart in the optical continuous spectrum. Violent fluctuations on the metre wavelengths may attain intensities a million times that of the radiation from the undisturbed Sun. Activity of this sort is generally recorded for several days before and after the passage of large spots across the central meridian. At higher frequencies (above 600 Mc/sec) the variations are smaller, and are approximately proportional to the size of the spot. Bright hydrogen flocculi and intense coronal regions, which sometimes survive for several days after the disappearance of the spot, appear to be closely related, or may themselves be the source of the radio waves.

The existence of a marked difference in the type of radiowave activity above and below the 400 to 500 Mc/sec frequency level appears to be well established.

The technical difficulties encountered in these radio observations are of various kinds: every wavelength requires apparatus and antennae expressly calculated for the purpose; the energy is so small that it is easily confused with the background noise of the receiver; and the resolving power of the instruments is very low. The resolving power of a telescope, whether for visual or radio frequencies, is given by

$$\epsilon = \frac{1 \cdot 22\lambda}{D}$$

where ϵ is the smallest angle that the instrument is capable of resolving, λ is the wavelength, and D is the aperture of the telescope. Thus for a wavelength of 10 cm and an aperture of 10 m the resolving threshold is about 1/100 of a radian, or half a degree. In order to attain resolving powers comparable with that of the naked eye (i.e. about 1') D would have to be increased beyond the practicable limit. One equipment, due to Reber, consists of large paraboloids which reflect the radio waves to the instrument's focus, where the antenna is located. Another arrangement is used at Cambridge by M. Ryle and his collaborators; it consists of a series of half-wave dipoles. When the distance between two of these antennae is equal to a whole number of wavelengths the resulting arrangement is similar to Michelson's stellar interferometer. By its means a resolution of about 6' is obtained.

Classification of Solar Radio Waves (Pawsey & Smerd)

Class	Characteristics and duration	Origin	Range of wavelengths
Basic thermal component	constant over years	whole Sun	unlimited
Variable component	slow variation, 27-day component	sunspots, small areas	3–60 cm (10,000–500 Mc/sec)
Noise storm (high intensity)	with or without numerous bursts; hours or days	large sunspots	1–15 m (300–20 Mc/sec)
Outburst (high intensity)	minutes no certain distinction	flare	8 mm–15 m (38,000–20 Mc/sec)
Isolated burst (high intensity)	seconds	unknown	1–15 m (300–20 Mc/sec)

We are still too near the beginning of these investigations of the radio-spectra of the Sun and stars to formulate hypotheses regarding the origin of the radio-frequency emissions. We may merely recall that in the corona there must exist free electrons whose velocities correspond to temperatures of the order necessary for the production of the radio noise, and that the great importance of the electromagnetic interpretation of the solar phenomena grows ever more apparent. Meanwhile it can be said that whereas the energy radiated by the Sun in the optical wavelength range is virtually constant—to which constancy we owe the possibility of life on our planet—the variations of the energy radiated in the radio wavelength range are of the order of several hundred, or even several thousand, per cent.

41. *Probability of Correlating Solar Phenomena with Terrestrial Meteorology

Correlations between the fluctuating activity of the Sun and meteorological conditions over the whole of the world must exist, but they are so complex that up to now it has proved impossible to reach any sure and well defined conclusions.

It is certain that the vicissitudes of our atmosphere do not coincide in any obvious way with those of the Sun throughout the 11-year cycle of the latter's activity, and the analysis of data relating to individual periods and groups of consecutive periods shows that cycles do indeed occur, but that these vary in amplitude and are occasionally of opposite phase. No explanation has so far been found that will give a reasonable account of the facts, which are different in different parts of the world and may exhibit opposite effects according to geographical position. It is indeed very difficult to foresee what effect an increase of solar activity might be expected to have on the weather of a particular locality; it is usually assumed that the temperature would rise in some areas and fall in others, but this also would vary according to the season.

The general circulation of the atmosphere would no doubt be intensified, but what sort of modifications this would introduce— for example in the distribution of pressure and rainfall—cannot at present be decided. Neither is it certain that an increase in the solar radiation reaching the Earth would mean an increase in the radiation received at its surface, for the upper atmosphere might at the same time become more opaque and thus transmit less. Hence although there is evidence that variations of terrestrial temperature must depend on variations of solar activity, it must nevertheless be concluded that fluctuations of the Sun's radiation are not the direct cause of variations in the elements of terrestrial meteorology.

Attempts have been made to establish numerous relationships: for example, the areas of glaciers in the polar basins as related to the number of sunspots, variations of atmospheric pressure, rainfall, the annual rings of trees, the levels of large lakes, floods, etc.

Investigations of the growth of trees have furnished some very interesting results. It is well known that each year a growing tree forms a new layer of wood, called the 'meristem'; these growth rings are alternately light and dark, so that merely by counting them one may determine the age of the tree. But in addition to this, from the width of the rings one may deduce whether the conditions during a given year were favourable or unfavourable to its growth. The species and age of the plant, conditions of the soil, the more or less direct action of the Sun's radiation, rainfall, and the variations of climatic conditions generally, are the factors which regulate the growth and therefore the size of the rings.

The study of the probable correlations between the development of the growth rings on the one hand, and soil and cosmic conditions on the other, was initiated in America, notably by A. E. Douglass. The new branch of the science of forestry thus created, termed 'dendrology', is of interest also for its astrophysical relevance. Leonardo da Vinci, when he attributed the increased growth of trees to the Sun and rain, was certainly one of the pioneers of dendrology, for he actually wrote, 'The southern side of plants shows greater vigour and youthfulness than the northern. The rings of sawn branches show the number of their years, and which were damper and which drier, according to their greater or smaller thickness. Thus is revealed the direction in the world which these were facing, for they are thicker towards the south than towards the north, and the centre of a tree is for this reason nearer to the bark on the north than on the south side.' During the last few decades dendrology has been considerably extended in the United States by the investigation of trees several thousand years old, such as *sequoia gigantea* and *pinus silvestris*. Other noteworthy work has recently been undertaken in Italy by U. Buli on the growth rhythms of trees in the pine forest of Ravenna, and elsewhere in Italy and Europe. The latter were undertaken by Buli using the method of periodic analysis evolved by F. Vercelli, who himself provided an example of this analysis as applied to one of the longest available sequences of growth rings—that of a *sequoia gigantea* stretching from 274 B.C. to A.D. 1914, i.e. the better part of 2200 years. In Figures 95 and 96 are shown, as an example, the results of this analysis of the early phase of the tree (274–144 B.C.) and of the final phase (A.D. 1780–1914).

The initial phase is the more interesting, showing the rapid growth of the young plant, which at times exceeded 4 mm per year and was subject to wide fluctuations. That shown by the median

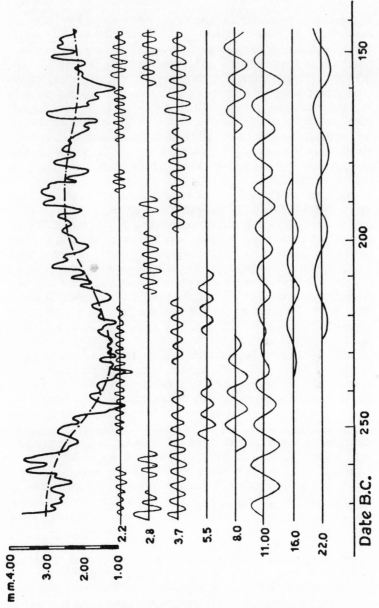

Fig. 95. *Periodic analysis of the dendrological sequence of a* Sequoia gigantea; *young phase (F. Vercelli).*

317

axis of the curve is not repetitive and therefore cannot be regarded as a periodic phenomenon. Extremely obvious, however, are the oscillations of about 11·1 years, which must be traced to solar causation, and the way in which the agreement with the curve of relative spot numbers is suppressed for a certain number of years, later to be resumed with increasing amplitude. The 11-year wave is taken as the principal one since the periods of all the others, both in the growth-ring curves and the solar curves, are linked harmonically with it. Figure 95 shows that the higher harmonics, within the limits of accuracy involved in the calculation, have very nearly the exact values $\frac{1}{2}, \frac{1}{3}, \frac{1}{4}, \frac{1}{5}$ of 11 years. The final phase also exhibits the typical 11-year wave, characteristic of the cyclic activity of the Sun, well developed over almost the whole of the diagram, but suppressed in the final section. Since, in this instance, we can avail ourselves of the solar data, we can observe how the maxima and minima of the corresponding phases of the 11-year wave of the relative spot numbers are, to a good degree of approximation, in phase with the main growth periods of the *sequoia*. Assuming that the agreement of phase observed during the last two centuries applies also to the preceding centuries, we may conclude that the positions of the 11-year wave throughout the whole 2000 years of the plant's life establish the principal phases of the solar activity curve. Herein lies the importance of the contribution of dendrological analysis to the study of solar physics. In this Figure will be noticed also the waves of about 16 and 8 years' duration which we have also encountered among solar phenomena, just as they occur in the secular climatic elements. Vercelli pointed out that the following characteristics are common to all the component waves: their typical period, their variable amplitude, and their discontinuity. The waves are in fact intermittent, and when they recur they are not necessarily of the same phase as the previous section; they cannot therefore be regarded as cyclic sequences. A difference to be noted between the solar curve and the dendrological and climatic curve is that the former is predominant and repeats itself indefinitely, though with varying amplitude, whereas the latter, even though of the same period, is discontinuous and therefore not to be regarded as cyclic in character.

From examples of *sequoia gigantea*, whose lifetime extends over a span of 3500 years, it is possible to trace the 11-year cycle back to 1000 B.C. Relatively few species of tree show so well defined a correlation, and this is to be explained by differences of climate in different regions, which are capable of suppressing the 11-year effect. In the American *sequoia*, for example, the dominant influence affecting its annual growth is moisture, since the regions in which it occurs are generally semi-arid, while the pines examined by Buli have their roots buried in a permanently damp stratum. The comparison of, and correlation between, plants of the same epoch but of diverse localities might therefore be extremely interesting.

Why trees grow more rapidly at epochs of sunspot maximum than of minimum, when it is so difficult to trace the climatic correlations, is not clear. It must be assumed that the variable conditions of the Sun's activity affect the growth of plants through the agency of factors which are at present unknown. For example, the exceptional emission of ultraviolet radiation may affect the quantity of ozone in the atmosphere in such a way as to make the ozone layer thinner at sunspot maximum, and thus increase the atmosphere's transparency to the ultraviolet rays.

Correlations between the rainfall in various parts of the world and the activity of the Sun have been the subject of much investigation, but with dubious and contradictory results. This may be explained by the fact that rainfall depends upon a variety of circumstances, and even meteorological stations that are relatively close to one another can give very different results. More promising is the research that has been carried out over wide areas such as the great basins that constitute the African lakes—Nyasa, Victoria and Albert. Evidence has accumulated showing that at some sunspot maxima the mean level of these lakes is about 3 feet higher than at minima. More recently the same trend has been discovered in the case of the Caspian Sea and other lakes.

It has also been noticed that at epochs of maximum solar activity the annual number of terrestrial cyclones is greater than at minima. This suggests that increased solar activity produces an increase in the circulation of the terrestrial atmosphere, and hence an increased production of tropical storms, and rainfall.

The correlation of solar phenomena with the intensity of cosmic radiation has also been the subject of investigation. A remarkable increase of cosmic radiation was, for instance, recorded in various parts of the world in February and March 1942 and in July 1946, almost simultaneously with the appearance of solar flares. Forbush, who made an analysis of the phenomenon, has advanced the hypothesis that all three increases could have been caused by charged particles emitted by the Sun with sufficient energy to reach the Earth in mid-geomagnetic latitudes. In this type of correlation, also, the question is extremely complex, and linked with the irregular fluctuations of the cosmic rays which are dependent upon variations of atmospheric pressure as well as the seasons. It is certainly not surprising that, as in the case of solar storms, we should

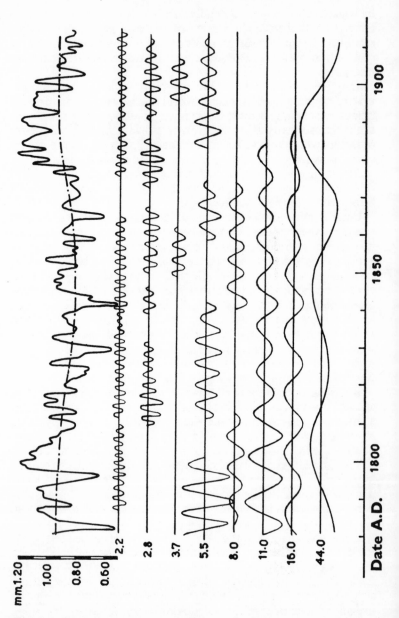

Fig. 96. *Periodic analysis of the dendrological sequence of a* Sequoia gigantea; *final phase (F. Vercelli).*

be concerned with penetrating charged particles; but observations have not yet progressed far enough to allow the formulation of satisfactory explanations or hypotheses.

This vast field of research demands, as may easily be imagined, extensive international cooperation, and this has only fairly recently been inaugurated. There is no doubt that with the development of this cooperation and of new methods, and ultimately new correlations, remarkable and important results will be reached, both from the theoretical and practical viewpoint of the influence of the Sun upon our planet.

42. *THE UTILISATION OF SOLAR HEAT

Numerous attempts have been made at different times to convert into the form of mechanical energy the vast quantities of energy that the Sun pours down upon the Earth in the form of heat and light. There are regions of the world where the continuous action of the Sun, uninterrupted by clouds, can produce

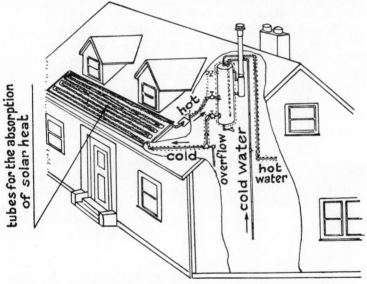

Fig. 97. The utilisation of solar energy for domestic purposes.

on a surface of 2 square metres energy corresponding to about 1 H.P. per day. But owing to the small temperature rise involved in such direct methods of utilising the Sun's heat, all 'solar machines' so far evolved have had too low an efficiency. It is for

35—T.S.   321

this reason that they have so far met with no practical success when, as is frequently the case, they are based on the employment of parabolic mirrors to converge the Sun's rays to a focus in order to heat water or other substances.

It should also be borne in mind that owing to the abundance and ease of employment of fuels and hydraulic forces that are today at our disposal, attempts to utilise the Sun's energy more or less directly will probably remain on the drawing-board for a long time to come.

On the other hand it is probable that for special purposes, and in particular localities of exceptional sunshine, an economic and practicable utilisation of solar heat will be achieved—has, indeed, already been achieved.

In the United States, special funds have been set aside for the study of this problem and for the development of new types of trees and plants which are better adapted to the utilisation of the Sun's heat. Attempts to concentrate the radiation by means of mirrors or lenses, so as to produce energy by the raising of the temperature, have not met with much success. The main difficulty is the storage of the heat that has been collected; the Sun shines only intermittently—whether because of clouds or the alternation of day and night—whereas for the plant to be efficient it must be working continuously. It therefore appears that at the present time a practicable installation cannot be constructed on these principles.

In the United States—particularly in Florida and California, where the incidence of sunshine is exceptional—living houses have been built which incorporate solar heating: they are provided with a large area of roof which faces south and is covered with glass like a greenhouse; into this roof are built blackened tubes through which air or water circulates. The heated material circulates as in an ordinary radiator and is collected in a special tank. It appears that in these regions the consumption of fuel required to maintain a given comfortable temperature and to furnish hot water for domestic purposes has in this way been cut by 50%.

In his youth Antonio Pacinotti, while working on the invention of the famous ring which bears his name, also pioneered this field, as is proved by his writings and lectures on the subject. In a series of letters to his father he expounded various projects for the utilisation of solar heat, among others that of exploiting the temperature difference between the surface and the depths of the sea or of a reservoir—a scheme that is still being tried at the present time.

At a meeting of the Società Agraria of Bologna, held in June

1870, he also outlined other schemes; one of these, which promised good results, was based on chemical decomposition to drive gas engines. He concluded with the words, 'I can make no estimate of the benefits that may accrue from these inventions, but I believe that in some suitable localities they could be used with advantage. And I am of the opinion that the benefit to be derived from the installation of a heat-absorbing pipe-system in the Sahara would be considerable, if the pipes were supported on pillars and spaced some distance apart so as to protect the ground beneath and thus render it suitable for the cultivation of plants or for human habitation.'

The essentials of Pacinotti's ideas are today beginning to be put into practice, as we shall see shortly, and there is no doubt that they will lead to concrete results. It has indeed been proposed to use evaporation basins situated below sea level—as, for example, the Lake of Tiberias, the Dead Sea, the Jordan valley, the Caspian Sea, and certain regions in Eritrea. In the case of the Jordan valley the scheme is to pump water from the Mediterranean into a reservoir, from which it would be discharged by turbines in two steps (of about 1000 and 600 feet) into the Lake of Tiberias and then into the Dead Sea; altogether about 20,000 H.P. would be developed, and the existing hydrological conditions of the region would remain unchanged owing to the rapid rate of evaporation. In this scheme, therefore, solar heat would only play the secondary role of maintaining the basins below a constant or fairly constant level.

Winds also—which owe their generation to the Sun's heat—are being used in various ways for producing mechanical energy, usually on a small scale. Their employment on a larger scale would be possible, according to modern plans, by using solar heat to induce ascending currents of air artificially. The air heated by the Sun at a low level and therefore at a relatively high atmospheric pressure, would be allowed to rise through suitable pipes to higher levels of lower pressure. The air passing through the pipes would develop a vortical motion similar to that with which tropical cyclones begin, and if the pipes were properly insulated against radiation the temperature difference between the air issuing from them and the surrounding air should produce an air current with a velocity of about 150 m.p.h. This current, which is comparable with those developed in natural cyclones, would be strong enough to drive turbines situated at the upper end of the pipes. The stations would have to be built in very hot regions where there are mountain slopes to support the pipelines. The Sahara would offer suitable conditions, and it appears that experiments along these lines are being made in the Atlas and Ahaggar Mountains with a view to supplying energy to Tunisia, Algeria and Morocco.

Another project for the indirect utilisation of solar heat which has been much talked about and experimented with of recent years, is the exploitation, for the production of thermal energy, of the difference of temperature between the surface waters (especially of tropical seas) and those at a selected depth. The temperature drop—which in the case of certain waters is computed to reach 20° C. at accessible depths—could provide sufficient steam pressure to drive machines. After accurate preliminary studies had been carried out, experiments were started on the island of Cuba, where the water temperature and the slope of the sea bed are specially suitable for the laying of the pipes required for the transport of the colder water.

The surface water, whose temperature was 28° C., was pumped out and made to boil by creating a vacuum over it. The steam was passed at low pressure through a turbine coupled to a generator and discharged into a condenser. Into this, cold water (at about 4° C.) from the sea bed was also passed, so as to condense the steam discharged by the turbine.

The tube—made of steel plates, and measuring over 3 feet in diameter—was laid to a depth of 2000 feet below the surface of the sea. Although the first results obtained with this experimental plant were rather disappointing it is nevertheless calculated that each cubic metre of water raised from the sea bed would, after deducting the work done in driving the auxiliary engine, provide sufficient electrical energy amply to repay the heavy installation costs.

The use of a liquid with a low boiling point, such as ammonia or sulphur dioxide, whose vapour would attain a high enough pressure to drive the turbine, seems to offer a likely direction for future experiments along these lines.

The cold of the polar regions has also been suggested as a source of energy, through the exploitation of the temperature difference between the sea and the air in these regions. Other projects will no doubt be worked out, such as the generation of electrical energy from the Sun's radiation by means of the photoelectric effect.

Another highly important branch of research is that devoted to the growth of plants in relation to solar radiation. It is well known that growing plants absorb carbonic acid from the air through the millions of stomata situated on the underneath of their leaves. But this absorption only occurs when the plant is exposed to certain rays contained in sunlight. The questions then arise, what is the wavelength of the most effective radiation ? what effect does their intensity, and the daily duration of exposure to them, have on the plant? what are the chemical processes whereby different parts of the plant are built up? how does direct radiation cause the bending of the plant towards the source of the light? These and other associated problems have been studied for some years past at the Smithsonian Institution of Washington and elsewhere.

The beneficial effect on living organisms of that part of the Sun's radiation which lies between violet and the ultraviolet which is still capable of penetrating the Earth's atmosphere, is nowadays fully appreciated by therapeutists: so much so, that when advantage cannot be taken of the Sun's rays themselves, artificial sources are used which reproduce them satisfactorily. That the body requires the Sun's radiation has been realised from the earliest times, but it has only recently been discovered that in addition to the visible tanning effect when the skin is exposed to direct sunlight, certain chemical substances in the skin are induced to manufacture vitamin D, which is essential to the smooth functioning of the human organism. When we receive too little solar radiation the microscopic laboratories in our skin stop producing vitamin D, and a general debilitation results. In this field also it may be said that research has barely started, though promising important results.

Thus whilst the study of solar physics leads to a fuller understanding of the constitution of the Sun and therefore of the other stars also, that of geophysics and of the possible applications of the Sun's radiation in the various ways briefly referred to above, increase our knowledge of the Sun's influence on the Earth, and also open the way to the utilisation of this immense source of energy, of which we can so lavishly avail ourselves to the ever greater advantage and well-being of mankind.

APPENDIX

(containing additions to various sections, and a new section)

Chapter II: 6. THE GRANULATION. The difficulties of investigating the characteristics of solar granulation, which is so important for our knowledge of the constitution of the Sun's surface, are partly due to disturbances in the troposphere; because of these, it used only to be possible to take photographs of the granulation at high-altitude stations and under exceptional meteorological conditions, and so few were taken (see Plate 23). But today the various probes we can send into the upper atmosphere or beyond have opened up new possibilities and have enabled us to increase our knowledge in this important subject. Recently, at the Observatory of the University of Princeton, under the guidance of M. Schwarzschild, photographs of the Sun's surface above the photosphere have been obtained. A reflector with a Newtonian mounting, and with a quartz mirror of 12 inches aperture, was employed. By means of a 35-mm ciné-camera and a suitable magnification system, a region of the Sun corresponding to an area of $35,000 \times 50,000$ miles of its surface was photographed; exposures of a thousandth of a second were used. The instrument, which had a special azimuth mounting, was suspended from a large balloon filled with helium, and the photographs of the surface of the Sun were taken automatically at a height of 82,000 feet. The instrument and ciné-camera were returned to Earth by means of a parachute. The numerous photographs show three main characteristics. The bright granules are very sharp and well-defined, and are of varying dimensions. Granules with a diameter of only 180 miles have never been photographed through our atmosphere before. From these very small dimensions the granules grow to up to a thousand miles in diameter. Most of them seem to be like irregular polygons; and the dark areas are decidedly different from the bright ones—they are like a network of narrow passages or canals between the bright granules.

Laboratory experiments prove that in its general aspects the network resembles the structures found in 'non-stationary convection'. We thus have new factors to help us in investigating how solar heat propagates from the interior towards the surface.

The evolution of photospheric granules has been investigated by R. Giovanelli at Sydney. He found there was considerable diversity in brightness, size and shape, over half of the granules showing no detectable changes during the periods for which they persisted as identifiable structures. Their life-span was found to be about ten minutes. The 'cell-size', defined as the average distance between the centres of adjacent granules, was measured for both photospheric and umbral granulation, the mean values being 2″9 and 2″3 respectively.

Chapter II: 8. THE POLAR FACULAE. The faculae at high latitudes may be named 'polar faculae'; they appear irregularly, and were particularly numerous at the end of the 18th cycle and the beginning of the 19th one. Their mean diameter is 1400 miles and their life-span varies from a few minutes to several days. The mean heliographic latitude at which the polar faculae appear is about ±66°, but there is an annual variation depending on the inclination of the solar axis. For latitudes higher than 68°—at the polar regions—the density of the faculae is high and almost uniform, while at lower latitudes it is much lower. A peculiar characteristic of these faculae is the appearance in them of a luminous point of great brilliancy between 2 inches and 5 inches in diameter; the more intense granules of their regular structures exceed by 40 to 50% the luminosity of the quiet photosphere.

The polar faculae already discovered by Fr Secchi seem to be related to the general magnetic field and to the polar rays of the corona.

In the years of transition between the 18th and the 19th cycle the polar faculae were exceptionally numerous, and in 1954 their zone was more active than the equatorial one. After that the polar faculae, which had reached latitudes of 70°–75°, disappeared completely in 1957.

Chapter II: 9. THE RELATIVE NUMBERS (R) FROM 1955 ONWARDS AND THE 19TH ELEVEN-YEAR CYCLE. Continuing the table on p. 80, we give here the relative numbers for the years after 1954:

Year	R
1955	38·0
1956	141·7
1957	190·2
1958	184·8
1959	159·0
1960	112·3
1961	53·9

This 19th cycle breaks the record for solar activity; there was greater activity during it than during any previous cycle known. The maximum of the activity was reached in the years 1957–58;

in November 1956 the activity had been so high that it seemed as if the maximum had been reached only three years after the minimum, which had occurred in 1954. But the renewed activity of June 1957 surpassed the intensity of that of November 1956, and, still increasing, reached the highest relative numbers ever recorded in October. Very exceptional events registered in this 19th cycle were two days in 1956 and eleven days in 1957 with $R > 300$: there was a further record on 24 and 25 December 1957 when the relative numbers reached 355.

Another event in this extraordinary cycle was the appearance of a spot on 21 June 1957 at the high latitude of 50°·3 N with an area of 50 millionths of the Sun's hemisphere; it seems that this group was at the highest latitude ever observed, if we except pores of limited life.

Moreover, in this cycle spots of large dimensions, such as were observed in the 18th and other cycles, were almost completely missing. This shows that the high relative numbers were due to the presence of numerous small spots. On 23 February 1956 there occurred the largest increase in cosmic ray neutron activity yet observed at the surface of the Earth. The night of 10–11 February 1958 produced an aurora of extraordinary proportions, accompanied by severe radio and telegraphic disturbances and Earth currents of unusual magnitude. On 22 August 1958 there occurred a flare (see p. 109) that initiated spectacular radio noise outbursts on a wide range of frequencies. The radio source apparently extended high into the solar atmosphere and occupied a volume of space roughly comparable to that occupied by the Sun itself. The great peak of flare activity of 13–16 July 1959 also produced strong proton emission and was accompanied by the largest decrease in cosmic ray intensity yet detected. Solar activity in August and November 1959 generated powerful long-wave solar radio noise emissions of an unusual nature.

Chapter III: 12. THE SOLAR SPECTRUM OUTSIDE THE TERRESTRIAL ATMOSPHERE. Considerable progress has been made in our knowledge of the solar spectrum through ever more advanced rockets and artificial satellites operating beyond our atmosphere. By these means it has been possible to analyse in detail the solar spectrum down to 100Å and explore it to a wavelength of 50Å. The continuous spectrum emitted by the solar photosphere diminishes very rapidly in intensity with decreasing ultra-violet wavelength, as would be expected of a black body with a temperature of about 5000°, and below 1700Å the spectrum consists almost entirely of emission lines emitted by the solar chromosphere.

Prominent are the resonance lines of Mg II and Si II and the
strong absorption doublet of Al I. The line Lyman α shows a
width of about 0·7Å with a broad self-reversal within which appears a very sharp absorption feature of still greater depth. The
resonance lines He I at 576Å and He II at 304Å are also intense;
the higher ionisation of light elements such as O VI, Si III and
C III must originate in the higher layers of the solar atmosphere.
Monochromatic photographs of the Sun in Lyman α light have
also been obtained—from a rocket at an altitude of 123 miles. The
disturbed areas are very similar to the spectroheliograms obtained
with the line K of Ca II, but are generally more extended. By
means of rockets the flux of 50Å of X-rays was measured at the
Naval Research Laboratory of the United States during the total
eclipse of 1958. This flux must originate from the regions of the
corona which are at a very high temperature. Again by means of
rockets, it has been possible to detect the X-ray emission from
flares; in the region from 2 to 10Å a strong increase in X-rays has
been noted. These important researches are being actively continued by means of artificial satellites.

Chapter III: 14. FLARES. There is active international collaboration
in the observation of the flares which appear on the surface of the
Sun. Naturally these appear with more frequency and intensity
in the periods of maximum solar activity. They are observed
continuously by means of the spectrohelioscope or the spectroheliograph, or by means of the Lyot interference filter, in about
forty-five observatories distributed all over the world. A list of
flares is published in the *Quarterly Bulletin on Solar Activity*
(see p. 109). The classification of flares is based mainly on their
area, reduced to the centre of the Sun's disc, and on their intensity.
The table below gives the area, the line width of *Hα*, and the
intensity in the centre of *Hα* for flares of different importances;
the intensity in the centre of *Hα* is given in units of the adjacent
continuum.

As their name implies, the flares appear suddenly; and they

Importance	Area 10^{-6} vis-hem	Line width $H\alpha$	Intensity in centre of $H\alpha$	Relative frequency
1⁻	< 100	1·5	0·6	—
1	100 to 250	3·0	0·8 to 1·5	0·72
2	250 to 600	4·5	1·2 to 2·0	0·25
3	600 to 1200	8	1·4 to 2·5	0·03
3⁺	> 1200	15	2 to 3	—

almost always appear in the neighbourhood of or inside the active group of spots as luminous points or lines, those of importance 3 appearing as more or less extended mottles of great brilliancy. Sometimes they reach the centre of the spot's umbra. Generally the flares appear in the first 10 or 15 days of the life of the spot groups. Very active groups may produce about fifty flares. They have a tendency to appear in the same regions several times and also in various regions of the centres of activity simultaneously.

According to Kiepenheuer the observations are best understood when it is assumed that the disturbance which causes the flare travels over the Sun's surface at a speed of from 600 to 1200 miles per second, triggering off other flares and destroying or activating other filaments up to distances of about a solar circumference. Because it has the same velocity, this kind of disturbance seems to be the same phenomenon as that observed in the type II bursts (see p. 339), the rising type IV bursts, and the corpuscular cloud producing geomagnetic storms and travelling from Sun to Earth in some 20 hours.

The spectra of the flares show the centre of the Fraunhofer line or the complete line in emission. Among the more intense lines are the ones of the Balmer series, the helium line 10,832Å, and the lines of Ca II. In a very bright flare about 100 bright lines have been observed between 5000 and 7000Å—among them many lines of neutral or ionised metals. Bright flares also show a very faint continuous spectrum.

To the class of flares may belong the phenomena sometimes observed in $H\alpha$ called 'bombs' by F. Ellerman. In the neighbourhood of $H\alpha$ and in a region extending for about 30Å, the continuum becomes extremely bright in a narrow band, while the $H\alpha$ and the other Fraunhofer lines remain unchanged. This may be due to an explosion of radiation taking place in the deep photosphere.

Generally during this phenomenon the absorption line is shifted towards the violet thus proving the existence of upward-moving vapours with a velocity of about 3 miles per second. But the bright emissions show velocities of about 600 miles per second. The amount of energy radiated by these phenomena must be of the same order as that developed in thermonuclear reactions. While the flares are typical chromospheric phenomena, the 'bombs', which are also called 'moustaches' from their appearance, must be photospheric or subphotospheric phenomena, and are probably connected with the first stage of the flare.

Chapter III: 16. SPICULES, FILAMENTS, PROMINENCES. The 'prairie fire' of Fr Secchi (p. 119) is formed by little flames rising

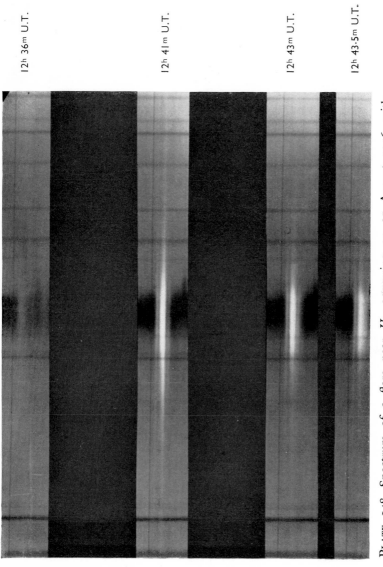

12h 36m U.T.

12h 41m U.T.

12h 43m U.T.

12h 43·5m U.T.

PLATE 148. Spectrum of a flare near $H\alpha$ occurring on 31 August 1956, with characteristic 'bombs' or 'moustaches'. (By courtesy of C. de Jager, Utrecht.)

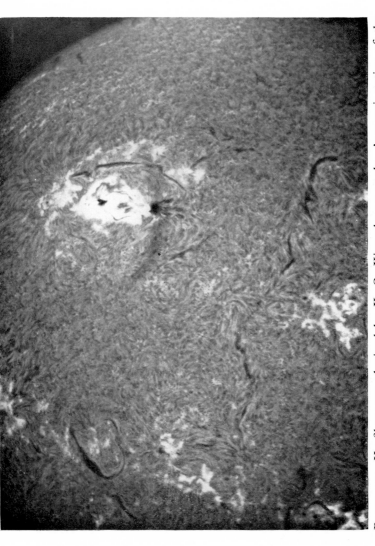

PLATE 149. *Hα* filtergram obtained by K. O. Kiepenheuer at the Anacapri station of the Fraunhofer Institut on 28 November 1958 at 13^h 55^m U.T. Large flare of importance 3$^+$ connecting two bipolar spots and various filaments.

to varying heights above the general level of the chromosphere. W. O. Roberts has called these flames 'spicules'. In the line $H\alpha$ they appear as bright little tongues. Their velocity of ascent is about 18 miles per second, their life-span 3 to 5 minutes; their height is anything up to about 6000 miles, their thickness 300 to 1200 miles and their temperature from 10,000° to 20,000° K. They show systematic inclinations, in most cases towards the equator; these inclinations may correspond to the direction of the local magnetic field. On the disc the spicules are arranged more or less regularly in a kind of network closely related to the general granulation. Observations made by R. Athay with the coronograph of Climax of the spectrum in the $H\alpha$, $H\beta$, D_3 and K lines, show that the extreme width of the line profiles of spicules contrasts sharply with the narrow profiles of quiescent prominences.

Chapter III: 19. RADIAL MOVEMENTS IN SUNSPOTS. Discussing the observations of the Evershed effect which were made at Arcetri, R. Michard shows that with the increase in the distance of a sunspot from the central meridian of the Sun, there is a decrease in the measured velocity. Taking into account the formation of the lines and the above mentioned distance from the central meridian, Michard found confirmation that the velocity varied with the depth as had already been deduced from St John's observations. Later, through observations made at the Pic du Midi, R. Servajean also found the existence of a small vertical downward component of the metallic vapours.

Chapter III: 21. THE MAGNETIC FIELDS AND MAGNETIC CLASSIFICATION OF SUNSPOTS. The majority of the more noteworthy magnetic areas may be classified as bipolar (BM), though some of them present a more complicated polarity. Some areas of limited intensity may be classified as unipolar (UM). Sunspots appear more frequently inside the BM regions when these regions are young, but it is also true that in several BM regions no spots occur; some of the larger ones may reach an area greater than a tenth of a hemisphere. If we compare the magnetic records (see p. 191 and Plate 109) with the monochromatic photographs taken in CA II light, the existence of a close connection between the regions covered by flocculi and those influenced by intense bipolar or unipolar fields becomes evident; we may conclude that calcium flocculi are present in every BM region of intensity greater than about 2 gauss. No magnetic characteristics are visible in the structure of photographs taken in calcium light, but such characteristics are visible in those taken in hydrogen light. From

331

the former, however, it is possible to make an approximate determination of the intensity of the field which determines the luminosity of the flocculi.

The brilliant coronal arcs which are so prominent during total eclipses, prove that the vertical extent of the BM fields in the corona is usually at least of the same order as their horizontal extent, and that it is often much greater. UM regions are rarer than BM ones and have a low magnetic intensity. They often cover a large area with ill-defined boundaries. These UM regions may retain a field intensity of a few gauss for several rotations of the Sun. Taking into consideration the correlation between the presence of these regions and the occurrence of terrestrial magnetic storms, the Babcocks think that the former may be identified with the so-called 'M-regions' (see p. 308). By comparing the monochromatic photographs in $H\alpha$ with the magnetograms, it is perhaps possible to find a connection between the UM regions and the filaments. Some filaments do in fact grow near, or on the border of, the magnetic regions, and sometimes they surround them. Others seem to be placed along lines dividing BM regions into two parts of opposite polarity; the absorbing hydrogen seems to pile up on the tops of the arching lines of force in the magnetic field.

Chapter III: 22. HYDROGEN VORTICES. After Hale's discovery of the solar vortices in the $H\alpha$ photographs of the Sun, further observations and research on the magnetic fields have brought changes in ideas and hypotheses as to their formation and structure. In view of the fact that only a small percentage of spots show any marked vortex structure, M. Ellison prefers to use the term 'striation pattern' rather than 'vortices', as being more generally applicable to such features. H. W. Babcock and H. D. Babcock have attributed the striation patterns to the alignment of the normal chromospheric mottling through the action of weak magnetic fields, which they have shown to extend far beyond the sunspots themselves.

In the brighter flares a sudden change has been observed occurring in one of these sunspot striation patterns a few minutes after the moment of peak intensity of the flare. According to Ellison a possible explanation—but one that should be put forward very tentatively—is to ascribe this change to the disappearance of the controlling magnetic field at the onset of the flare. A. Severny describing his own researches (carried out with the magnetograph of the Crimean Astrophysical Observatory) into the magnetic fields in active regions before and after the occurrence of flares, concludes:

(1) Flares occur at neutral points in the sunspot's magnetic field.

(2) When the magnetic field gradient is sufficiently large in the vicinity of such points, an instability of the plasma sets in; this leads to the flash phase through the operation of the pinch effect. 'Plasma' is a completely ionised gas composed almost exclusively of protons and electrons.

(3) The appearance of the flare brings about a destruction of the surrounding magnetic field.

The present interpretation of solar vortices may be more compatible with the radial motion of the metallic vapours in sunspots.

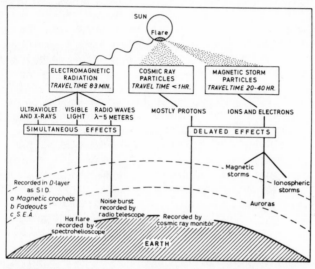

Fig. 98. *Effects of solar flare on the Earth. Dashed ring indicates the ionosphere.* SID=*sudden ionospheric disturbances.* SEA=*sudden enhancement of atmospherics.* (*M. A. Ellison, by courtesy of* Sky and Telescope).

Chapter III: 23. THE SUN'S GENERAL MAGNETIC FIELD. H. D. Babcock and H. W. Babcock have continued their researches into the magnetic fields of the Sun. A change of polarity in the general field has been observed in recent years. The south polar field reversed in mid 1957, and the north polar field in November 1958. The Sun's general field is now parallel to that of the Earth, the opposite of the situation from 1953 to 1957. For over a year, during the greatest activity, opposite rotation poles of the Sun had the same magnetic polarity. A new model of the Sun's magnetic field, based on observations made with the magnetograph over several years, and incorporating a synthesis and extension of current theories put forward by Cowling, Parker and others, has been proposed by H. W. Babcock. The model accounts for the reversal of the main dipole, the sunspot polarity laws, and a number of other incidental features.

At the Astrophysical Observatory in the Crimea, A. Severny and his collaborators have found a tendency for the flares to originate in the steep magnetic field gradients where the field passes through 'neutral points'.

R. Leighton at the Mount Wilson Observatory has proposed a new method of mapping the solar magnetic fields, and presented preliminary results (1959). Relatively strong fields up to 100 or 200 gauss are found in extensive areas throughout the flocculi regions, the pattern of the field being in striking agreement with the pattern of Ca II emission, that is, over the same regions as those of the calcium flocculi.

Chapter IV: 27. THE CORONA. In photographs of the corona taken during total eclipses of the Sun, concentric arcs protruding from the dark limb of the Moon are often visible above the prominences; they are alternately bright and dark, and seem to pulsate with a velocity of the order of 0·3 to 2 miles per second. These bright and dark arcs could be explained on the supposition that the electron density in the neighbourhood of the filament-prominences was strongly diminished. Permanent coronal condensations in the shape of caps with a diameter of from 60,000 to 120,000 miles that are directly connected with the centres of activity present at the Sun's limb at the moment of eclipse, may be observed issuing from the chromosphere. Their electron density is from 10 to 20 times that of the quiet corona and rises from 5.10^9 to 2.10^{10} electrons/cm³. These permanent condensations reach their maximum development when the connected spot group has gone beyond its maximum development and is in decreasing activity. Sporadic condensations are sometimes noted in the permanent ones at 5303Å and 6374Å.

The use of monochromatic polarising filters on these coronal bright lines has increased our knowledge of the structure and motions of the corona. On several occasions during observations of the structure of the corona at the Sacramento Peak Observatory, arcs over active regions that are usually fairly low have been seen to disrupt violently with a whip-like motion.

The fact that the light emitted by the corona shows a partial polarisation, leads us to the conclusion that this light is not completely due to thermal emission as was formerly supposed, but that it must originate instead from the light diffused by free electrons. On the basis of this hypothesis and having revised his theory, Baumbach computed the degree of polarisation P as a function of the distance from the solar limb. Although the results obtained do not show a good agreement with the observations, his theory is in the main proved by the observations. These also prove that the characteristics of the corona's polarisation may be qualitatively explained by assuming the coronal light to be a mixture of a partially-polarised component originating from the light scattered by the free electrons, and a non-polarised component produced by the inner zodiacal light. Another result is certain: the polarisation at the poles is considerably weaker than that at the equator; this may be due to the fact that the corona is brighter at the equator than at the poles.

Chapter VIII: 39. CORRELATIONS BETWEEN SOLAR PHENOMENA AND DISTURBANCES OF THE IONOSPHERE, TERRESTRIAL MAGNETISM AND AURORAE. Statistical results of the correlation between solar phenomena and terrestrial magnetic storms lead to the following conclusions:

(1) Terrestrial magnetic storms begin about 1·5 days after the transit of large sunspots across the Sun's central meridian; and the maximum intensity is generally recorded two days later.

(2) There is a correlation between the presence of spots and geomagnetic disturbances when the spots are large and have an area of about 1000 millionths of the solar disc, but not when they have a smaller area.

(3) A better correlation is obtained by limiting the comparison to spots with flares. When these are exceptionally intense they are always followed by great magnetic storms, while the more frequent flares of lesser intensity are statistically associated with increasing geomagnetic activity.

(4) At sunspot minima, when practically no flares occur, there may still be magnetic storms. Usually these are weak, but they are not dependent on the presence of flares.

The observations show that the corpuscular cloud is emitted by the Sun in a cone with a half-angle aperture of about 45°. Only with flares of importance 3 or 3$^+$ is the entire cone filled with sufficient density to cause a geomagnetic storm. The ionised layers of the upper terrestrial atmosphere form the 'ionosphere', which is becoming better and better known today through the use of rockets and artificial satellites. The ionosphere has been divided into four main layers: D, E, F_1 and F_2. Their height is greater in winter than in summer, and varies from approximately 60 to 120 miles with electron concentrations which are well defined. During the maximum solar activity the F_2 layer may reach a height of 240 miles and a maximum electron concentration per cm^3 of $6\cdot8 \times 10^5$. According to Menzel the chromosphere may be compared to a sieve whose meshes screen the radio waves. Depending on their frequencies these either pass through or return to the Earth. The ones with a short wavelength speed on through, to be lost in the depths of interplanetary space.

When the Sun is quiet, the size of the ionosphere mesh is almost constant, but when it is disturbed, real ionospheric storms take place (these are associated with magnetic storms). They may completely destroy the various layers of the ionosphere, and may last several days; the layers of the ionosphere will later re-form. With the continuous survey possible today of the Sun on the one hand, and of the critical frequency of the ionosphere on the other, it is possible to foresee the conditions that so affect terrestrial radio communications. A theory for ionospheric storms has been developed by S. Chapman.

Chapter VIII: 40. THE SUN'S RADIO-SPECTRUM. Remarkable progress has been made in recent years in the field of solar radio-astronomy.

New and powerful instruments are actually working in many observatories throughout the world, so that in the field of radio-waves, too, there is a continuous record of solar phenomena. Thanks to the widespread collaboration established for the International Geophysical Year (1957–58), it has been possible during the present very active 19th cycle to clarify the various types of radio-emissions and analyse the circumstances of their origin and emission, and also all their properties. All these researches enable us to give a fairly precise description of what may be called a 'centre of radio-electric solar activity'. But it is true that no satisfactory interpretation of the various emissions has yet been given; nor is it yet possible to understand their physical significance.

In the *Quarterly Bulletin on Solar Activity*, published by the Zurich Federal Observatory, records of 'solar radio emission' collected from about thirty observatories scattered throughout the world are given. The *Bulletin* shows the 'flux density' coming from the Sun for each day, using as its unit:

$$10^{-22} \text{ watts metre}^{-2} \text{ (c/sec)}^{-1};$$

the 'variability' relative to the median flux density is shown by indices on a scale 0 to 3, where 0=quiet, and 3=violent variability;

the direction and degree of polarisation is indicated. The 'outstanding occurrences' are also given; these may be compared with the observed optical phenomena, and their location compared with that of emitting regions.

The values of the flux density S can be readily converted into apparent disc temperatures, T_D, by means of the relation:

$$S = 2 \cdot 09 \times 10^{-32} f^2 T_D$$

where f is the frequency in megacycles per second.[*]

At wavelengths of less than about 2 cm all the radiation may be ascribed to the basic component. At wavelengths of between 3 and 60 cm the intensity variations due to the slowly varying component are closely connected with the sunspot area, and the basic component may be computed by extrapolating for zero area of the spots. The correlation between the fluctuations in intensity of short waves of about 10 cm (300 Mc/sec) and the number of spots is so good that we can determine the numbers of sunspots even when the sky is overcast.

It is also possible to recognise the fundamental component at the metre wavelengths, so that we may conclude that in the range of wavelengths from 1 cm to a few metres all or almost all the thermal radiation comes from the chromosphere or the corona. The apparent temperature consists of the temperature of the 'quiet Sun' plus that which is approximately proportional to the area of the sunspots. At these wavelengths, therefore, it is possible to separate a component of the solar radiation which varies with the sunspot area and which may have a circular polarisation that depends upon the cycle and position of the sunspots.

Sometimes bursts are so intense that they are called 'outbursts'; together with the flares, they are received on Earth on a wide range of frequencies, or wavelengths, from 30 metres (10 Mc/sec) to about 1 cm (30,000 Mc/sec). The highest frequencies originate from the relatively dense layers of the chromosphere, while the lower ones can only originate from the outer and more rarefied layers of the corona. Regular time lags between the appearance of the flare and that of the outburst have been observed; they may be explained as being due to the ascent of the disturbances from the

[*] The frequency is given in cycles per second (c/sec) or in hertz (1 Hz = 1 c/sec). Often the multiples are given: kilocycles (1 kc/sec = 10^3 c/sec), and megacycles (1 Mc/sec = 10^6 c/sec). When f is given in MHz and λ in metres we have:

$$\lambda = \frac{300}{f_{\text{MHz}}}$$

chromosphere to the corona; as soon as this is reached, the successive lower frequencies can escape. The supposed velocity of this ascent is of the order of 600 miles per second which is approximately the same as that of the corpuscular streams which arrive at the Earth from the Sun and produce aurorae and magnetic storms. The intensity of these bursts is so great that they cannot be explained as a thermal property of solar matter.

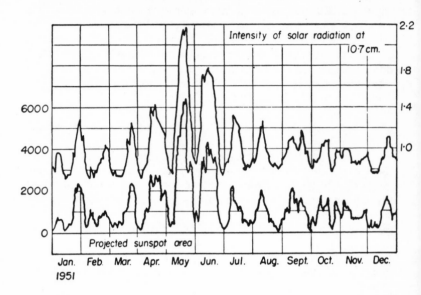

Fig. 99. Intensity of solar radiation at wave length 10·7 cm and projected area of sunspots (after K. O. Kiepenheuer, Die Sonne).

Powerful sources of radio-waves have been identified in streams of matter in rapid motion and collision; something of the same kind may cause these solar phenomena, for which there is at the moment no clear explanation.

In order to investigate how the streams of particles originating in the active centres of the Sun are transmitted through the various layers of its surface, J. Wild has conceived and built a 'radio-spectrograph' with which it is possible to change the frequency in a few seconds—from 600 Mc to 50 Mc, for example. It is composed of an aerial with a wide reception band, and one or more receivers which are tuned on decreasing frequencies. The resulting diagrams are very interesting and prove that some phenomena have a relatively slow variation of frequency, while others have a very rapid one. With bursts of type II, relatively low velocities of the order of 240 to 300 miles per second are found; with those of type III, the velocities reach 60,000 miles per second.

F. Denisse of the Meudon Observatory has classified the sources of radio-emissions according to their life-span as follows:

(a) thermal emissions of the whole solar atmosphere;

(b) thermal emissions of chromospheric and coronal origin which seem to be associated with flocculi and have the same life-span;

(c) emissions with a shorter life-span (about a week) which occur only during the periods of high sunspot activity;

(d) a whole series of events in close association with the individual eruptions; the outbursts of type II, III, IV and V.

The radio noise bursts are classified by Denisse as follows:

Burst type	Time, duration and size	Polarisation	Wavelengths	Associated phenomena
I	tenths of seconds	circular	bursts are at metre wave-lengths, but associated centres often emit weak continua.	associated with centres in the corona, and roughly overlie active regions.
II slow drift bursts or outbursts	minutes	usually not strongly polar-ised	centimetres to tens of metres.	exhibit harmonics are associated with flares of approximately 300 miles per second in corona with magnetic storm producing solar corpuscles.
III fast drifts, bursts	seconds	irregular	metres to tens of metres sweep in frequency at 100 Mc/sec^2	associated with early early stages of flares; are probably sources moving at substantial fraction of speed of light; perhaps associated with high-speed proton showers on earth.

[continued overleaf

Burst type	Time, duration and size	Polarisation	Wavelengths	Associated phenomena
IV continuum outbursts or storm-phase bursts	minutes to hours; size: up to ap-proxi-mately 6×10^4 miles	often circu-larly polar-ised	continuum from centimetres to tens of metres	associated with certain very strong flares, starts approximately 15 min. after flash phase; perhaps associated with synchroton emission and cosmic ray generation; sources sometimes displace in atmosphere at speeds of approxi-mately 60-600 miles per second; often associated with type II bursts.
V centi-metric bursts	minutes; size: approx-3×10^4 miles	variable	broad band continua but enhanced at centimetre wavelengths	ascending sources of speeds approximately 1800 miles per second; often follow type III bursts.

While the radiation of the 'quiet Sun' and of the slowly varying component may be explained as due to a thermal mechanism of emission, the radio-storms and the bursts of various types have apparent temperatures which cannot be explained as being due to a thermal mechanism. Wild notes that one mechanism alone cannot explain the characteristics of the various phenomena observed. While the monochromatic emission, that is, the emission coming from a band of a few Mc/sec (as it does with types I, II, and III), may be interpreted as plasma oscillations in the surrounding coronal gas, while the continuous emission as it occurs in the radio-storms and bursts of types IV and V, could be interpreted as a synchrotron radiation from electrons spiralling in a magnetic field.

Chapter VIII: 41. PROBABILITY OF CORRELATING SOLAR PHENO-MENA WITH TERRESTRIAL METEOROLOGY. It is recognised that the correlation between the Sun's activity and climatic conditions on the Earth is still uncertain. But the fast accumulating data will shed more light on the problem. We can, for instance, quote some facts resulting from the present exceptional 19th cycle of solar activity. In the month of May 1957 alone, there were 230 tornadoes in the United States, and the yearly total of 924 was greater than that for any year for which statistical data are available. Also in 1957 the American meteorological stations registered a new record for rainfall and exceptional minima and maxima of temperature. The rainfall in Libya in the middle of the summer of the same year was exceptional. Other unusual meteorological conditions occurred in various parts of the globe such as England, for instance, where there were numerous and varied electrical phenomena.

Chapter VIII: 42. THE UTILISATION OF SOLAR HEAT. The necessity for the multiplication of sources of energy, in order to satisfy the ever increasing needs of human society, has led in the past few years to great progress being made in researches into the utilisation of solar energy. An international conference dealing with this was held at Tucson, Arizona, in 1955, and conferences on new sources of energy have been sponsored by the United Nations.

I will now mention those of the experiments that have been carried out in various countries on the uses of solar energy, that seem to be most promising, and most likely to lead to developments and improvements.

Solar energy may be used for cooking where other sources of energy are not available. Heat is generally obtained by means of a metal parabolic mirror which is directed towards the Sun and follows its apparent diurnal motion; at the focus of the mirror is placed a pot which is heated by the concentrated solar radiation. On a much larger scale, but based on the same principle, are the solar furnaces, like the one at the laboratory for solar energy at Mont Louis in the eastern Pyrenees, 5280 ft above sea level. This solar furnace consists of a parabolic mirror with an aperture of 969 square feet composed of 3000 small curved mirrors, which together make up the curve of the great mirror. The rays of the sun are directed onto the parabolic mirror by a reflecting surface composed of 500 small plane mirrors. At the focus of the parabolic mirror the temperature exceeds 3500°C, and so this furnace is specially employed for metallurgical operations, for firing ceramics and for chemical reactions. Being able to melt substances without a crucible in a controlled atmosphere or in the open air, makes it possible to prepare innumerable mixtures of refractory compounds for the study of their phase diagrams and the determination of various of their physical properties.

Remarkable progress has been made in the use of solar energy for heating and cooling houses. Heat pumps with an operating cycle identical with a conventional refrigeration cycle are mounted in thousands of houses in the United States. Operating with either the winter heating cycle or the summer cooling cycle, these maintain a constant temperature in the house from season to season. The majority of these plants are to be found in the hotter southern states, where there is more sunshine, and a greater need for cooling, and conditioned air is more in demand. Air or water or a mixture of various elements is employed as the source of heat in these heat pumps.

The supply for cooling purposes of sun-heated air to an absorption dehumidifier employing a hygroscopic liquid has been experimentally investigated and found to be feasible. This use of solar energy will certainly be greatly developed.

Numerous experiments concerned with the economical conversion of sea water or saline water into fresh water by means of solar energy have been made. A method of doing this would be particularly useful in arid lands where the lack of water is primarily caused by the Sun itself which desiccates the land. It has been proved that in the Sahara desert solar stills are the best and cheapest fixed installations for this purpose. In experiments made in California with plane stills properly tilted, an average of about a gallon of fresh water is produced daily for each 14 square feet of the surface of the collecting tray. Simple evaporating trays directly heated by the Sun with self-contained condensers appear to be the most economical, producing pure water at 1.65 dollars per thousand gallons. At the Phoenix meeting Maria Telkes concluded her report on solar stills with these words: 'We may look forward to a time, not too far away, when previously arid regions will be supplied by rivers of fresh water flowing backward from the oceans. Saline water will be changed by solar stills into fresh water—the source of all life."

The conversion of solar radiation into electrical power holds much promise, too. Three devices for this purpose are well known: the thermopile, the photogalvanic cell and the barrier photovoltaic cell. Until a few years ago it was only possible to obtain an efficiency of about 1% with these devices; then in 1954 D. Chapin, C. Fuller and G. Pearson of the Bell Telephone Laboratories succeeded in raising the efficiency of the photovoltaic cell to about 11%. They obtained this remarkable result through the use of silicon prepared in a special manner. Silicon is one of the commonest elements on Earth. Solar batteries are built up of cells of silicon in crystalline form and of extreme purity, mixed with a small amount of arsenic, the ratio being about one part of arsenic to a million parts of silicon. To give an example of the efficiency of these solar batteries, the solar energy falling on 11 square feet of the Earth's surface at Phoenix (Arizona) on a clear day is about 1000 watts, and a silicon photovoltaic cell of this area would have an electrical output of about 110 watts. Today these solar batteries are employed for several purposes; one important use is that of energy source in the artificial satellites.

The great efficiency of chlorophyl is well known. It can absorb three-quarters of the energy received from the Sun in the form of light, and convert it into chemical energy directly assimilable by man. Another method of utilising solar energy can be based on the photosynthesis processes. In the United States, Russia, France and Japan, experiments are being carried out for the application on a large scale of the photosynthesis of chlorophyl to plants which can be cultivated easily and can grow very rapidly in special installations, in order to increase the food available to humanity on Earth.

THE SUN AND COSMIC RAYS.—The magnetic fields of the Sun are without doubt responsible for the various solar phenomena, and for the guidance, acceleration and general control of the emission of solar particles as for instance in the case of cosmic rays. But the origin of the latter and their ultimate relation to solar phenomena, and to flares in particular, is being investigated and further knowledge of them is expected to be gained from artificial satellites. It is known that cosmic rays are atomic nuclei stripped of their electrons, that move at a speed near to that of light. Generally they are protons and heavy nuclei endowed with the highest energies. They collide with the terrestrial atmosphere and, being charged, are subjected to the Earth's magnetic field.

Their origin is still mysterious, but it seems certain that the cosmic rays of the highest energy are not of solar origin, or influenced by solar activity. From observations made during the most recent cycles of solar activity, it has been discovered that flares of high intensity produce cosmic ray particles. A typical case is the flare of intensity 3^+ that occurred on 23 February 1956. Accompanied by a sudden disturbance in the ionosphere and radio-burst at various frequencies, a flux of cosmic rays of higher intensity than any previously observed reached the Earth. At stations with mean geomagnetic latitudes the following increase was observed:

neutrons	600%
all mesons	58%
hard mesons	38%

and the maximum was reached 10 minutes after the maximum activity of the flare. The cloud must have accelerated near the

Sun and spread almost immediately with a velocity not much below that of light. With regard to the correlation between flares and cosmic rays it seems possible to draw the following conclusions from the few cases observed:

(1) With flares of importance 3 or 3^+ there occurs an increase in cosmic radiation 1 to 2 hours after the maximum activity of the flare.

(2) The energy of the solar charged particle must be less than 10–15 BeV.* Their extra-terrestrial intensity is at least of the order of 1 particle/cm^2 sec. The total energy of such solar explosions is estimated at 10^{33}–10^{34} ergs.

(3) In all cases the intensity of the observed effect increases considerably with the height of the station, and is also dependent on the geomagnetic latitude and longitude.

(4) Not all flares cause an increase in cosmic radiation.

The effects of the 'M-regions' of the Sun (see p. 308) are also perceived in the intensity variations in cosmic radiation. These variations, having a period of 27 days, are of the order of 5%; their amplitude varies according to the yearly cycle and may eventually reach 20–30%. These variations, which are recorded at all the terrestrial stations, occur in the energies of the primary radiation at 10–12 BeV.

As a result of the observations on cosmic rays made at the Department of Terrestrial Magnetism, Washington, it has become clear that there is a close correlation between the yearly rate of cosmic ray intensity and the relative spot numbers; when the first decreases, the second increases. The observations were made in the two cycles between 1937 amd 1957. It has, in fact, been observed that the years of maximum cosmic ray activity coincide with those with minimum relative spot numbers. Moreover, the intensity minima for cosmic rays in 1947 and 1957 were lower than the maximum for 1937. This fits in with the fact that the relative numbers of sunspots were greater in 1947 and 1957 than in 1937. The decrease in the intensity of cosmic radiation between 1955 and 1957 evidently comes about a year after the corresponding increase in the number of sunspots in that period.

* eV = electronvolt   MeV = 10^6 eV   BeV = 10^9 eV

BIBLIOGRAPHY

OF GENERAL WORKS, ARRANGED IN CHRONOLOGICAL ORDER

Fr A. SECCHI, S.J., *Le Soleil.* Two volumes, Gauthier-Villars, Paris, 1875–7.

Sir N. LOCKYER, *Chemistry of the Sun.* Macmillan, London, 1887.

C. A. YOUNG, *The Sun.* Appleton, New York, 1895.

Sir N. LOCKYER, *The Sun's Place in Nature.* Macmillan, London, 1897.

Sir N. LOCKYER, *Recent and Coming Eclipses.* Macmillan, London, 1900.

E. PRINGSHEIM, *Physik der Sonne.* Teubner, Leipzig, 1910.

J. BOSLER, *Les Théories modernes du Soleil.* Doin, Paris, 1910.

G. ABBOT, *The Sun.* Appleton, New York, 1911.

A. BRESTER, *Le Soleil.* Van Stockum, The Hague, 1924.

RUSSELL, DUGAN & STEWART, *Astronomy.* Two volumes, Ginn, Boston, 1926–7.

W. H. JULIUS, *Zonnephysica.* Noordhoff, Groningen, 1928.

ABETTI, BERNHEIMER, GRAFF, KOPFF & MITCHELL, *Handbuch der Astrophysik: Das Sonnensystem.* Springer, Berlin, 1929.

S. A. MITCHELL, *Eclipses of the Sun.* Columbia University Press, 4th edn., New York, 1935.

M. MINNAERT, *De Natuurkunde van de Zon.* Van Stockum, The Hague, 1936.

A. UNSÖLD, *Physik der Sternatmosphären.* Springer, Berlin, 1938.

G. GAMOW, *The Birth and Death of the Sun.* Viking Press, New York, 1940.

M. NICOLET, *Introduction à l'étude des relations entre les phénomènes solaires et terrestres: Le Soleil.* Ciel et Terre, Uccle, 1943.

M. WALDMEIER, *Sonne und Erde.* Büchergilde Gutenberg, Zurich, 1946.

F. HOYLE, *Some Recent Researches in Solar Physics.* University Press, Cambridge, 1949.

D. H. MENZEL, *Our Sun.* Harvard Books on Astronomy. Blakiston, Philadelphia, 1949.

G. BRUHAT & L. D'AZAMBUJA, *Le Soleil.* Presses Universitaires de France, Paris, 1951.

G. D. KUIPER, *The Sun.* University of Chicago Press, 1953.

M. WALDMEIER, *Radiowellen aus dem Weltraum.* A. G. Fretz, Zürich, 1954.

M. WALDMEIER, *Ergebnisse und Probleme der Sonnenforschung.* Akademische Verlagsgesellschaft, Leipzig, 1955.

World symposium on applied solar energy. Phoenix, Arizona, November 1955.

K. O. KIEPENHEUER, *Die Sonne*. Springer, Berlin, 1957.

D. H. MENZEL, *Our Sun* (revised edition). Harvard University Press, Cambridge, Massachusetts, 1959.

W. ROBERTS & H. ZIRIN, 'Recent Progress in Solar Physics', *Journal of Geophysical Research*, June 1960.

'Radioastronomia solare', *Rendiconti Scuola Internazionale di Fisica 'E. Fermi'* (articles by M. Minnaert, K. O. Kiepenheuer, R. Coutrez, etc.). Zanichelli, Bologna, 1960.

M. HACK, *La radioastronomia alla scoperta di un nuovo aspetto dell' universo*. Laterza, Bari, 1960.

M. RIGUTTI, *Il Sole e la Terra*. Laterza, Bari, 1960.

Science in Space, edited by Lloyd Berkner and H. Odishaw. McGraw-Hill, N.Y., 1961.

Report of A. SEVERNY in: 'Commission de l'activité solaire', *Draft Reports, International Astronomical Union, Eleventh General Assembly*, p. 51 (with bibliography 1958–1961). Berkeley, June 1961.

Report of L. GOLDBERG in: 'Commission de la radiation et de la structure de l'atmosphère solaire', *Draft Reports, International Astronomical Union, Eleventh General Assembly*, p. 63 (with bibliography 1958–1961). Berkeley, June 1961.

Report of J. DENISSE in: 'Commission de radio-astronomie', *Draft Reports, International Astronomical Union, Eleventh General Assembly*, p. 451 (with bibliography 1958–1960). Berkeley, June 1961.

R. THOMAS & R. GRANT ATHAY, *Physics of the Solar Chromosphere*. Interscience Publication, New York, 1961.

References to new appendix are in a separate index following this one

INDEX .

INDEX TO THE APPENDIX